Studies in Inductive Logic and Probability

VOLUME II

Studies in Inductive Logic and Probability

VOLUME II

Richard C. Jeffrey, Editor

UNIVERSITY OF CALIFORNIA PRESS

BERKELEY . LOS ANGELES . LONDON

University of California Press
Berkeley and Los Angeles, California

University of California Press, Ltd.
London, England

ISBN: 0-520-03826-6
Library of Congress Catalog Card Number: 77-136025

Printed in the United States of America

Designed by Dave Comstock

Contents

Introduction

Much delayed, here is the second, final volume of *Studies in Inductive Logic and Probability*. Carnap projected the series ca. 1959 as a nonperiodical journal for quick publication of advanced work in inductive logic. A medium for cooperative research, it would replace the abandoned second volume of the work ("Probability and Induction") of which his *Logical Foundations of Probability* (1950) was to have been Volume I, and in which *The Continuum of Inductive Methods* (1952) was to have been part of Volume II. First on Carnap's new agenda was composition of an account, for publication in 1960 or 1961, of how the project then stood. A first draft ("An Axiom System of Inductive Logic") was circulated privately for criticism, section by section as written. Upon finishing that he began a massive revision ("A Basic System of Inductive Logic") that received the same treatment. His deteriorating physical condition, and the death of his wife, delayed matters far beyond his early, unrealistic estimate of 1961 as a publication date. Ten years after beginning, he decided to publish Volume I with only the then complete first half of "A Basic System": Article 2. While seeing Volume I through the press he would revise the rest for publication soon thereafter in Volume II. But he died in 1970, with Volume I still in press and with his "Basic System" still incomplete. Thus Volume I was a decade late, and the foundations were laid for a similar delay in the appearance of Volume II. For the magnitude of that second delay I must apologize, especially to those who contributed earliest to this volume: Jens Erik Fenstad and Godehard Link.

The articles here are numbered successively with the five of Volume I, and an index to both volumes is provided at the end of this one.

Article 6 completes article 2 of the first volume: "A Basic System of Inductive Logic". Carnap revised §§14–18 for this volume, but died while he was revising §19. As he had done only the first few pages of that, and it was unclear just how he would have proceeded, I have kept to the first draft of §19, except for inevitable changes, for example, in the numbering of backward references. Carnap would surely have shortened §19, but I do not know how, and so have left it much as he did. The case is similar for §20, but there I have done a bit more serious editing, mainly at the beginning.

In an obvious sense, "A Basic System of Inductive Logic" is Carnap's last word on the subject. But it got that status by accident. Carnap meant it to be a new *first* word: no grand overview but merely a revision of the ABCs. The last section, §21, was §8 of Carnap's first draft, "An Axiom System of Inductive Logic". He dropped that section in order to expedite publication of Volume I, but had meant to revise it for publication later. I have included it here in order to convey an idea of some of the directions that Carnap envisioned, some twenty years ago, for more advanced inquiries.

The basic system concerns a single family of predicates P_j ($j = 1, \ldots, k$), precisely one of which applies to each individual a_i. The function $\mathscr{C}$ is assumed to be symmetrical with respect to permutations of the a_i (i.e., the a_i are assumed to be exchangeable), so that all $\mathscr{C}$ values are determined by the so-called *singular predictive inference*, i.e., the values

$$C_j(s_1, \ldots, s_k) = \mathscr{C}(P_j a_{s+1} \mid P_{h_1} a_1 \cdot \ldots \cdot P_{h_s} a_s)$$

where $s = s_1 + \ldots + s_k$ and where for $j = 1, \ldots, k$, s_j is the number of occurrences of the number j in the sequence $\langle h_1, \ldots, h_s \rangle$. Thus the conjunction in the second argument-place of $\mathscr{C}$ above identifies a particular s_j of the first s individuals as having the property P_j. The members P_j of the family may have distinct *logical widths* γ_j (nonnegative reals that sum to 1). In the $\lambda - \gamma$ systems of Carnap's §19, C_j is determined as T19–5f:

$$C_j(s_1, \ldots s_k) = \frac{s_j + \lambda \gamma_j}{s + \lambda}$$

One can think of these $\mathscr{C}$-functions as modifications of the *straight rule* (the rule according to which C_j is simply the relative frequency of P_j in the first s individuals) in which we augment the s *real* individuals with λ *virtual* individuals, among which $\lambda \gamma_j$ have the property P_j for each $j = 1, \ldots, k$. Then the value of $C_j(s_1, \ldots, s_k)$ given above is simply the relative frequency of P_j among the $s + \lambda$ *real and virtual* individuals. Mathematically, these $\lambda - \gamma$ systems are indistinguishable from Pólya urn models with double replacement: initially the urn contains λ balls, of which $\lambda \gamma_j$ are of type j for each $j = 1, \ldots, k$; after the ith ball is drawn, it is returned to the urn together with one more ball of its type. Then after the ith drawing and double replacement, the proportion of balls in the urn of type P_j will be as specified by $C_j(s_1, \ldots, s_k)$ above.

The crucial aspect of the $\lambda - \gamma$ systems is that in them, C_j is a function of its jth argument s_j and of the sum s of all k arguments, but is independent of how the $s - s_j$ items in the sample that are not of type P_j are assorted among the other $k - 1$ types. As Carnap points out in §§16 and 17 of article 6, there are cases where it seems unreasonable to overlook the *similarity* of observed individuals that are not of type P_j. Example: roulette, with segments numbered 1 to 100 consecutively, and segment number j making an angle of $2\pi\gamma_j$ with the center of the wheel. With $s = 60$ and $s_1 = 0$, one might reasonably give higher credence to $P_1 a_{61}$ in case the 60 observed trials are scattered among the P_j in a disorderly manner than if all were of one type (say type P_{51}, so that $s_{51} = s = 60$). Carnap considers such *analogy by similarity* at length (e.g., in connection with the parameters η), but considers *analogy by proximity* very briefly (at the end of §17), as consideration of "proximity influence" requires dropping the assumption of exchangeability of the individuals a_i. Thus, in the roulette example, analogy by proximity would lend greater credence to $P_1 a_{61}$ in case one had observed $P_{61} a_1 \cdot P_{60} a_2 \cdot \ldots \cdot P_2 a_{60}$ (so that the turn of P_1 seems to have come, with a_{61}) than if one had observed $P_2 a_1 \cdot P_3 a_2 \cdot \ldots \cdot P_{61} a_{60}$. Here we have the same values for all s_j in each case, so that there is no distinction via similarity influence.

From motives akin to those that have led some (notably Bruno de Finetti and L. J. Savage) to reject sigma-additivity as a general requirement for probability functions, Carnap in §21 speculates about nonarchimedian-valued probability measures (this was in 1960). Another motive concerns the probabilities of nontrivial universal generalizations, e.g., $(x)P_1 x$, which are always 0 in the $\lambda - \gamma$ systems. Here Jaakko Hintikka and his collaborators, starting in the mid-1960s, have explored a variety of systems in which universal generalizations can have positive confirmation on finite evidence. In article 7, Hintikka and Ilkka Niiniluoto present a very natural modification of Carnap's λ-system (with $\gamma_j = 1/k$ for all j) in which C_j is taken to depend upon *the number c of its arguments that* *are nonzero* as well as upon its *j*th argument s_j and the sum s of all of its arguments. Thus the λ principle is weakened just enough to allow universal generalizations to have positive prior probabilities. (Article 7 was presented at a conference on *Formal Methods in the Methodology of Empirical Sciences* at Warsaw, June 17–21, 1974, and is reprinted here with the kind permission of the authors, and the publishers of the Proceedings of that conference: Ossolineum in Warsaw and D. Reidel in Dordrecht. 1976.) Related, independent work by Theo A. F. Kuipers is summarized in article 8. Clearly (see the third paragraph of §21, article 6) these sorts of inquiries were on Carnap's agenda, too.

Carnap himself seemed undecided about the desirability of adopting $\mathcal{M}$-functions that assign positive real values to nontrivial universal generalizations. Technically, he knew, the thing was feasible: de Finetti's representation theorem for exchangeable random variables showed how. A family of k predicates is in effect a random variable capable of taking values $1, \ldots, k$. In the de Finetti representation, C_j is determined by a probability distribution over the $k-1$ dimensional simplex of which the vertices are the points $(1, 0, \ldots, 0)$, $(0, 1, \ldots, 0)$, $\ldots, (0, 0, \ldots, 1)$ corresponding to the unit vectors on the coördinate axes of Euclidian k-space. Thus, with $k = 3$ we have a triangle. To obtain positive $\mathcal{M}$-values for the three universal generalizations of form $(x)P_j x$ we assign positive mass to the three vertices $(1, 0, 0)$, $(0, 1, 0)$, $(0, 0, 1)$ in the de Finetti representation. And to obtain positive $\mathcal{M}$-values for the three hypotheses of form "P_j is empty, but neither of the other two members of the family is empty" we assign some positive probability to each of the three sides of the triangle, endpoints excluded. (As Haim Gaifman has shown, this is best done by "smearing" some probability over each side, leaving no gaps of positive length: see the editor's note at the beginning of Carnap's §20 here.) And finally we obtain positive $\mathcal{M}$-value for the existential hypothesis that no member of the family is empty by smearing some probability over the whole interior of the triangle. And in general, one can ensure that the various nontrivial generalizations get positive $\mathcal{M}$-values while ensuring that the Reichenbach axiom holds, by such assignments of mass to interiors and boundaries of subsimplices of dimension $1, 2, \ldots$ of the full $k-1$ dimensional simplex to which probability 1 is assigned in the de Finetti representation of a k-valued random variable. But as §21 testifies, Carnap hoped for a more radical treatment of the problem of confirming generalizations.

Untouched in "A Basic System of Inductive Logic" is the problem of accounting for analogy influence between families.

There Carnap looked to de Finetti's representation theorem for *partially* exchangeable random variables. With the author's kind permission, there is included here (article 9) a translation of de Finetti's original paper on partial exchangeability, which was presented at the Geneva Colloquium on Probability Theory of October 1937 (*Actualités scientifiques et industrielles*, No. 739 [Paris: Hermann & Cie. 1938]). New proofs of the de Finetti representation theorems are given in Godehard Link's article 10 (Link's proof, using Choquet's representation theorem for convex sets, dates from 1975), and in article 11, by Persi Diaconis and David Freedman, where treatment of the infinite case is based illuminatingly upon the finite case and partial exchangeability is studied in a very general form.

In the early 1960s Carnap abandoned his old framework, in which probabilities are assigned to sentences of a formal language instead of to propositions ("events" in the customary terminology of mathematical probability theory), as in articles 2 and 6. But meanwhile, Gaifman and (independently) Jerzy Łoś were showing how to make better use of the old framework. (Item: by the compactness theorem for first-order logic, sigma-additivity is a trivial consequence of finite additivity, in this framework.) These developments— especially the line initiated by Łoś, to which Fenstad has contributed in earlier publications—is represented here by Fenstad's article 12. There open formulas as well as sentences are assigned c-values, which are interpreted as averages of relative frequencies with which the formulas are satisfied in finite models, under certain finiteness conditions; and from this, yet another proof of de Finetti's representation theorem for exchangeable sequences of events is forthcoming. An intriguing aspect of this point of view is the possibility of interpreting Carnap's individual constants a_i as free variables, thus making sense of Carnap's idea that exchangeability of the a_i is a "logical" assumption on a par with (say) finite additivity. (If feasible, this is a matter of doing without the k_n in Fenstad's symmetry condition, e.g., perhaps formulating it so: "$c(e) = c(e')$ for all formulas e, e' that are obtainable from each other by permutation of variables." Does this do the work of (I) in Fenstad's treatment?)

Finally, in article 13 David Lewis places the objectivistic concept of probability (chance, propensity) in a subjectivistic or inductive framework by systematic exploitation of what he calls "The Principal Principle," thereby shedding light on such matters as the relationship between chances and frequencies, and the prospects for reducing the objectivistic probability concept to the subjectivistic one.

(Added in press, October 1979.) Douglas Hoover kindly read §21 of Article 6 in galley proof. His observations (appended here as Article 14) answer the questions that Carnap raised there, in the light of recent developments in nonstandard measure theory.

Richard Jeffrey

Princeton, N.J.
June 1978

6

A Basic System
of Inductive Logic
Part II

BY RUDOLF CARNAP

Editor's Note. This completes article 2. Here §§14–18 are as revised by Carnap for this volume, but §§19 and 20C are as in Carnap's first draft. Carnap would have ended this article with §20, and published a revision (surely a considerable revision) of what is here §21 later in the series. Thanks are due to Lary Kuhns and Gordon Matthews for their generous help with obscure parts of the text.

The other articles in these volumes can be read independently of this one, and of one another.

14

The Attribute Space;
Distances and Widths of Attributes.

A. THE COLOR SPACE.

The assignment of values of $\mathcal{C}$ or $\mathcal{M}$ to propositions involving attributes of a given family is frequently influenced by certain features of these attributes and relations among them, e.g., relations of similarity. In this section we make a digression from the field of pure inductive logic to that of applied IL (§4) in order to gain a clearer picture, though still a simple and informal picture, of these features and relations. In the next section we shall discuss the nature of the rules of applied IL which guide the choice of certain $\mathcal{C}$- or $\mathcal{M}$-values with regard to those relations among the attributes. And in subsequent sections we shall develop further our system of IL, and make use of special rules of applied IL.

As an example of an attribute space, we considered earlier (2–1) the *color space* $\mathbf{U}^1$, and the family of the six colors Red, Orange, Yellow, Green, Blue, Violet. This family corresponds to a partition of $\mathbf{U}^1$ into six regions. The colors mentioned (in the given order) are designated in language $\mathscr{L}_1$ by the predicates 'P_1', . . . , 'P_6', respectively. We shall now consider the features of this space in somewhat more detail, but still only in outline. The color space is three-dimensional and has (according to some analyses) the shape of a double cone (figure 14-1). The saturated hues are represented by the points on the circumference of a circular area A with center C (figure 14-2). The points of the segment of the circumference marked "Red" represent saturated red hues, from yellowish red to bluish red (near violet). The center C represents neutral gray. Moving from the circumference to C, we come from saturated red through less and less saturated, more and more grayish red to neutral gray, all of the same brightness. Imagine the circular area A lying in a horizontal plane; then the axis of the double cone is a vertical line through C. The points of the axis represent nonchromatic (gray) colors, from white through darker and darker grays to black. The interior points of the cone above A represent brighter colors, those below A darker ones.

When we study the similarity relations among elementary qualities of a given kind, we find it often not difficult to make merely *comparative* judgments to the effect that the similarity in a given pair of qualities is equal to that in another pair, or that the first pair shows a higher (or a lower) similarity than the second (compare

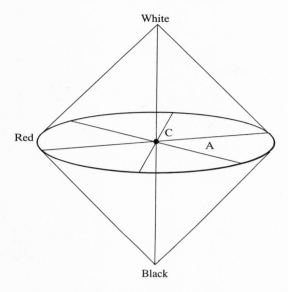

Fig. 14-1.   The Color Space.

(5-4) and the discussion following it). E.g., looking at four cards showing one each of the following four elementary colors: a pure red R_1, a bluish red R_2, a reddish violet V_1, a pure neutral violet V_2, and a pure, neutral blue B_1, we shall not hesitate, if asked, to arrange them according to similarities. It is clear that R_2 is more similar to R_1 than either V_1 or V_2 or B_1 is; and that V_1 is more

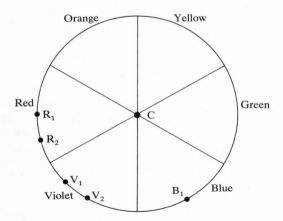

Fig. 14-2.   Area A of the Color Space.

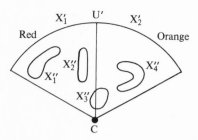

Fig. 14-3.   Subspaces of the Color Space.

similar to R_2 (and likewise to R_1) than V_2 is. It is more difficult to compare similarities of an intermediate color in the series with two other colors on different sides of it. We shall certainly judge that R_2 is more similar to R_1 than to B_1. But for some violet V_2 (less reddish than V_1) we may feel unable to say whether it is more similar to R_1 than to B_1, or less similar, or equally similar. On the other hand, there are cases of three colors, especially if they are nearer to each other than those in the last example, e.g., R_1, R_2, and V_1 for which we may feel able to judge that the intermediate color (R_2) has the same degree of similarity to each of the two other colors (R_1 and V_1). In this case we shall say that the *distance* between R_1 and R_2 is equal to that between R_2 and V_1. In the former example we shall say that the distance between R_1 and R_2 is smaller than that between R_2 and B_1. These are comparative judgments on distances, that is, similarities.

B. DISTANCE AND WIDTH

Sometimes it is possible to go beyond merely comparative judgments and make *quantitative* judgments. In the most favorable case one can define a *quantitative* (or metric) *concept of distance*, i.e., one that has a numerical value for any pair of elementary qualities so that we can make a statement of the form: "The distance between P_j and P_l is 2.3". For this we shall write "$d(P_j, P_l) = 2.3$" or simply "$d_{jl} = 2.3$". The following definition states the general conditions for a distance concept of this kind in any space.

D14-1. Let Ω be any abstract space and d be a function on $\Omega \times \Omega$ with nonnegative real numbers as values. We say that d is a (quantitative) *distance function* for Ω, and that Ω has a *metric* (is a metric space) based upon d if-if the following three conditions are fulfilled for any points u, v, w in Ω:

    (a) *Zero distance.* $d(u, v) = 0$ if-if u is identical with v.

    (b) *Commutativity.* $d(u, v) = d(v, u)$.

    (c) *Triangle condition.* $d(u, v) + d(v, w) \geq d(u, w)$.

Psychologists have introduced a metric of this kind for some fields of sensory qualities, e.g., a three-dimensional metric for colors and a one-dimensional metric (a metric scale) for the pitch of musical notes. Such a metric may be based, e.g., on the subjective judgments of the test person about equality of distances; another method is based on the least discriminable differences of elementary qualities; $d(P_j, P_l)$ is determined by the number of pairs in the shortest chain of pairs with such differences, connecting P_j with P_l. It seems that these two methods lead to essentially the same results.

If the attribute space **U** is the value space of a measurable magnitude G, it is often easier to find a natural distance function. For many magnitudes, especially in physics, there is a generally accepted scale, as for spatial length, temporal duration, mass, temperature (the Kelvin scale), etc. In a case of this kind it seems most natural, to adopt as the metric of the space **U**, for the purposes of inductive logic, the scale form chosen by the physicists, in other words, to take as distance in the space **U** for G the numerical difference between two values of G according to the standard scale. (The choice of the unit is irrelevant; its influence disappears through normalization of the width function and the distance function; see below, D3 and D4, respectively.)

The points of an attribute space represent elementary attributes. Usually, however, the attributes designated by primitive predicates of a language are not elementary, they have less than maximum specificity. Therefore they are represented in the attribute space not by points, but by extended *regions*. (Just as most of the propositions for which we wish to determine $\mathcal{M}$- or $\mathscr{C}$-values, are represented not by points in the probability space **Z** but by larger subsets of **Z**.)

A partition (D1-1d) of the attribute space **U** or, for short, an *attribute partition* is a countable, disjoint class $\mathscr{D}$ of subsets of **U** such that $\bigcup \mathscr{D} = \mathbf{U}$. Thus, in particular, any family is represented by an attribute partition. For example, if we divide the color space **U** by three planes through the vertical axis, each of them through one of the three diameters marked in the diagram of the area A (figure 11-2), we have a partition of six regions in **U**, representing the six color attributes.

Suppose that two attributes P_1 and P_2 are represented in the attribute space $\mathbf{U}$ by the regions X_1 and X_2 respectively. We shall see later, and it seems intuitively plausible, that it is relevant for the assignment of $\mathcal{M}$-values to propositions involving P_1 or P_2, whether X_1 is equal in size to X_2, or larger than X_2, or smaller. Here again we may be able to make only comparative judgments about the sizes of the two regions, or we may be able to make also quantitative judgments. We shall understand the **width** of an attribute as the size (volume) of the regions representing it. A width function is said to be **normalized** if-if the width of the whole space $\mathbf{U}$ is 1.

Suppose that a metric for the space $\mathbf{U}$ is given, based on a (quantitative) distance function d. Then a width function can often be defined with the help of d. Let us consider first the case of a *one-dimensional continuous space*. We introduce a coordinate x such that the following holds:

(14-1) For any two points in $\mathbf{U}$ with the coordinates x_1 and x_2, $d(x_1, x_2) = |x_2 - x_1|$.

By the coordinate x, the attribute space $\mathbf{U}$ is mapped in a one-to-one correspondence onto a subset of $\mathbf{R}$. We now decide:

(14-2) **a.** The *width function* w on $\mathbf{U}$ is to correspond to the *Lebesgue measure* on $\mathbf{R}$.
   Therefore we have:
  b. The width function w is a measure function.
  c. For a region X in $\mathbf{U}$ corresponding to an interval (closed, half-closed, or open) in $\mathbf{R}$, $w(X)$ is the length of the interval.
  d. w is σ-additive.

Suppose that $\mathbf{U}$ is an n-dimensional attribute space, with a distance function d, (e.g., the three-dimensional color space). We introduce an n-dimensional Cartesian coordinate system, so that, to each point u of $\mathbf{U}$ an n-tuple $\langle x_1, \ldots, x_n \rangle$ in $\mathbf{R}^n$ is assigned in such a way that d is a function of the coordinates. Usually we shall use a *Euclidean metric*; that is to say, the relation between the distance function d and the coordinates is as follows:

D14-2. If the point u in $\mathbf{U}$ has the coordinates $\langle x_1, \ldots, x_n \rangle$, and the point v has $\langle y_1, \ldots, y_n \rangle$, then $d^2(u, v) = \mathrm{Df} \sum_{nm=1} (y_m - x_m)^2$.

(14.3) For an n-dimensional metric space $\mathbf{U}$ we take as the *n-dimensional width function* $w^{(n)}$ the *n*-dimensional Lebesgue measure function. Then the following holds:

(14-4)   **a.**   Suppose the region $X \subset U$ is an *n*-dimensional interval (u, v), with the coordinates as in D2. (This means that the corresponding region X' in $\mathbf{R}^n$ is the Cartesian product of *n* intervals, one on each of the *n* coordinate axes: $X' = (x_1, y_1) \times (x_2, y_2) \times \ldots \times (x_n, y_n)$.) Then: $w^{(n)}(X) =$

$$w^{(n)}(u, v) = \prod_{m=1}^{n} |y_m - x_m|.$$

 b.   Let $\mathscr{A} = \{X_1, X_2 \ldots\}$ be a countable sequence of disjoint subsets of U, and let $X = \bigcup \mathscr{A}$. Then $w^{(n)}(X) = \sum_p w^{(n)}(X_p)$ (where the sum covers all $X_p \in \mathscr{A}$).

In some cases this simplest form of $w^{(n)}$ may not be appropriate. It may then be necessary to define $w^{(n)}$ in another way; but it should be a measure function (D1-7) and σ-additive (D1-8).

Suppose that, for a given attribute space U, we have first the distance function d, and then the width function w based upon d. Suppose that we find that w is not normalized, but that $w(U)$ is finite. Then it may be that we would prefer to use instead of w a *normalized width function* w'. We define:

D14-3.   For any region X in U, $w'(X) =_{\text{Df}} \dfrac{w(X)}{w(U)}.$

We have obviously $w'(U) = 1$; thus w' is normalized. However, this new function w' does not fit our original function d. Therefore it seems advisable, to introduce a *normalized distance function d'*, i.e., one that is in accord with the normalized width function w'. If the space U is *n*-dimensional, we define (in terms of the original functions d and w):

D14-4.   For any points $u, v \in U$,

$$d'(u, v) =_{\text{Df}} \frac{d(u, v)}{w(U)^{1/n}}.$$

Let Y be any *n*-dimensional interval in U; let the *n* component intervals of Y have the lengths (measured by d) $b_1, \ldots, b_n$, respectively. Let the normalized functions w' and d' be defined by D3 and D4, respectively. Then we have $w'(Y) = w(Y)/w(\mathbf{U}) = b_1 b_2 \ldots b_n/w(\mathbf{U})$ (by (4)(a)) $= \prod_{m=1}^{n} [b_n/w(\mathbf{U})^{1/n}] = b_1 b_2' \ldots b_n'$, where $b_1', \ldots, b_n'$ are measured by d'. This shows that the function d' defined by D4 is in accord with w'.

In some cases the normalization procedure proposed in D3 does not work. Suppose that the set B of the possible values of a real-valued function G, say a physical magnitude, is not bounded, and that the Lebesgue measure of B is infinite. Then w, based on the Lebesgue measure, is not normalized. Here D3 is not applicable since $w(B)$ is infinite and hence, for any finite interval A, D3 would yield: $w'(A) = 0$. In a situation of this kind, two ways are open to us. First, we may transform G into G' with the help of a suitable function f which maps B onto a set of Lebesgue measure 1:

(14-5) For any individual a_i,

$$G'(a_i) =_{\mathrm{Df}} f(G(a_i)).$$

Let B' be the value space for G', and let w' for subsets of B' be defined as Lebesgue measure. Then $w'(B') = 1$, and thus w' is normalized.

On the other hand, it may be that we do not find any function f such that the resulting magnitude G' appears as natural. In this case we might prefer to retain the original G and the width function w in spite of its failure to be normalized. Then the function $\mathcal{M}$ based upon w will likewise be non-normalized, and thus not be a probability measure (PM, D1-7) and not be counted as an "$\mathcal{M}$-function" (D1-10). But it may still be the case that the corresponding $\mathscr{C}$-function has normal values for pairs of propositions H, E of the following kind. Let X_1 be any subset of $\mathbf{R}$ with infinite Lebesgue measure; let $X_2 \subset X_1$; for a given individual a_i, let E be the proposition that, $G(a_i) \in X_1$, and H be the analogous proposition for X_2. Then we may define $\mathscr{C}$ as follows:*

(14-6) $$\mathscr{C}_{(H|e)} =_{\mathrm{Df}} \lim_{x \to \infty} \frac{w(X_2 \cap B_x)}{w(X_1 \cap B_x)},$$

where the values of x are the positive real numbers (or the positive integers) and B_x is the closed interval $[-x, +x] \subset \mathbf{R}$.

---

* To ensure existence of the limit, this definition may require modification, e.g., as indicated in Emanuel Parzen, *Modern Probability Theory and its Applications*, (New York: Wiley, 1960), p. 335. (Ed.)

Sometimes, for the purpose of a certain investigation, we wish to consider as possible only some of the attributes of a certain modality, say the colors. In this case we use, instead of the original attribute space U only a proper subspace U'. For example, for the study of a certain kind of objects, say flowers, we may wish to take a subspace U' containing only the two sectors Red and Orange, or perhaps a still narrower subspace U'' consisting of four separate regions X_1'', X_2'', X_3'' and X_4'' within these sectors (as shown in Fig. 11-3, where the third dimension is disregarded). U' consists of the whole sector shown; U'' is the union of the four regions X_1'', X_2'', X_3'', X_4''. Suppose we had a width function w for the whole color space. Then we may simply retain w as a width function for U' and for U'', if we do not care for normalization. If, however, we wish normalized width functions w' and w'' for U' and U'', respectively, we define them as follows in accordance with D3 (it does not matter whether w is normalized or not):

(14-7)   For any region $X' \subset U'$,

$$w'(X') =_{\text{Df}} \frac{w(X')}{w(U')}.$$

(14-8)   For any region $X'' \subset U''$,

$$w''(X'') =_{\text{Df}} \frac{w(X'')}{w(U'')},$$

where $w(U'') = w(X_1'') + w(X_2'') + w(X_3'') + w(X_4'')$.

The color space U is partitioned into six equal sectors for the six color attributes. Thus, for each sector X, $w(X) = 1/6$. The space U' consists of two of those six sectors; hence $w(U) = 1/3$. Therefore, by (7), for each of these two sectors X', $w'(X') = 1/2$. Suppose that, in U'', for $j = 1, 2, 3, 4$ $w(X_j'') = 3/180, 2/180, 1/180, 4/180$, respectively; thus together $w(U'') = 10/180$ $(= 1/18)$. Then by (8): $w''(X_j'') = 3/10, 2/10, 1/10, 4/10$, respectively; thus together $w''(U'') = 1$. This shows that w'' is indeed normalized for U''.

[The restriction of the attribute space to U' is a transition to a *sublanguage of the fourth kind*; this was dealt with in §6, see D6-4 and Example (6-10). Sublanguages of this kind are not conservative (6-13d); therefore the rule R6-1 is not applicable. But a method for forming an adequate $\mathscr{C}$-function for a sublanguage of this kind was given in (6-15). —The restriction of the space U' to U'' is not of the same kind, but more complicated. We assume that X_1'', X_2'', X_3'', and X_4'' have been defined. Let $X_{3a}'' =_{\text{Df}} X_3'' \cap X_1'$, and $X_{3b}'' =_{\text{Df}} X_3'' \cap X_2'$.

Our first step consists in splitting X_1' into four parts: X_1'', X_2'', X_{3a}'', and the rest, X_1^* (i.e., $X_1' - (X_1'' \cup X_2'' \cup X_{3a}'')$). This procedure is the inverse of the transition to a sublanguage of the third kind (D6-3) by the merger of several attributes. The second step is similar. Here X_2' is subdivided into three parts: X_{3b}'', X_4'', and the rest, X_2^*. Thus we have a seven-part partition of $\mathbf{U}'$. Now we take the main step: we restrict $\mathbf{U}'$ to $\mathbf{U}''$ with the five-part partition $\{X_1'', X_2'', X_{3a}'', X_{3b}'', X_4''\}$. This step is of the same kind as the transition from $\mathbf{U}$ to $\mathbf{U}'$. Finally, we make a merger, of X_{3a}'' and X_{3b}'' into X_3''. This leads to the four-part partition $\{X_1'', X_2'', X_3'', X_4''\}$.]

Suppose that F is a family of k qualitative attributes, for which we have not found a natural metric, but only a comparative serial order. As examples, consider the sequence of five attributes {Hot, Warm, Lukewarm, Cool, Cold} (before a concept of temperature was introduced) or the sequence {Easy, Medium, Difficult} for examination questions, based on subjective impressions. In spite of their subjective nature, we may wish to apply inductive methods to such families, and therefore to assign concepts of width and distance. The following procedure may be considered for this purpose. This procedure, and (b) in particular, is suggested by the partition of a finite interval in $\mathbf{R}$, which might be the value space of a quantitative magnitude, into k equal parts.

(14-9) For a serial family of k attributes without a metric, we may define a normalized width function w and a normalized distance function d as follows.

  a. For each of the k attributes, we take $w = 1/k$.
  b. For any two adjacent attributes in the series, we take $d = 1/k$.
  c. In the case of a family of two attributes, where we do not see any reason for ascribing to the one a larger width than to the other, we shall take (as in (a) and (b)) $w = 1/2$ for each, and $d_{1,2} = 1/2$.

C. SEVERAL FAMILIES.

For the rest of this section, we shall use, not the one-family-language $\mathscr{L}_1$, but the full language $\mathscr{L}$ containing n families F^m ($m = 1, \ldots, n$). [Since the concepts here introduced refer to several families, they will hardly be used in subsequent sections of this article.] Suppose the individuals are material objects which are investigated with respect to n different features, each represented by one of the n families in $\mathscr{L}$. Each feature may be either qualitative or quantitative. Each family F^m is represented in its attribute space $\mathbf{U}^m$ by a countable partition $\{X_1^m, X_2^m, \ldots\}$. For example, a given class of persons at a given time is to be studied with respect to the following features: (1) sex, (2) age (in years), (3) height (in centimeters), (4) weight (in grams), etc. (1) is a qualitative concept, with a family of two attributes: $F^1 = P_1^1$, P_2^1, P_1^1 is the attribute Male, P_2^1 Female. (2), (3), and (4) are quantitative concepts, which may be expressed by functors 'G_2', 'G_3', 'G_4'. The spaces of G_2, G_3, and G_4 are intervals of $\mathbf{R}$; $\mathbf{U}^2$ may be the interval $[0, 120]$, $\mathbf{U}^3$ the interval $[20, 200]$, $\mathbf{U}^4$ $[1000, 160000]$, The normalized coordinates in these three spaces are defined as follows: $G_2'(x) =_{\mathrm{Df}} G_2(x)/120$; $G_3'(x) =_{\mathrm{Df}} G_3(x-20)/180$; $G_4'(x) =_{\mathrm{Df}} G_4(x-1000)/150{,}000$. We assume that, for each of the qualitative features in the investigation, we have a metric attribute space $\mathbf{U}^m$, with a normalized width function w_m and a normalized distance function d_m. [Since F^1 contains only two attributes, we have, in accordance with (9)(c), $w(P_1^1) = w(P_2^1) = 1/2$, and $d_{1,2} = 1/2$.]

As the overall attribute space for those n concepts in language $\mathscr{L}$, we take the n-fold *product space* $\mathbf{U} = \mathbf{U}^1 \times \mathbf{U}^2 \times \ldots \times \mathbf{U}^n$. The points of $\mathbf{U}$ are the n-tuples $\langle u_1, \ldots, u_n \rangle$, where u_m $(m = 1, \ldots, n)$ is a point of $\mathbf{U}^m$. Each point of $\mathbf{U}$ represents a specific possibility for an individual, in all n respects together (e.g., "Sex: male; Age: 2.735 years; Height: 158.3 cm; ... ").

Since we have a metric for each space $\mathbf{U}^m$ $(m = 1, \ldots, n)$, we can define a metric for $\mathbf{U}$. It will seem natural to use for this definition the Euclidean form, as in D2:

D14-5. The *Euclidean distance function d* for a product space $\mathbf{U} = \mathbf{U}^1 \times \ldots \times \mathbf{U}^n$ is defined as follows. Let u be a point in $\mathbf{U}$ with the coordinate n-tuple '$\langle u_1, \ldots, u_n \rangle$' and v with $\langle v_1, \ldots, v_n \rangle$; then:

$$d^2(u_1, \ldots, u_n; v_1, \ldots, v_n) =_{\mathrm{Df}} \sum_{m=1}^{n} d_m^2(u_m, v_m),$$

where $d_m(u_m, v_m)$ is the distance between the points u_m and v_m in the component space $\mathbf{U}^m$.

In particular cases, a non-Euclidean metric may be chosen.

Let us now consider a difficulty that appears in connection with a distance definition for a product space, if physical magnitudes of different physical dimensions are involved. In the above example, the dimensions of G_2, G_3, and G_4 are temporal duration (T), length (L), and weight, or, in terms of physics, mass (M), respectively. In physics, one usually avoids adding numerical values which are not of the same dimension. In D5, however, we add: $T^2 + L^2 + M^2$. A sum of this kind does not occur in the customary formulations in physics. But I believe that we need something of this form in inductive logic. This will become clear in the next sections when we consider the influence of attribute distances on $\mathscr{C}$-values. If we change over to a new unit in one of the magnitudes, say in G_4 from gram to kilogram, while we keep the old units for G_2 and G_3, then any statement in physics, say a prediction of an observable event, remains unchanged (provided that a suitable adjustment in the coefficients of G_4 is made). In contrast to this, there would be a change in the result of an application of inductive logic (no change, of course, in pure inductive logic itself). Therefore we need here a convention establishing something like equivalent units for different magnitudes. This difficulty would disappear if in a future system of physics we had natural units at least for the fundamental magnitudes. Today we have a natural unit for electric charge by the elementary charge; and for velocity by the velocity of light, which is the upper bound for all velocities of motions and signals. [A solution of a different kind, which might sometimes be practically useful, although its theoretical justification is doubtful, would consist in guiding the choice of a unit for a certain magnitude G_m in the context of an investigation of a given domain of individuals, by the standard deviation observed in a sample or estimated for the population.] For the time being, the best procedure for an objective comparison between values of magnitudes of different dimensions seems to me to be the use of normalized distance functions (D4) in the various value spaces for a given investigation.

The value-space $\mathbf{U}^m$ of a magnitude G_m is usually an interval in $\mathbf{R}$, mostly a finite one. With respect to a qualitative space $\mathbf{U}$, e.g., the color space, usually a sentence in $\mathscr{L}$ can ascribe to an individual only an attribute represented by an extended region, not a point-attribute. The same holds for a quantitative concept G_m. In the context of a certain investigation, we are in general content with a description of the individuals in terms of a countable (usually finite) partition of $\mathbf{U}^m$ which is in this case a subset of $\mathbf{R}_1$ into intervals, neglecting the finer distinctions between different values of G_m within an interval (see the example [2-3] of an interval partition for age).

Let us now assume that for each of the n features, we have a space $\mathbf{U}^m$ with a metric based upon a normalized distance function d_m and a normalized width function w_m; hence we have $w_m(\mathbf{U}^m) = 1$. Furthermore, suppose we have chosen, for each of these spaces $\mathbf{U}^m$ a countable partition $\mathscr{D}^m$. Since the space is finite, the partition will usually also be finite; let k_m be the number of the parts in $\mathscr{D}^m$. Thus $\mathscr{D}^m = \{X_1^m, X_2^m, \ldots, X_{k_m}^m\}$. Each region X_j^m represents an attribute P_j^m. In a qualitative family this is a qualitative attribute, in a quantitative family it is a quantitative attribute. In the example (2-3) for a partition of the value space, P_3^2 is the property of having an age higher than 30 and not higher than 35 years. Thus we assimilate the quantitative families to the qualitative ones. And also inversely, for a quantative family F^m we introduce a real-valued function G_m with attribute indices as values:

(14-10) $$(G_m(a_i) = j) =_{\text{Df}} P_j^m(a_i).$$

Any individual can now be characterized by one attribute in each family, thus by an n-tuple of attributes, say $\langle P_{j_1}^1, P_{j_2}^2, \ldots, P_{j_n}^n \rangle$. These n-tuples are obviously the elements of the Cartesian product $F^1 \times F^2 + \ldots \times F^n$. To each n-tuple $\langle P_{j_1}^1, P_{j_2}^2, \ldots, P_{j_n}^n \rangle$, or simply to the n-tuple of indices $\langle j_1, j_2, \ldots, j_n \rangle$, there is a corresponding attribute $Q_{j_1 j_2 \ldots j_n}$. We call these attributes Q-*attributes*.

We define:

D14-16.   For any a_i, $Q_{j_1 j_2 \ldots j_n}(a_i) =_{\text{Df}}$

$$P_{j_1}^1(a_i) \cap P_{j_2}^2(a_i) \cap \ldots \cap P_{j_n}^n(a_i).$$

Thus a Q-attribute characterizes an individual completely within the frame-work of the n families. (The Q-predicates were first defined in [1950, §31], but only for families with $k = 2$; the general case is briefly indicated in [1950, §18C].)

(14-11)   The number of Q-attributes is $k = \prod\limits_{m=1}^{n} k_m$.

In each space $\mathbf{U}^m$, there is a partition $\mathscr{D}^m = \{X_1^m, \ldots, X_{k_m}^m\}$ into k_m parts. These partitions generate a k-partition $\mathscr{D} = \mathscr{D}^1 \times \mathscr{D}^2 \times \ldots \times \mathscr{D}^n$ of the product space $\mathbf{U} = \mathbf{U}^1 \times \mathbf{U}^2 \times \ldots \times \mathbf{U}^n$. Each part, e.g., $\langle X_{j_1}^1, X_{j_2}^2, \ldots, X_{j_n}^n \rangle$, represents one of the k Q-attributes, viz. $Q_{j_1 j_2 \ldots j_n}$. We call the partition $\mathscr{D}$ the product partition or Q-partition.

It seems natural to define a width function w for the product space $\mathbf{U}$ in the following way.

(14-12) $$w(X_{j_1 \ldots j_n}) = \prod_{m=1}^{n} w_m(X_{j_m}^m).$$

[The present concept of width is a generalization of my earlier concept of "relative logical width" (1950, §32), which was based on a special form of Q-partition.]

15
Basic Regions and Admissible Regions in the Attribute Space

A. BASIC REGIONS

We go back to our language $\mathscr{L}$, with one family F of k attributes: $F = \{P_1, P_2, \ldots, P_k\}$. We shall consider the question as to which properties of these attributes are relevant for IL or, more specifically, for the determination of values of the functions $\mathscr{C}$ and $\mathscr{M}$ for any propositions involving attributes of F. These k attributes are represented by the regions of a partition of the attribute space $\mathbf{U}$, say $\{X_1, \ldots, X_k\}$. We shall now consider the question of which properties of the k attributes P_j and the regions X_j $(j = 1, \ldots, k)$ are relevant for IL.

I cannot give a definitive answer to these questions. But I wish to state partial and tentative answers in the form of *three conjectures*, C1, C2, and C3. I have used them in recent years as, so to speak, working hypotheses for intuitive, pre-systematic speculations. I state them in spite of their uncertainty, because I have found them useful in searching for rules of IL. Perhaps others might be willing to use them for the time being, "until further notice", or to suggest modifications.

C15-1. *First Conjecture.* Only those properties of P_m (those relations between P_m and P_n) are essential for IL, i.e., for the determination of values of $\mathscr{C}$ for propositions involving P_m (and P_n), which are reflected in the topological and metric properties of X_m (in the topological and metric relations between X_m and X_n).

Among the essential properties of X_m (in the sense of C1) are these: the number of separate subregions of which X_m consists, and for each connected subregion: its width, its shape, its location in $\mathbf{U}$, etc. Among the essential relations between X_m and X_n or between two separate subregions $X_{m,1}$ and $X_{m,2}$ of X_m are: relations of width, relations of location to each other, relations based on distances (e.g., maximum distance, minimum distance, mean distance, etc.). The class of possibilities for some of these characteristics is obviously enormous, for example, the totality of possible shapes for three-dimensional connected regions of fixed width in a three-dimensional space. Thus the question arises whether it is necessary to state rules for this vast variety of regions. We shall find that it is sufficient to state such rules for regions of a special kind, of small size and simple shape, which we shall call "basic regions". The class of basic regions will be chosen in such a way that the values of $\mathscr{C}$ for propositions involving any partition $\mathscr{D}'$ of **U** which might be scientifically useful, are determined by the values of $\mathscr{C}$ for propositions involving some partition $\mathscr{D}$ consisting of basic regions such that $\mathscr{D}$ is a refinement of $\mathscr{D}'$ (i.e., every set of $\mathscr{D}$ is a subset of some set of $\mathscr{D}'$).

Let us say, for short, "*useful*" instead of "scientifically useful". A useful partition, or region (of the partition), or attribute (represented by the region) is here meant as one that could conceivably occur in the context of a scientific investigation where the scientist would be interested in $\mathscr{C}$- and $\mathscr{M}$-values for propositions involving the attributes of this partition. For example, in the space **R**, let X be the interval $(3, 4]$. Then X is useful, since the investigator might be interested in the hypothesis that a certain measurement of a physical magnitude G will yield a number in X; e.g., "$G(a_5) \in X$". In contrast, let X' be the set of the rational numbers of X: $X' =_{Df} X \cap$ **Q**. Then X' is not useful. Although the statement that the result of the measurement will be in X', is mathematically meaningful, it has no scientific (e.g., physical) significance. Likewise, a degenerate interval is not useful. True, a scientist writes often something like "$G(a_5) = 4.13$" as a statement (assertion or hypothesis) of a measurement result. But this is to be understood, not really as a point statement, but rather as an abbreviation for a statement on a nondegenerate interval, maybe for "$G(a_5) \in [4.125, 4.135]$".

I prefer to take as *primitive* predicates in the languages here considered only those with a *connected* region. Suppose the predicate 'M' has a region consisting of several separate parts $X_1, X_2, \ldots, X_p$, each of them a connected region, then we shall take p predicates 'P_1', $\ldots$, 'P_p', each represented by one of those regions, among our primitive predicates and define 'M' as their disjunction. Unless otherwise indicated, I shall understand the term "region" in the sense of "connected region". Furthermore, I usually assume that the region of an attribute, and even the whole attribute space **U**, is finite. (Otherwise, a normalized width function for **U** is not possible.)

We shall now consider the properties of useful regions. In **R**, just the intervals are connected regions; and just the finite, nondegenerate intervals are useful. The interesting problems appear for $\mathbf{R}^n$ with $n > 1$. We shall now consider $\mathbf{R}^2$; for $n > 2$, the situation is analogous, but more complicated.

It seems plausible to make the following assumptions. (We might also put it this way: Let us understand the term "useful" in such a way that these assumptions hold.)

(15-1)   We assume that the following holds for every useful (connected) region X in $\mathbf{R}^2$.

    (a) X is two-dimensional at every one of its points.

    (b) Let μ be the two-dimensional Lebesgue measure function. Then $\mu(X)$ is positive finite.

    (c) X is bordered by a curve C such that:

        (i) C is a simple closed curve (i.e., topologically equivalent to a circle).

        (ii) C has, at each of its points, either one or two tangents.

Suppose that an attribute space $\mathbf{U}$ is given. We shall now consider possible ways of defining for $\mathbf{U}$ a class $\mathscr{B}$ of *basic regions* and later a class $\mathscr{A}$ of *admissible regions* such that $\mathscr{A}$ contains all those subsets of $\mathbf{U}$ that might be useful (in the sense indicated above).

C15-2.   *Second Conjecture.* For a given attribute space $\mathbf{U}$, *a class $\mathscr{B}$ of basic regions* in $\mathbf{U}$ may be chosen in one of the following ways.

    a. Suppose that we have *no metric* for $\mathbf{U}$ but are able to make *comparative judgements* on widths, at least for regions of simple shape. We choose an arbitrary small region X of a simple shape and take as $\mathscr{B}$ the class of all regions B of a simple shape such that the width of B appears to us as clearly positive and as clearly smaller than that of X.

    b. Suppose that we have a *metric* for $\mathbf{U}$, i.e., a normalized *distance function* d and, based upon d, a normalized *width function* w. We choose a small positive real number x and a class $\mathscr{B}'$ of regions characterized by a chosen simple convex shape. Then we take as $\mathscr{B}$ the class of all regions B of $\mathscr{B}'$ such that $0 < w(B) \leqq x$.

    c. Special case of (b), for a one-dimensional space $\mathbf{U}$. We proceed as in (b), with the class of all rational intervals as $\mathscr{B}'$.

    d. Suppose that $\mathbf{U}$ is an n fold product space $\mathbf{U}_1 \times \ldots \times \mathbf{U}_n$, and that for each component space $\mathbf{U}_m$ ($m = 1, \ldots, n$), a class $\mathscr{B}_m$ has been chosen according to (a) or (b) or (c). We take $\mathscr{B} = \{B_1 \times \ldots \times B_n : \text{for every } m\ (m = 1, \ldots, n),\ B_m \in \mathscr{B}_m\}$.

In the case of a discrete, countable attribute space $\mathbf{U}$ it does not seem necessary to distinguish between basic and other regions; any subset of $\mathbf{U}$ may be taken as an admissible region. The problem of basic regions is important in the case of a continuous space. For a space of this kind I shall now give a schema in which the class of basic regions is defined (D1). Later, the general class of admissible regions will be defined (D3). This schema does not claim to be the best solution. It is merely intended to give a suitable framework for future concrete examples.

D15-1. For *the attribute space* **U**, we make the following assumptions (i) through (vii); m runs always from 1 to n.

> **(i)** **U** is an *n-dimensional continuous space* (n positive finite).
>
> **(ii)** In **U** an n-dimensional, rectangular, Cartesian *coordinate-system* is given; thus **U** is mapped onto a subset **R′** of **R**^{n}.
>
> **(iii)** On the m-th coordinate axis, let μ_m be the Lebesgue measure function. Thus, for any interval B_m on this axis, $\mu_m(B_m)$ is the length of B_m.
>
> **(iv)** In **R**^{n}, let μ be the n-dimensional Lebesgue measure function. Thus, for any n-dimensional interval B in **R**^{n}, with the interval components $B_1, \ldots, B_n$,
>
> $$\mu(B) = \prod_m \mu(B_m).$$
>
> **(v)** For the sake of simplicity we shall identify **U** with **R′**; that is to say, we shall speak of any point $u \in $ **U** as being (instead of merely "corresponding to") an n-tuple of real numbers: $u = \langle x_1, \ldots, x_n \rangle \in $ **R′**.
>
> **(vi)** We assume that $\mu($**R′**$)$, and hence $\mu($**U**$)$, is finite (and positive).
>
> **(vii)** μ, as defined in (iv), is a non-normalized width function for n-dimensional intervals in **R**^{n}.

Now we define as follows.

> **a.** For any m, on the mth coordinate axis in **R**^{n} we take as the class $\mathscr{B}_m'$ of basic component regions the class of all rational intervals of all four kinds, that is, (x, y), $[x, y)$, $(x, y]$, and $[x, y]$, where $x, y \in $ **Q** and $x < y$.
>
> **b.** We take as the class $\mathscr{B}'$ of *basic regions in* **R**^{n} the n-dimensional rational intervals of all 4^n kinds. For any two distinct rational points u, v in **R**^{n}, say $u = \langle x_1, \ldots, x_n \rangle$ and $v = \langle y_1, \ldots, y_n \rangle$, where for any m, x_m and y_m are rational numbers, $x_m < y_m$, and $B_m \in \mathscr{B}_m'$ (B_m

is anyone of the four intervals with x_m and y_m, as in (a)), we define:

$$\text{the basic region } B_{u,v} =_{Df} B_1 \times \ldots \times B_n.$$

We call the n intervals $B_1, \ldots, B_n$ the component intervals of $B_{u,v}$.

c. On the basis of (vi) and (vii), we define the width function w for $\mathbf{R}'$ and $\mathbf{U}$. For any Lebesgue-measurable set $A \subset \mathbf{R}'$,

$$w(A) =_{Df} \frac{\mu(A)}{\mu(\mathbf{R}')}.$$

Hence $w(\mathbf{R}') = 1$; thus w is *normalized*.

d. We define the class $\mathcal{B}$ of *basic regions in* $\mathbf{U}$ as the class of these basic regions B in $\mathbf{R}^n$ which satisfy the following additional conditions:

(1) $B \subset \mathbf{U}$.

(2) $w(B) \leqq \epsilon^n$, where ϵ is a positive small fraction chosen once and for all (for example, .01).

(3) For any given basic region B in $\mathbf{R}^n$, let w_j be the greatest and w_l the least width among the n component intervals of B. Then it is required that $w_j/w_l \leqq \beta$, where β is a real number $\geqq 1$, to be chosen once and for all.

[Some remarks on d(3). The purpose of the requirement (3) is to exclude elongated shapes for basic regions, because they would lead to difficulties at a certain point. We shall find an example of such a difficulty in connection with the definition of distance between basic regions (D2d). It seems that a value in the interval $[1, 2]$ would be suitable. The requirement is the stronger the nearer to 1 β is chosen. Even the extreme value $\beta = 1$ may be chosen. In this case, for any basic region, all component intervals have equal length; thus all basic regions in $\mathbf{R}^n$ are n-dimensional cubes or hypercubes, in $\mathbf{R}^2$ they are squares.]

D15-2. *Distance functions* for points and for basic regions

a. On the mth coordinate axis we take the natural distance function:

$$d_{(m)}(x_m, y_m) =_{Df} |y_m - x_m|.$$

b. For the *distance function d in* $\mathbf{R}^n$ (and hence in $\mathbf{U}$), we take the Euclidean definition (D14-2).

c. If $u = \langle x_1, \ldots, x_n \rangle$ and $v = \langle y_1, \ldots, y_n \rangle$, $x_m < y_m$, then the *center* of the n-dimensional interval $B_{u,v}$ is the point $t = \langle z_1, \ldots, z_n \rangle$, where for every m, $z_m = (x_m + y_m)/2$.

d. We introduce the concept of the *distance between disjoint basic regions* (for simplicity, we shall use here the same symbol 'd' as for the distance between points). For any two disjoint B, $B' \in \mathscr{B}$,

$$d(B, B') =_{\text{Df}} d(t, t'),$$

where t is the center of B, and t' that of B'.

Strictly speaking, the distance between two n-dimensional intervals A and A' in $\mathbf{R}^n$, in the sense of the mean distance for all pairs of points u, u', where $u = \langle x_1, x_2, \ldots, x_n \rangle$ is in A and $u' = \langle y_1, y_2, \ldots, y_n \rangle$ in A', is to be determined by a $2n$-fold integral (with the variables $x_1, \ldots, x_n$, $y_1, \ldots, y_n$). This leads to rather complicated formulas. However, in the case of two disjoint *basic* regions B and B', the distance between their centers yields a convenient approximation, which is sufficient in most practical cases, in view of the fact that a basic region is small (D1d(2)) and not elongated (D1d(3)). If the latter condition were not required, our definition D2d would lead to unacceptable results. For example, let B in $\mathbf{R}^2$ be a rectangle with the lengths of the sides being $w_1 = 16b$ and $w_2 = 2b$ (for some b). Thus $w_1/w_2 = 8$; hence D1d(3) is not satisfied. Let B' be a tiny square with the length of the sides being a small fraction of b; let B' be located adjacent to B, one side of B' coinciding with a central part of a long side of B. Then the distance between the centers of B and of B' is roughly b; but the mean distance is roughly $4b$.

B. ADMISSIBLE REGIONS

Earlier we discussed a kind of regions in $\mathbf{U}$ which we called "(scientifically) useful regions". We did not give a definition of this concept, but indicated its meaning only in inexact, intuitive terms. Now we shall contemplate the concept of *admissible regions* in $\mathbf{U}$ and then give a definition for it, with the symbol '$\mathscr{A}$'. This concept is intended to be closely connected with the concept of useful regions. The class $\mathscr{A}$ is, however, not intended as an explicatum for the concept of useful regions. We wish $\mathscr{A}$ to contain all useful regions.

But we shall not object to the inclusion of some nonuseful regions if thereby the definition of $\mathscr{A}$ gains in simplicity. Scientific concepts are frequently formed in such a way that they include also some cases that the man on the street would exclude. For example, the scientific concept of metal, which is based on the micro-structure of bodies rather than their directly observable properties, includes also substances like sodium, although its behavior under ordinary conditions deviates far from that of the familiar metals by being soft and inflammable.

We shall now indicate two guiding ideas for our search of a suitable definition of the class of admissible regions.

(15-2)   We wish the sought for definition of the class of admissible regions in **U** to fulfill the following two conditions.

> **(a)** If we see clearly that a given region X is useful, then $\mathscr{A}$ should contain X.
>
> **(b)** Beyond this requirement, $\mathscr{A}$ should be as simple as possible.

Thus the practical procedure is this. Among the classes that we recognize at some time as satisfying condition **(a)**, we choose that which appears to be the simplest. This leaves open the possibility that later we discover a class that is even simpler and still satisfies **(a)**. From this point of view the following definition seems to my friends and me at the present moment the most satisfactory one. (It refers to the class $\mathscr{B}'$ defined in D1b.)

D15-3.   Definition of *admissible regions*.

> **a.** We define the class $\mathscr{A}'$ of the admissible regions in $\mathbf{R}^n$:
>
> $$\mathscr{A}' =_{\mathrm{Df}} \{A: \text{ for some countable sequence } \mathscr{B}^* = \{B_1, B_2, \ldots\} \text{ of disjoint basic regions in } \mathscr{B}', A = \bigcup \mathscr{B}^*.$$
>
> **b.** We take as the class $\mathscr{A}$ of the admissible regions in **U** the class of those sets in $\mathscr{A}'$ which are subsets of **U**.

Now let us informally consider the question whether the definition D3 is adequate and, more specifically, whether it fulfills the requirements (2). We shall restrict our consideration to the case of $\mathbf{R}^2$, as we did in (1). Suppose that X is a useful (connected) region in $\mathbf{R}^2$. Then, according to our assumptions (1), X satisfies the conditions there stated and, in particular, the condition (1c): X is bordered by a curve C of the kind there specified. Hence, even without a formal proof, it seems intuitively plausible that X can be partitioned by a countable sequence of basic regions, that is, two-dimensional rational intervals satisfying the conditions in D1. Therefore $X \in \mathscr{A}'$ (D3a). Thus the requirement (2a) is satisfied. Since the regions of all primitive attributes in a family considered in IL are useful, we shall always assume that such regions belong to $\mathscr{A}$. And in general, whenever we speak of "regions" in a continuous attribute space with a metric, we mean admissible regions.

Does D3 also satisfy (2b), the requirement of simplicity? It seems to me that D3 is surprisingly simple. We can hardly expect to find a simpler definition for a class that still satisfies (2a). If we were to simplify the definition of $\mathscr{A}'$ by referring to a *finite* sequence $\mathscr{B}^*$ instead of a countable one as in D3a, then this would certainly be an inadequate definition; it would violate (2a), since for $\mathbf{R}^2$ it would exclude triangles and circles.

The following results hold in virtue of the preceding definitions.

T15-1. Let X be any *admissible region* in the attribute space $\mathbf{U}$.
    a. There is a countable disjoint sequence $\mathscr{B}^* = \{B_1, B_2, \ldots\}$ such that $\mathscr{B}^* \subset \mathscr{B}$ and $X = \bigcup \mathscr{B}^*$. (From D3a).)
    b. w is σ-additive.

Proof. The Lebesgue measure is σ-additive (D1-8); therefore likewise μ (D1(iv)) and w (D1c). ∎

    c. $w(X) = \sum w(B_1)$, with the sum covering all B_i in $\mathscr{B}^*$. (From (a) and (b).)
    d. $w(X) > 0$.

Proof. For any B_i in $\mathscr{B}^*$ and any component interval $B_{i,m}$ of B_i, $\mu(B_{i,m}) > 0$ (by D1a), and hence $\mu(B_i) > 0$ (D1b) and $w(B_i) > 0$. Hence the assertion by (c). ∎

    e. $w(X) \leqq 1$. (From D1c.)
    f. For any positive real number z, there is a finite disjoint class $\mathscr{B}^{**} \subset \mathscr{B}$ such that $w(X) - w(\bigcup \mathscr{B}^{**}) < z$. This means that any admissible region X can be approximated, to any degree desired, by some finite union of disjoint basic regions.

Proof. We write '$\bigcup\limits_{p}$' for the union with i running from 1 to p; analogously '$\sum\limits_{p}$', '$\bigcup\limits_{\infty}$', and '$\sum\limits_{\infty}$'; further 'lim' for the limit with $p \to \infty$.

For the given X, let $\mathscr{B}^*$ be as in (a). For any $p \in \mathbf{N}$, let $\mathscr{B}_p^* = \bigcup_p B_i$, the union of the first p sets in the sequence $\mathscr{B}^*$. Hence $w(B_p^*) = \sum_p w(B_i)$. Now we have by (c):

$$w(X) = \lim_p \sum_p w(B_i) = \lim w(B_p^*).$$

Thus, for any given z, there is a number p' such that $w(B_{p'}^*) > w(X) - z$; therefore $w(X) - w(B_{p'}^*) < z$. Hence the assertion. ∎

[One might perhaps be inclined to consider an alternative to D3a, taking as $\mathscr{A}'$ the σ-field generated by $\mathscr{B}'$ (D1-3b), thus the class of the n-dimensional Borel sets (or the subclass containing those of these sets that have finite positive Legesgue measure). For this class $\mathscr{A}'$, T1f would still hold, but not T1a. However, the property of admissible regions stated in T1a will turn out to be of great importance in the next section, in the investigation of the similarity influence. Therefore the alternative definition of $\mathscr{A}'$ is not suitable.]

T15-2. Suppose that the following conditions (i) to (vii) are satisfied.

  (i) $\mathbf{U}$ is an attribute space.
  (ii) $\mathscr{B}$ is the class of the basic regions for $\mathbf{U}$.
  (iii) $\mathscr{A}$ is the class of the admissible regions for $\mathbf{U}$.
  (iv) F' is a family $\{P_1', \ldots, P_j', \ldots\}$ with index set D'.
  (v) $\mathscr{D}' = \{X_1', \ldots, X_j', \ldots\}$ is the partition of $\mathbf{U}$ corresponding to F', with the same index set D'.
  (vi) $\mathscr{D}' \subset \mathscr{A}$.
  (vii) $\mathscr{L}'$ is a language of the kind $\mathscr{L}_1'$ (§10) with F' as the only family.

Then the following holds.

  a. There is a partition $\mathscr{D}$ of $\mathbf{U}$ such that (1) $\mathscr{D} \subset \mathscr{B}$, and (2) $\mathscr{D}$ is a refinement of $\mathscr{D}'$ (that is to say, every set in $\mathscr{D}$ is a subset of a set in $\mathscr{D}'$).

Proof. Let X_j' ($j \in D'$) be any element of the partition $\mathscr{D}'$. Then X_j' is an admissible region. Hence, by T1a, there is a basic partition of X_j', i.e., a countable disjoint sequence $\mathscr{B}_j^* = \{X_{j,1}, X_{j,2}, \ldots\}$ with the index set D_j^*, such that $\mathscr{B}_j^* \subset \mathscr{B}$ and $X_j' = \bigcup \mathscr{B}_j^*$. Let $\mathscr{D} =_{\mathrm{Df}} \bigcup_{j \in D'} (\mathscr{B}_j^*)$. Then $\mathscr{D}$ is a partition of $\mathbf{U}$ formed by subdividing the regions of the partition $\mathscr{D}'$ into basic regions. Thus (1) and (2) hold. ∎

b. Let F be a family of attributes corresponding to the partition $\mathcal{D}$ of basic regions; let $\mathcal{L}$ be the language with the same set of individuals as $\mathcal{L}'$, but with F as the only family. (This is not an essential restriction, because, according to the rule R6-1 of sublanguages, the $\mathcal{C}$-values and $\mathcal{M}$-values for propositions involving only F are not affected by the presence of other families.) Let $\mathcal{C}$ be any $\mathcal{C}$-function for $\mathcal{L}$ satisfying our axioms. Then the function $\mathcal{C}'$ for $\mathcal{L}'$ corresponding to $\mathcal{C}$ is uniquely determined by R6-1.

Proof. $\mathcal{L}'$ is a sublanguage of $\mathcal{L}$ of the third kind (D6-3), and thus a conservative sublanguage (6-13c). Therefore, by rule R6-1, the $\mathcal{C}$- and $\mathcal{M}$-values for any propositions in the sublanguage $\mathcal{L}'$ are equal to those for the corresponding propositions in $\mathcal{L}$. ∎

(15-3) *Example* for T2b. Let us consider an atomic proposition in $\mathcal{L}'$, say $P_5'a_8$. Now the region X_5' of the attribute P_5' is subdivided in $\mathcal{D}$ (see proof of T2a) by the basic partition $\mathscr{B}_5^* = \{X_{5,1}, X_{5,2}, \ldots\}$ with the index set D_5^*. (D_5^* in **N** if X_5' is subdivided by a denumerable class of basic regions; it is $\mathbf{N}_p$ if X_5' is subdivided into a finite class of p basic regions.) These basic regions represent the attributes $P_{5,1}, P_{5,2}, \ldots$ in $\mathcal{L}$. The proposition in $\mathcal{L}$ corresponding to $P_5'a_8$ (in the symbolism of D6-3: the proposition $T_3(P_5'a_8)$) is the union $\bigcup_{i \in D^*} (P_{5,i}a_8)$. Therefore $\mathcal{M}'(P_5'a_8) = \sum_{i \in D^*} \mathcal{M}(P_{5,i}a_8)$. Let E be any nonatomic proposition in $\mathcal{L}'$. Then the proposition $T_3(E)$ in $\mathcal{L}$ corresponding to E is determined by the rules (6-4) (compare also (6-5)).

Our next question is: what kinds of properties of basic regions or relations among them may be regarded as essential for rules of IL? We give here a tentative answer to this question.

C15-3. *Third conjecture.* It is sufficient to take as *basic magnitudes*, to be used in rules of inductive logic, the following two, applied to basic regions:
  (a) the *width* w of a region,
  (b) the *distance* between two disjoint regions (see D2d).

C3 is not meant to imply that any other characteristics are irrelevant for IL. It means merely that any valid rule concerning the effect of other characteristics on $\mathscr{C}$- and $\mathscr{M}$-values would be derivable from a suitable set of rules involving the two basic characteristics.

If C3 is valid, it would mean a great simplification in the kinds of rules to be taken into consideration. We would then not need to bother about the enormous variety of possible shapes of regions.

However, the three stated conjectures are far from certain. They should, in the course of future applications, be constantly reexamined. It is quite possible that they will have to be modified. Especially in the case of C3, it may well be that we find another feature of regions, not definable in terms of width and distance, that must be taken as relevant.

I wish to point out more explicitly what is, and what is not, implied by the three conjectures. Let F be a family of k basic attributes, corresponding to a partition $\mathscr{B}$ of the attribute space $\mathbf{U}$ into k basic regions. Suppose that we have a metric for $\mathbf{U}$, and that the values of w_j (width) and d_{jl} (distance) for these regions are given. Suppose further that we wish to state rules for the determination of $\mathscr{C}(H \mid E)$ for any propositions H and E $(E \neq \varnothing)$ not involving any other family than F. The three conjectures imply that for this purpose we need no other information about the attributes than the values of w_j and d_{jl} Suppose that $\mathbf{U}'$ is another attribute space, and that F' is a family (with the number k' of attributes of a different kind) corresponding to a basic partition $\mathscr{B}'$ of $\mathbf{U}'$, and that here likewise the values of w_j' and d_{jl}' are given. Suppose further that the situation happens to be such that $k' = k$ and, for any j and l, $w_j' = w_j$ and $d_{jl}' = d_{jl}$. Let H be a proposition involving only attributes of F. Let H' be completely analogous to H, but involving, instead of the attributes of F in H', the corresponding attributes of F'. Let similarly E' be analogous to E. Then the conjectures imply that $\mathscr{C}(H' \mid E') = \mathscr{C}(H \mid E)$. However, they do not imply that the $\mathscr{C}$-values for propositions involving only F are uniquely determined by the values of w_j and d_{jl}, and that therefore two persons who use the same metric for the space $\mathbf{U}$ and thus apply the same values of w_j and d_{jl}, must necessarily arrive at the same $\mathscr{C}$-values. It may be that the $\mathscr{C}$-values depend upon additional parameters. If so, the conjectures imply merely that for the determination of the parameter values no knowledge about the attributes beyond the w- and d-values are required. It may be that the parameter values may be chosen by each person; either chosen freely, or chosen with consideration given to other factors than the nature of the attributes. [We shall later (in §19) discuss the parameter λ, which is important for the determination of $\mathscr{C}$-values. It seems that the choice of a value for λ by a person is influenced by his personal "inductive inertia".]

Furthermore, the conjectures do not imply that we are in possession of a sufficient set of rules stating exactly the connections between the magnitudes mentioned and the $\mathscr{C}$-values. We have today only some tentative rules of this kind.

16

The Analogy Influence

A. GAMMA- AND ETA-PARAMETERS

We shall now introduce two new kinds of parameters, symbolized by 'γ' and 'η' with subscripts. They provide a simple notation for the values of C_j^0 and C_j^1. Since these values are important characteristics of a $\mathscr{C}$-function, the symbols will frequently occur as parameters in formulas in this and subsequent sections and in later articles. We shall see that the γ-symbols are closely connected with the widths of attributes, and the η-symbols with distances between attributes. [In effect, D16–1 comes to this: $\gamma_j = \mathcal{M}(P_j a)$ and $\eta_{jl} = \mathcal{M}(P_j a \cdot P_l b)/\mathcal{M}(P_j a)\mathcal{M}(P_l b)$, where a and b are arbitrary, distinct individuals (ed.)]

D16-1. Let $\mathscr{C}$ be a given symmetric and regular $\mathscr{C}$-function, and let C be the representative function of $\mathscr{C}$ (D12-1). We define for any attribute indices j and l (not necessarily distinct) in $\mathbf{N}_k$:

    a. $\gamma_j =_{\mathrm{Df}} C_j^0(\mathbf{s}_0)$. (See (3.7c).)

    b. $\eta_{jl} =_{\mathrm{Df}} \dfrac{C_j^1(\mathbf{s}_0^l)}{C_j^0(\mathbf{s}_0)}$.

We give some formulas for γ and η (based on D12-3b).

T16-1. For given functions $\mathscr{C}$ and C, symmetric and regular, the following holds for any j and l (not necessarily distinct) in $\mathbf{N}_k$:

    a. $\gamma_j = \mathrm{MI}(\mathbf{s}_0^j)$.

    b. $0 < \gamma_j < 1$.

  +c. $\sum_j \gamma_j = 1$. (From the sum condition D12-3b1.)

  +d. $\eta_{lj} = \eta_{jl}$.

Proof. $\eta_{lj} = C_l^1(\mathbf{s}_0^j)/C_l^0(\mathbf{s}_0)$,

          $= C_j^1(\mathbf{s}_0^l)/C_j^0(\mathbf{s}_0)$ (by the quotient condition D12-3b2''),

          $= \eta_{jl}$. (From D1b.) ■

    e. $C_j(\mathbf{s}_0^l) = \gamma_j \eta_{jl}$. (From D1a and b.)

    f. $0 < \eta_{jl} < \dfrac{1}{\max(\gamma_j, \gamma_l)}$.

Proof.   1. From (e), since $0 < C_j(\mathbf{s}_0^l)$, $0 < \eta_{jl}$.
  2. From (e), since $C_j(\mathbf{s}_0^l) < 1$, $\eta_{jl} < 1/\gamma_j$. Similarly, $\eta_{lj} < 1/\gamma_l$. But $\eta_{jl} = \eta_{lj}$ (d). Hence the assertion follows. ∎

  g. For any l, $\sum\limits_{j}(\gamma_j \eta_{jl}) = 1$. (From (e) and the sum condition D12-3b1.) This says that, for a given l, the weighted mean of $\eta_{1l}, \eta_{2l}, \dots, \eta_{kl}$ with the weights $\gamma_1, \dots, \gamma_k$, is 1.

  h. $\dfrac{C_j(\mathbf{s}_0^l)}{C_l(\mathbf{s}_0^j)} = \dfrac{\gamma_j}{\gamma_l}$.   (From (e) and (d).)

  i. $C_j(\mathbf{s}_0^j) = \gamma_j \eta_{jj}$.   (From (e).)

  j. If $\mathscr{C}$ satisfies the principle of instantial relevance (P13-1), then $1 < \eta_{jj} < \dfrac{1}{\gamma_j}$.

Proof.   1. By P13-1(a) and (b), $C_j(\mathbf{s}_0^j) > C_j(\mathbf{s}_0)$. Hence, with (i), $\gamma_j \eta_{jj} > \gamma_j$; hence $\eta_{jj} > 1$.
  2. $\eta_{jj} < 1/\gamma_j$, by (f). ∎

  k. Let $\mathscr{C}$ be as in (j). Then, for any l, there is a j (distinct from l) such that $\eta_{jl} < 1$.

Proof.   By (g), the weighted mean of $\eta_{1l}, \dots, \eta_{ll}, \dots, \eta_{kl}$ is 1, and by (j) $\eta_{ll} > 1$. Hence at least one of the other values must be <1. ∎

  l. $\mathrm{MI}(\mathbf{s}_0^{jl}) = \gamma_j \gamma_l \eta_{jl}$. (From (e), since $C_j(\mathbf{s}_0^l) = \mathrm{MI}(\mathbf{s}_0^{lj})/\mathrm{MI}(\mathbf{s}_0^l)$; and (a). See (13.2a).)
  m. $\mathrm{MI}(\mathbf{s}_0^{jj}) = \gamma_j^2 \eta_{jj}$. (From (l).)

We shall now state rules which connect $\mathscr{C}$-values with certain features of the attributes involved. In accordance with the conjecture C15-3 (near the end of §15), we think in the first place of widths and distances. Here we shall give rules referring to width. The question of rules involving distances is somewhat more complicated and requires considerations of the analogy influence. This will be discussed later (in §16B).

According to D1a (or T1a), γ_j is the initial probability of any atomic proposition with the attribute P_j. It is clear that γ_j should be the greater, the greater the width of P_j, $w(P_j)$. Unless for some family there are particular reasons against it, it would seem natural to take γ_j as proportional to $w(P_j)$; the proportionality factor would be determined by the requirement that the sum of the γ's be 1 (T1c). Therefore, if the concept of width for the family in question is defined in such a way that it is normalized, we should take $\gamma_j = w(P_j)$. These considerations suggest the following rule.

R16-1. *Rules for γ, based on width.* Let F be a family of k attributes; let P_j and P_l be two distinct attributes in F.

      a. Suppose that we have no quantitative concept of width for the space **U**, but we see no reason (with respect to the attributes P_j and P_l themselves, disregarding any knowledge about their distribution among the individuals) for expecting the occurrence of one of these attributes more than that of the other, then we take $\gamma_j = \gamma_l$. It follows that, if the described relation holds for each pair of distinct attributes in F, we take each $\gamma = 1/k$.

      b. If we have no quantitative concept w but are able to make the comparative judgment that P_j has a greater width than P_l, then we take $\gamma_j > \gamma_l$.

      c. If we have a quantitative (not necessarily normalized) width function w, then we take $\gamma_j = aw(P_j)$, where
$$a = 1 \Big/ \sum_{l=1}^{k} w(P_l).$$

      d. If we have a normalized width function w, then we take $\gamma_j = w(P_j)$.

The given rules R1 are to be applied in the first place to the *primitive* attributes of a family F in a language $\mathcal{L}_1$ containing F as the only family. But now, for the subsequent rules R2, we consider a language $\mathcal{L}$ which possibly contains *several families*. Here the rules R1 must be applied to each of the families in $\mathcal{L}$ separately. We assume that the γ's for all primitive attributes of each of the families in $\mathcal{L}$ have been determined according to the rules R1.

Now let us investigate *molecular attributes* in $\mathcal{L}$. An attribute Q is called molecular if it is either primitive or definable on the basis of a finite number of primitive attributes with the help of negation and conjunction (without the use of identity). We are interested in the determinations of γ-values for molecular attributes on the basis of given γ-values for the primitive attributes. In general, for this determination we need the rules of IL for a combination of families, which will be given in a later article.* However, we can do without these rules if the following special conditions are fulfilled. First, let

---

  * Unwritten (ed.).

us assume, as we usually do, that, among the attributes of distinct
families, there are no dependencies through logical, phenomenological, or meaning relations. (If there were dependencies of this kind,
they would have to be expressed by B-principles, see §5). This does
not exclude either statistical dependencies (i.e., dependencies in
terms of frequencies or statistical probabilities) or inductive dependencies (i.e., dependencies in terms of $\mathscr{C}$-values). Under the assumption stated, the following simple rules hold.

R16-2. Let Q, Q', and Q'' be any molecular attributes with γ, γ',
and γ'', respectively.
    a. If Q is necessary, its $\gamma = 1$; if Q is impossible, $\gamma = 0$.
    b. If the definitions of Q' and of Q'' do not involve the
    same family, and Q is defined as $Q' \cdot Q''$ (the conjunc-
    tion of Q' and Q''), then $\gamma = \gamma'\gamma''$.
    c. If Q is defined as $Q' \vee Q''$ (the disjunction of Q' and
    Q'') and Q' and Q'' are incompatible (i.e., their con-
    junction is impossible), then $\gamma = \gamma' + \gamma''$.
    d. If Q is defined as the negation of Q', then $\gamma = 1 - \gamma'$.
    (From (a) and (c).)

    Let $\mathbf{U}$, $\mathscr{B}$, $\mathscr{A}$, F', $\mathscr{D}'$, and $\mathscr{L}'$ fulfill the conditions (i) through (vii)
in T15-2. Then, according to T15-2a, there is a partition of $\mathbf{U}$, say
$\mathscr{D}$, such that $\mathscr{D}$ is a refinement of $\mathscr{D}'$, and $\mathscr{D} \subset \mathscr{B}$. (We shall therefore
speak of the sets in $\mathscr{D}$ as basic regions; but note that the subsequent
considerations and, in particular, the results in T3, T4, and T5
concerning η'_{12} and η'_{11} hold generally for an arbitrary refinement $\mathscr{D}$
of $\mathscr{D}'$.) Let the language $\mathscr{L}$ contain only the family F corresponding
to $\mathscr{D}$. Let $\mathscr{C}$ be a $\mathscr{C}$-function and $\mathscr{M}$ an $\mathscr{M}$-function for $\mathscr{L}$. Then, on
the basis of $\mathscr{C}$ and $\mathscr{M}$, the corresponding functions $\mathscr{C}'$ and $\mathscr{M}'$ for $\mathscr{L}'$
are uniquely determined by R6-1 (T15-2b). And, in particular, the
values of the γ- and η-parameters for the attributes in F are
uniquely determined by the values for the basic attributes in F'. We
shall now derive formulas for these determinations.
    We consider two attributes in F', say P'_1 and P'_2; the results
hold, of course, likewise for any other pair of distinct attributes. Let
the regions in $\mathbf{U}$ corresponding to these two attributes be X'_1 and
X'_2; both are in $\mathscr{D}'$. X'_1 is partioned by $\mathscr{D}$ into a countable
sequence; let this be $\mathscr{B}_1 = \{X_{1,1}, X_{1,2}, \ldots\}$; then $\mathscr{B}_1 \subset \mathscr{D} \subset \mathscr{B}$. Let the
index set of $\mathscr{B}_1$ be D_1. If $\mathscr{B}_1$ is denumerable, $D_1 = \mathbf{N}$; if $\mathscr{B}_1$ contains a
finite number k_1 of subregions, then $D_1 = \mathbf{N}_{k_1}$. Similarly, let X'_2 be
partitioned into the sequence $\mathscr{B}_2 = \{X_{2,1}, X_{2,2}, \ldots\}$ with index set D_2.

Thus we have:

$$X_1' = \bigcup_m X_{1,m}; \qquad X_2' = \bigcup_p X_{2,p}.$$

(Here and hereafter, unless otherwise indicated, the variables 'm' and 'n' under a union symbol or a sum symbol run through the numbers in D_1, and 'p' runs through the numbers in D_2.)

In the following formulas we shall use E-symbols for atomic propositions with the individual a_1, and H-symbols for those with a_2; specifically, E_j' and H_j' ($j = 1, 2$) are atomic propositions in $\mathscr{L}'$ with the attribute P_j'. The following are atomic propositions in $\mathscr{L}$: $E_{1,m}$ and $H_{1,m}$ ($m \in D_1$) with the attribute corresponding to the basic region $X_{1,m}$, and $E_{2,p}$ and $H_{2,p}$ ($p \in D_2$) with the attribute corresponding to $X_{2,p}$. Then each of the following four pairs (a), (b), (c), (d) contains two corresponding propositions (compare Example (15-3)), the first belonging to $\mathscr{L}'$, the second to $\mathscr{L}$:

(16-1)   (a) E_1', $\bigcup_m E_{1,m}$;   (b) E_2', $\bigcup_p E_{2,p}$;

(c) H_1', $\bigcup_m H_{1,m}$;   (d) H_2', $\bigcup_p H_{2,p}$.

According to the rule R6-1 for sublanguages, corresponding propositions in $\mathscr{L}'$ and $\mathscr{L}$ have equal $\mathscr{M}$-values:

(16-2)   Let A' be any proposition in $\mathscr{L}'$, and A be the proposition in $\mathscr{L}$ corresponding to A'. Then $\mathscr{M}'(A') = \mathscr{M}(A)$.

Hence with (1a):

(16-3)   (a) $\mathscr{M}'(E_1') = \sum_m \mathscr{M}(E_{1,m})$; and analogously
(b) for E_2'; (c) for H_1'; (d) for H_2'.

In T2 and T3 we shall show how the γ's and η's for the attributes in F' are determined by those for the basic attributes in F. For this purpose, we introduce in (4) notations for these γ's and η's.

(16-4)   (a) Let γ_1' be the γ-value of the attribute P_1' in F', hence the normalized width of the region X_1'.
(b) Likewise γ_2' for P_2' (and X_2').
(c) Similarly in F, $\gamma_{1,m}$ for the region $X_{1,m}$.
(d) $\gamma_{2,p}$ for $X_{2,p}$.

(e) Let $\eta_{1,m;2,p}$ be the η-value for the attributes represented by the basic regions $X_{1,m}$ and $X_{2,p}$.

(f) Likewise $\eta_{1,m;1,n}$ for the regions $X_{1,m}$ and $X_{1,n}$.

(g) Let η'_{12} be the η-value for the attributes P'_1 and P'_2 in the original family F'.

(h) Likewise, η'_{11} for P'_1 with itself.

T16-2. **a.**
$$\gamma'_1 = \sum_m \gamma_{1,m}. \quad \text{(From (3a).)}$$

b.
$$\gamma'_2 = \sum_p \gamma_{2,p}. \quad \text{(From (3b).)}$$

Any η-value for any pair of attributes in any family is definable (according to T11 and m) in terms of γ-values and $\mathcal{M}(E \cap H)$, where E and H are atomic propositions with the two attributes:

(16-5) **a.**
$$\eta_{12} = \frac{1}{\gamma_1 \gamma_2} \mathcal{M}(E_1 \cap H_2).$$

b.
$$\eta'_{12} = \frac{1}{\gamma'_1 \gamma'_2} \mathcal{M}'(E'_1 \cap H'_2).$$

+T16-3.
$$\eta'_{12} = \frac{\sum_m \sum_p \gamma_{1,m} \gamma_{2,p} \eta_{1,m;2,p}}{\sum_m \gamma_{1,m} \sum_p \gamma_{2,p}}$$

Proof. By (1a) and (1d), the proposition $E'_1 \cap H'_2$ corresponds to $\bigcup_m E_{1,m} \cap \bigcup_p H_{2,p}$, which is $\bigcup_m \bigcup_p (E_{1,m} \cap H_{2,p})$. Therefore: $\mathcal{M}'(E'_1 \cap H'_2) = \sum_m \sum_p \mathcal{M}(E_{1,m} H_{2,p})$. Then with (5b):

$$\eta'_{12} = \frac{1}{\gamma'_1 \gamma'_2} \sum_m \sum_p \mathcal{M}(E_{1,m} \cap H_{2,p}).$$

We have for language $\mathscr{L}$ (in analogy to (5a), again by T11) for any $m \in D_1$, $p \in D_2$:

$$\mathcal{M}(E_{1,m} \cap H_{2,p}) = \gamma_{1,m} \gamma_{2,p} \eta_{1,m;2,p}.$$

Hence the theorem. ■

T3 gives the value of η'_{12} for the large regions X'_1 and X'_2 in terms of γ's and η's for their basic subregions. We see from T3 that

η'_{12} is the weighted mean of the values $\eta_{1,m;2,p}$ with the weights $\gamma_{1,m}\gamma_{2,p}$.

We shall now determine $\eta'_{1,1}$ is a similar way.

+T16-4.
$$\eta'_{11} = \frac{\sum\limits_{m}\sum\limits_{n} \gamma_{1,m}\gamma_{1,n}\eta_{1,m;1,n}}{\sum\limits_{m}\sum\limits_{n} \gamma_{1,m}\gamma_{1,n}}.$$

Proof. By T1m:

$$\eta'_{11} = \frac{1}{(\gamma'_1)^2} \mathcal{M}'(E'_1 \cap H'_1).$$

Here the two atomic propositions E'_1 and H'_1 involve the same attribute P'_1; hence both variables 'm' and 'n' run through D_1. The proposition H'_1 corresponds to $\bigcup\limits_{n} H_{1,n}$. Hence:

$$\mathcal{M}'(E'_1 \cap H'_1) = \sum_{m}\sum_{n} \mathcal{M}(E_{1,m} \cap H_{1,n}).$$

By T1m, for any m and n in D_1 (distinct or identical),

$$\mathcal{M}(E_{1,m} \cap H_{1,n}) = \gamma_{1,m}\gamma_{1,n}\eta_{1,m;1,n}.$$

Hence, by T2, the theorem. ∎

Thus η'_{11} is the weighted mean of the values $\eta_{1,m;1,n}$ with the weights $\gamma_{1,m}\gamma_{1,n}$. [Note that m and n run through D_1 independently. For two distinct numbers in D_1, say 5 and 7, both values $\eta_{1,5;1,7}$ and $\eta_{1,7;1,5}$ occur, although they are equal. And also the value $\eta_{1,5;1,5}$ occurs.]

Here is an alternative form (which avoids the duplication just mentioned):

T16-5. $\quad \eta'_{11} = \dfrac{1}{\left(\sum\limits_{m} \gamma_{1,m}\right)^2}\left[\sum\limits_{m} (\gamma_{1,m})^2 \eta_{1,m;1,m} + 2 \sum\limits_{\substack{m,n \\ (m<n)}} \gamma_{1,m}\gamma_{1,n}\eta_{1,m;1,n}\right].$

(The η-values under the first sum in the square bracket are of the kind η_{jj}, those under the second sum are of the kind η_{jl}, $j \neq l$.)

Now let us consider the *special case* in which all the (basic) attributes of the family F have *equal γ-values*. This case can occur only if the number of attributes in F is finite, say k. Then every (basic) region in $\mathcal{D}$ has the width $1/k$; hence every γ-value is $1/k$. Suppose that the partition $\mathcal{B}_1$ divides the region X'_1 of the attribute P'_1 into k_1 basic regions; then the index set D_1 is $\mathbf{N}_{k_1}$. Likewise, let

$\mathscr{B}_2$ divide X'_2 into k_2 basic regions; then $D_2 = \mathbf{N}_{k_2}$. Hence by T2:

$$\gamma'_1 = k_1/k; \qquad \gamma'_2 = k_2/k.$$

Thus from T3, with every weight $\gamma_{1,m}\gamma_{2,p} = 1/k^2$:

(16-6) $$\eta'_{12} = \frac{1}{k_1 k_2} \sum_m \sum_p \eta_{1,m;2,p}.$$

Similarly from T4:

(16-7) $$\eta'_{11} = \frac{1}{k_1^2} \sum_m \sum_n \eta_{1,m;1,n}.$$

And from T5 the alternative form:

(16-8) $$\eta'_{11} = \frac{1}{k_1^2}\left[\sum_m \eta_{1,m;1,m} + 2 \sum_{\substack{m,n \\ (m<n)}} \eta_{1,m;1,n} \right].$$

B. RULES FOR THE ETA-PARAMETER

We have earlier given a rule (R1) for γ-values. Now we shall make an informal analysis of a situation in which it seems plausible to apply a reasoning by analogy based upon the similarity of attributes. These considerations will lead us to a rule for η-values.

We are here concerned with analogy within one family of attributes. Most of the cases of reasoning by analogy, both in everyday life and in science, involve several families. For example, if two bodies agree in several features, say in shape, size, color, density, then it is regarded as probable that they will agree also in some other features. (This kind of analogy inference will be discussed in a later article on the basis of an inductive method for several families. A crude method for this inference was indicated in [1950] §110D.)

Suppose an observer looks for objects of a certain kind, e.g., insects of a certain species; they constitute the domain of individuals for this investigation. He may be interested in various features of these objects, e.g., the length of the bodies, the color of the wings, and the like. But at present he concentrates on one of these features, represented by the attribute space $\mathbf{U}$. This space may be a part of a more general attribute space; for example, $\mathbf{U}$ may consist of some colors, or it may be an interval of positive real numbers as values of length in millimeters. Suppose the observer partitions $\mathbf{U}$ into k regions forming a linear series (e.g., the interval $\mathbf{U}$ is divided into k smaller intervals, or the part $\mathbf{U}$ of the color space consists of k regions, representing color shades from pure blue through more and more greenish blue and bluish green to pure green). Thus we have an *ordered family* of k attributes. For simplicity, let us assume the k regions have equal width; then by R1d, for each attribute P_j ($j = 1, \ldots, k$), $\gamma_j = 1/k$. Suppose, with $k = 9$, a sample of 20 individuals has been observed, with the distribution shown in the diagram (figure 16-1).

3	6	2	4	3	0	0	2	0
P_1	P_2	P_3	P_4	P_5	P_6	P_7	P_8	P_9

Fig. 16-1

Let E be the sample proposition with this distribution; the k-tuple of E is $\mathbf{s} = \langle 3, 6, 2, 4, 3, 0, 0, 2, 0 \rangle$. Let H_j ($j = 1, \ldots, k$) be an atomic proposition with the attribute P_j and with any new individual. Suppose that we have not yet chosen a fixed, defined $\mathscr{C}$-function. But we are pondering the question of the relations that should hold among the values $\mathscr{C}(H_j \mid E) = C_j(\mathbf{s})$ with the $\mathbf{s}$ just mentioned. In particular, let us consider $C_3(\mathbf{s})$ and $C_8(\mathbf{s})$ from a commonsense point of view, leaving tradition and theory aside. At first glance, it might appear plausible to take these two values as equal, because $s_3 = s_8 = 2$. But I think it would be advisable to take $C_3(\mathbf{s})$ as slightly-higher than $C_8(\mathbf{s})$, i.e., to take the probability of the prediction H_3 on E as slightly higher than that of H_8, for the following reason. Although the occupation numbers of P_3 and of P_8 themselves, which are, of course, the main factors determining the C-values, are equal, those of the attributes P_2 and P_4, which are close to P_3, are higher than those of P_7 and P_9, close to P_8. We might reason as follows. The sample indicates that the attributes on the left side (the smaller lengths, or the bluish colors) occur more frequently in the sample, and therefore presumably also in the population, than those on the right side. In view of this situation, the fact that the sample contains only 2 individuals with P_3 may be just incidental. On the other hand, it may not be; in other words, the proportion of P_3 in the population may be about as low as in the sample. On the basis of this rather small sample, we shall not be willing to risk high stakes in a bet at even odds on the prediction that the next individual found to have either P_3 or P_8, will have P_3. However, suppose that someone offers me the choice between this prediction, call it $H_{3,8}$, and the opposite prediction $H_{8,3}$, without any risk for me, and with the promise to give me \$10 if the prediction I shall choose comes out true, and further, to give me, independently of the outcome, a bonus of 10c if I choose $H_{8,3}$. Then I would, in spite of the bonus, choose $H_{3,8}$.

Generally speaking, it seems reasonable to make the rules such that $C_j(\mathbf{s})$ is dependent, not only on s_j, but also on the occupation numbers of attributes closely similar to P_j. Thus we should take into consideration the various degrees of similarity between attributes, in other words, the various distances between the representing regions in the attribute space. The influence that similarities between attributes have on $\mathscr{C}$-values in cases of the kind just discussed, will be labeled "*similarity influence*". This is the first of two kinds of *analogy influence*. (The second, called "proximity influence", will be briefly explained in §17C.) Both kinds of analogy influence have only secondary significance. C_j is primarily determined by the numbers s_j and s. The change in the value of C_j through the influence of the occupation numbers of other nearby attributes is usually very small, and it decreases with increasing s. If s is large, the influence may be practically neglected in many cases.

On the basis of the preceding informal considerations, we shall now try to formulate general rules. In the previous example we compared. $\mathscr{C}$-values for two attributes on the basis of one fixed evidence such that the occupation numbers of the two attributes were equal, while those of their neighbor attributes showed great differences. In the example, I made these differences great, and the distance for the similarity influence as small as possible (contiguous intervals) in order to make the influence plausible. But if there is a noticeable influence under such circumstances, then there should also be an influence, though possibly much smaller in amount, in other situations where the occupation number of a neighbor attribute is small and its distance not quite as small as in the example.

The rules R3 will refer to these attributes P_j, P_m, P_n. We consider first an example with a *diagram* (figure 16-2), where the

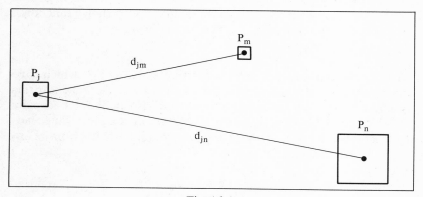

Fig. 16-2

attribute space is represented by the large rectangle, and the (basic) regions of the three attributes are represented by three small squares. Their widths, and hence their γ-values, are not necessarily equal. We consider two $\mathscr{C}$-values for the prediction H_j with P_j, with respect to two different evidence propositions E and E', both with $s = 1$. E ascribes to the one observed individual the attribute P_m, and E' ascribes P_n. Thus the k-tuple of E is $\mathbf{s}_0^m$ (see (3-7)b and c), and that of E' is $\mathbf{s}_0^n$. Suppose that P_j is more similar to P_m than to P_n. Then the distances d_{jm} is smaller than d_{jn}. Our earlier analysis, using the example of a series of attributes (figure 16-1), makes it plausible that in this situation H_j has a higher probability on E than on E'; thus $C_j(\mathbf{s}_0^m) > C_j(\mathbf{s}_0^n)$. Hence, with D1b, $\eta_{jm} > \eta_{jn}$. This is the reason for the following *rules for η-values between basic attributes, based upon their distances.*

R16-3. *Rules for the similarity influence.* Let F be a family of k basic attributes; let P_j, P_m, P_n be three distinct attributes in F. If we have a quantitative distance function d for the attribute space $\mathbf{U}$ of F, let $d_{jm} =_{\mathrm{Df}} d(P_j, P_m)$.

    a. Suppose that we have no quantitative distance function for the attribute space $\mathbf{U}$ of F, but we see no reason for regarding the attribute P_j as more similar or as less similar to P_m than to P_n, then we take $\eta_{jm} = \eta_{jn}$.

    b. If we have no quantitative distance function, but are able to make the comparative judgment that P_j is as similar to P_m as to P_n, then we take $\eta_{jm} = \eta_{jn}$.

    c. If we have no quantitative distance function, but are able to make the comparative judgment that P_j is more similar to P_m than to P_n, then we take $\eta_{jm} > \eta_{jn}$.

    d. Here (and in the subsequent rules (e), (f), and (g)) it is assumed that we have a quantitative distance function d for $\mathbf{U}$. If $d_{jm} = d_{jn}$, then we take $\eta_{jm} = \eta_{jn}$.

    e. If $d_{jm} < d_{jn}$, we take $\eta_{jm} > \eta_{jn}$.

The principle (d) says that, for two attributes P_m and P_n which have equal distances from P_j, the η-values should be equal. Now it seems intuitively plausible that the same should also hold for two pairs (P_j, P_m) and (P_l, P_n) which have no attribute in common. This leads to the following rule (f). A similar consideration leads from (e) to the more general (g).

    f. If $d_{jm} = d_{ln}$, then we take $\eta_{jm} = \eta_{ln}$.

    g. If $d_{jm} < d_{ln}$, then we take $\eta_{jm} > \eta_{ln}$.

These rules are meant as tentative, for two reasons. First, the concept of comparable (or even quantitative) degrees of similarity of attributes is somewhat problematic. If we succeed in finding a plausible metric for a certain kind (modality) of attributes, this will not necessarily help us in doing the same for another kind. It seems that we have to solve this problem again and again for further kinds. The second reason lies in the fact that today we are not yet quite certain that these rules are valid without restriction. This uncertainty is connected with that about the third conjecture (C15-3). If it were found that not only widths and distances, but also other factors must influence the $\mathscr{C}$-values, then the rules just stated would presumably have to be modified.

We shall call R3d and e together *the strong η-rule*. In some cases we might hesitate to accept this rule, but be willing to accept the following *weak η-rule*:

(16-9) If $d_{jm} \leqq d_{jn}$, we take $\eta_{jm} \geqq \eta_{jn}$.

R3d follows from this rule, but R3e does not. On the basis of (9), $d_{jm} < d_{jn}$ is only a necessary condition for $\eta_{jm} > \eta_{jn}$, but not a sufficient one. Someone might prefer (9), if he thinks that in certain cases it would be appropriate to have equal values of η (and hence of C_j) in spite of a difference between the two distances; for instance, in cases where the difference is below a certain threshold value or both distances are rather large (this will be discussed later). But even if someone accepts the strong rule theoretically, he may in practice disregard the similarity influence in many cases of the kind indicated. This is similar to the customary procedure of a physicist who usually disregards in his calculations certain disturbing factors although he knows that the amount of their influence is actually not zero.

The earlier rule R1 and the rule R3 here make a connection between, on the one side, the $\mathscr{C}$-functions together with the parameters γ and η defined by them and, on the other side, the functions of width and distance, whose values are established in applied IL. Here in our investigations, which are devoted to pure IL, we do not study in detail the procedure of establishing those functions. It is the task of psychologists to find a suitable measuring scale for distance, for example in the color space. We simply assume here, that the distance function d and, on its basis, the width function w have been constructed, and that their values for any basic regions relevant for a given scientific investigation, are known. Then the rules R1 and R2 help us in determining first certain values of γ and η, and thereby some $\mathscr{C}$-values for small s. Thus, in our present considerations, we do not assume, as we usually do, that a $\mathscr{C}$-function is given. We rather assume now that applied IL has given us some values of width and distance for some attributes in our conceptual system; and the two rules help us in adjusting our construction of a $\mathscr{C}$-function to these values.

Suppose that, in a given family F of k basic attributes, for every ordered triple (j, m, n) of distinct attribute indices the conditions in R3a (or in R3b, or in R3d) are fulfilled. Then all η_{jl} $(j \neq l)$ in F are equal. Note that this does not imply that all values $C_j(\mathbf{s}_0^l)$ $(j \neq l)$ are equal. This is the case only if, furthermore, all γ-values are equal. Suppose that we have (as in figure 16-3) $d_{12} = d_{23} = d_{34}$, but $\gamma_1 = \gamma_2 < \gamma_3 = \gamma_4$. Then $\eta_{12} = \eta_{23} = \eta_{34}$. On the other hand, $C_j(\mathbf{s}_0^l) = \gamma_j \eta_{jl}$ (T1e). Therefore $C_1(\mathbf{s}_0^2) = C_2(\mathbf{s}_0^1) = C_2(\mathbf{s}_0^3) < C_3(\mathbf{s}_0^2) = C_3(\mathbf{s}_0^4) = C_4(\mathbf{s}_0^3)$.

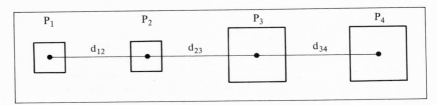

Fig. 16-3

The rule for γ-values (R1) determines all γ-values, provided that a quantitative width function is given. In contrast, our present rule for η-values (R3) gives for the case of different distances only an inequality, even if a quantitative distance function is given. The problem of the determination of numerical η-values on the basis of given widths and distances (with normalized width and distance functions) will be investigated in §17.

C. THE SEARCH FOR PRINCIPLES OF ANALOGY
BY SIMILARITY

We shall now discuss another important problem, for which so far no general solution has been found. Suppose that for a certain family of k basic attributes $(k > 2)$ all γ- and η-values are given (in accordance with the rules R1 and R3), with at least some of the values η_{jm} $(j \neq m)$ unequal. Then all C_j-values for $s = 0$ and $s = 1$ are given; in other words, all values of MI for $s = 1$ and $s = 2$. Let us look at the relations between these C_j-values or MI-values and those for higher s. According to our conjecture C15-3, the widths w

and distances d for basic regions should be sufficient as a basis for all C-values. Now the values of w and d for the family F have been used to determine the lower C_j-values. Therefore it might in principle be possible to determine all C_j-values from the lower ones. However, the following considerations have a much more modest aim. I shall propose some tentative new principles, not for acceptance but merely for consideration. They are still very far from a complete determination; they merely state some relations among higher C_j-functions, relations which represent the similarity influence. They are tentative steps on the way toward the final aim, which is a general rule for the determination of higher C_j-values for a family in which the distances are very different and some of them are very small. (For families not of this kind, general methods will be given in the λ-system, §19.)

It would be of interest to investigate whether one of the two subsequent *tentative principles* (a) and (b) in (10) could be taken as an axiom (it seems that it is not possible to take both); and if so, to find out how much (if any) freedom would then be left for the choice of the function C_j.

(16-10) Suppose that the following six conditions are fulfilled.

(i) F is a family with k basic attributes ($k > 2$);

(ii) $s > 1$.

(iii) $\mathbf{s} = \langle s_1, \ldots, s_k \rangle \in {}^0\mathbf{N}^{k,s}$ (see (3-7a)).

(iv) m and n are two distinct attribute indices in F such that $s_m + s_n > 1$.

(v) $s_{m,n} =_{\text{Df}} s_m + s_n$.

(vi) We define the $s_{m,n} + 1$ k-tuples $\mathbf{s}_p^{(m,n)}$ ($p = 0, 1, \ldots, s_{m,n}$) in ${}^0\mathbf{N}^{k,s}$ on the basis of $\mathbf{s}$ as follows:

$\mathbf{s}_p^{(m,n)} =_{\text{Df}}$ that k-tuple which is like $\mathbf{s}$, except with p instead of s_m and with $s_{m,n} - p$ instead of s_n. (Thus $\mathbf{s}^{(m,n)} \in {}^0\mathbf{N}^{k,s}$.)

a. Under the conditions stated, for any j distinct from m and n, $C_j(\mathbf{s}_p^{(m,n)})$ is a *linear function* of p; i.e., the $s_{m,n} + 1$ values $C_j(\mathbf{s}_p^{(m,n)})$ (with $p = 0, \ldots, s_{m,n}$) form an arithmetic progression.

b. Under the same conditions, $C_m(\mathbf{s}_p^{(m,n)})$ is a *linear function* of p.

Of these two tentative principles, (a) seems to me more plausible than (b), because (a) is somewhat similar to the linearity of C_j (for $j = m$) in the λ-system (T19-10).

We might also consider taking as an axiom a principle of the following form, with a suitable choice of the restricting condition B^*.

(16-11) *Principle of analogy.*[*] Suppose that, for a family F of k basic attributes $(k > 2)$, all γ- and η-values are given. Then, for any three distinct attribute indices j, m, n, for any $s > 0$, for any $\mathbf{s}$ in ${}^0\mathbf{N}^{k,s}$, and for $p \geqq p'$ such that the values of γ, η, s, $\mathbf{s}$, and p' fulfill a condition B^* (to be specified), the following holds.

    (a) If $\eta_{jm} = \eta_{jn}$, then $C_j(\mathbf{s}^{m_p}) = C_j(\mathbf{s}^{n_p})$.

    (b) If $\eta_{jm} < \eta_{jn}$, then $C_j(\mathbf{s}^{m_p}) < C_j(\mathbf{s}^{n_p})$.

Note that, according to (13-2b), the k-tuple $\mathbf{s}^{m_p}$ is formed from $\mathbf{s}$ by replacing s_m with $s_m + p$. Thus the two $(s+p)$-tuples $\mathbf{s}^{m_p}$ and $\mathbf{s}^{n_p}$ characterize two sample propositions for $s + p$ individuals such that the second s.p. is formed from the first by shifting p individuals from the attribute P_m to P_n.

At the present moment it is not yet clear what the best choice for the condition B^* is. I shall indicate five conditions $B_1, \ldots, B_5$. B_1^* is B_1; for $i = 2, \ldots, 5$, B_i^* is the conjunction of the first i conditions. (11_i) is the version of the principle (11) with condition B_i^*.

B_1 is the tautology. Thus (11_1) is the strongest, unrestricted version of the principle. This version looks attractive because of its great simplicity. However, it is violated by certain kinds of $\mathscr{C}$-functions which I (and some of my friends) have used for years for certain situations. [This is the case for certain mixtures (convex combinations) of $\mathscr{M}$-functions of the λ-system. (This system, but not the combination, will be explained in §19.) It is also the case for my old solution of the problem of two families, which is indicated in Carnap–Stegmüller [1959, Anhang B, VIII]. At that place I also stated an axiom NA16, which is a special case of the present principle (11_1); but I discovered later that this axiom is not in agreement with the solution given there.] We do not yet know whether it is preferable to retain the older methods and abandon (or weaken) the strong principle (11_1), or whether it is safe to accept the strong principle and give up the earlier methods.

    (B_2) $p' = 1$.

---

[*] In effect, (16–11) comes to this: If $\mathscr{C}(P_j a \mid P_m b)$ equals (or, is less than) $\mathscr{C}(P_j a \mid P_n b)$ then $\mathscr{C}(P_j c \mid E)$ equals (or, is less than) $\mathscr{C}(P_j c \mid E')$, where $a \neq b$, E' comes from the sample proposition E by shifting p individuals from P_m to P_n, and c is outside the sample (ed.).

Here the principle (11b) applies even if only one individual is shifted. This condition B_2 is very weak; therefore the principle (11_2) is very strong. The subsequent conditions B_3, B_4, and B_5 are step for step stronger; thus the principle becomes weaker each time.

(B_3) $s_m = s_n$.

Here $s_m + p = s_n + p$. Thus here the second s.p. is formed from the first by exchanging the cardinal numbers of P_m and P_n.

(B_4) $s_m = s_n$; and $\gamma_m = \gamma_n$.

This version (11_4) of the principle seems rather plausible. But it is still not fulfilled by some of the earlier methods.

(B_5) All γ's are equal, and all k numbers in **s** are equal.

The principle (11_5) with this strongest condition is very weak, and hence quite plausible. If I am not mistaken, this principle is fulfilled by all methods accepted at the present time.

We shall refer to the versions (11_2) and (11_3) of the principle later, but without deciding on their acceptance.

The following principle is, as we shall see, an alternative formulation for one of the forms of (11).

(16-12) For any triple j, m, n of distinct indices, exactly one of the following three cases holds (but for distinct triples distinct cases may hold): either

    (a) for every $s \geq 0$ and every **s** in ${}^0\mathbf{N}^{k,s}$, $C_j(\mathbf{s}^m) = C_j(\mathbf{s}^n)$, or

    (b) for every s and **s**, $C_j(\mathbf{s}^m) < C_j(\mathbf{s}^n)$, or

    (c) for every s and **s**, $C_j(\mathbf{s}^m) > C_j(\mathbf{s}^n)$.

(16-13) The statement (12) is logically equivalent to (11_2) (with $p' = 1$).

Proof. For the given triple j, m, n, one of the following three cases holds: either (1) the two values η_{jm} and η_{jn} are equal, or (2) the first is smaller, or (3) the second is smaller. By T1e, (1) holds if-if the two values $C_j(\mathbf{s}_0^m)$ and $C_j(\mathbf{s}_0^n)$ are equal; (2) holds if-if the first is smaller; and (3) holds if-if the second is smaller. Thus (11_1) (a) (with $p = 1$) says that, if the two $\mathscr{C}$-values $C_j^{s+1}(\mathbf{s}^m)$ and $C_j^{s+1}(\mathbf{s}^n)$ are equal for $s = 0$ and $\mathbf{s} = \mathbf{s}_0$, then also for any s and any **s**; similarly (b) says that, if the first $\mathscr{C}$-value is smaller for $s = 0$, then also for any s and any **s**; and (b) with m and n exchanged says that, if the second $\mathscr{C}$-value is smaller for $s = 0$, then also for any s and any **s**. Thus (11_2) logically implies (12). It is easily seen that the inverse implication holds too. ∎

Let us suppose that we have a quantitative distance function for the attribute space, and let us remember the relations between η_{jm} and the distance d_{jm} between the regions of the basic attributes P_m and P_n, stated in the rule R3. Then we see that (11_2) (and hence also (12)) says the following. (1) By the shift of one individual from P_m to P_n, C_j is increased if $d_{jm} > d_{jn}$; in other words, if by the shift the individual is moved closer to P_j; (2) C_j is diminished if $d_{jm} < d_{jn}$; and (3) C_j remains unchanged if the two distances are equal. It seems to me that these considerations give some plausibility even to the strong version (11_1).

My thinking about the similarity influence in inductive logic as dependent upon the distance in the attributive space has been guided for years by the analogy to the dependence of a physical effect of one body on another upon the distance between the bodies. (This is, of course, only a formal analogy; the two fields are fundamentally different, since inductive logic is not an empirical science, and its principles are not laws of nature.) The idea that the primary rules for the similarity influence, viz. the rules R3 for η-values and the exact rules, still sought for, which are to determine an η-value as a function of the distance, should refer only to the small basic regions, came to me from a reflection on the analogous method that has been used long and successfully in physics, namely the method of basing the whole of mechanics on particle mechanics. This method, a special case of the analytic method, was used by Newton when he formulated his general law of gravitation only for particles or mass points; Coulomb did the same in his law of electrostatic forces. In both cases the resulting forces for bodies of arbitrary size and shape can then easily be determined by summation of forces exerted by one particle on another particle (or by integration with respect to mass density or electric charge density, if a continuous distribution of mass or charge is assumed). The analogue to this procedure is our determination of derived γ- and η-values in T2a, T3, and T4.

The simplest form of distinction in similarity between attributes is this:

(16-14) Every basic attribute is more similar to itself than to any other basic attribute of the same family.

This is also applicable if we have no metric for the attribute space, and even if we are unable to make a comparative judgment of the form: "P_j is more similar to P_m than P_l to P_n." (where $j \neq m$ and $l \neq n$, but possibly $j = l$). With the help of the rules R3, (14) leads to the *principle of self-similarity:*

P16-1. For any two distinct basic attributes P_j and P_l of the same family, $\eta_{jj} > \eta_{jl}$.

P1 (with T1e) yields the following.

T16-6. Let P_j and P_l be two distinct basic attributes of the same family.

    a. $C_j(\mathbf{s}_0^i) > C_j(\mathbf{s}_0^l)$.
    b. If $\gamma_j = \gamma_l$, then $C_j(\mathbf{s}_0^i) > C_l(\mathbf{s}_0^i)$.

The restricting condition in T6b is necessary. If γ_l is sufficiently larger than γ_j, then it can occur that $C_j(\mathbf{s}_0^i) < C_l(\mathbf{s}_0^i)$; see (17-6) below. In the latter case we have different predictions on the same evidence, while in T6a we have the same prediction with two different evidences.

P1 is a principle of *pure* inductive logic, not of applied IL, because P1, in contrast to R3 and (14), does not depend upon the specific interpretation of the primitive predicates. P1 might be taken as an axiom. I have not done this because it is at present not clear whether it is not derivable from the other axioms, perhaps with the help of the principle of instantial relevance P13-1 (which in turn is derivable, as indicated in §13). In any case, P1 is closely related to P13-1; I have found that some special cases of P1 are derivable from P13-1 (e.g., the special case for η-equality, see below).

The principle P1 is here restricted to basic attributes, those represented by basic regions in the attribute space. It holds also for those kinds of nonbasic attributes which we ordinarily use in our examples. Therefore we shall often apply the principle to such attributes in our examples, with a simple reference to P1 or T2. However, there are some kinds of attributes or regions for which P1 does not hold. In case of doubt, we must divide the regions in question into basic regions, assign to the latter plausible η-values, and then determine the η-values for the nonbasic attributes with the help of T3 and T4. However, in order to assign plausible η-values to basic regions, we must have a suitable general function yielding η-values on the basis of given distances. In the next section we shall make an attempt to construct such a function.

17
The Eta Function

A. GENERAL CONSIDERATIONS

We assume here that for the language $\mathscr{L}$ with one family F and the attribute space $\mathbf{U}$, we have a normalized distance function d, applicable to pairs of points and also (by D15-2d) to the attribute regions. According to the rules R16-3f, g (in §16B), the following holds: (1) if in two pairs of attributes the distance is the same, then the η-value for the two pairs is the same; and if the distance in one pair is smaller than in another, the η-value for the first pair is greater than for the second. This suggests the idea that, for the given F, $\mathbf{U}$, and d, there may be a function, say f, such that, for any two attributes P_j and P_m, we have $\eta_{jm} = f(d_{jm})$. Such a function will be called an η-function for F. We shall consider possibilities for such a function, and, in particular, we shall study a general form for the function. This form involves some parameters; and we shall make suggestions for the choice of values of these parameters. In this analysis, we consider a *one-dimensional attribute space* $\mathbf{U}$. (But the results can then be applied, with suitable modifications, also to two- and more-dimensional spaces.)

The space $\mathbf{U}$ is partitioned into a large number k of intervals X_j which represent the k attributes P_j of a family F. This is similar to the series of intervals shown in figure 16-1, which served as basis for the analysis leading to rule R16-3 (in §16B).

We shall here consider chiefly C_j-values with $s = 0$ or $s = 1$. These values are expressible in terms of γ- and η-values (D16-1a and T16-1e).

(17-1) We make the following assumptions:
    a. The attribute intervals have the same length.
    b. Our width function w is normalized: $w(\mathbf{U}) = 1$.
    Hence we have for each attribute P_j with interval X_j (by R16-1d):
    c. $w(X_j) = 1/k$.
    d. $\gamma_j = 1/k$.
    e. We introduce a coordinate x based on w.
    f. Let the positive end of $\mathbf{U}$ (in figure 17-1 the right-hand end) be at $x = b$ ($b < 1$). Then the negative (left-hand) end is at $x = b - 1$. Thus $\mathbf{U} = [b - 1, b]$.

Throughout this analysis, we study as an example the fixed evidence E_0, which is an atomic proposition with the individual a_1

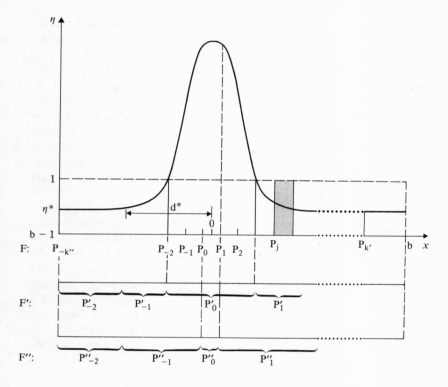

Fig. 17-1.   The Eta-Curve.

and an attribute chosen arbitrarily (with some restrictions to be explained later). Let this evidence attribute be P_0; thus E_0 is $P_0 a_1$. As in figure 17-1, let $P_1, P_2, \ldots, P_{K'}$ be the attributes on the right side of P_0, beginning with the one next to P_0; and similarly $P_{-1}, P_{-2}, \ldots, P_{-k''}$ those on the left. Thus $k = k' + k'' + 1$.

As hypotheses we consider the atomic propositions $H_j = P_j a_2$ ($j = 0, 1, 2, \ldots, k', -1, -2, \ldots, -k''$). For any two attributes P_j and P_m, their distance, i.e., the distance between their center points, is equal to the length of $j - m$ attribute intervals; thus:

(17-2)   **a.** $d_{jm} = |j - m|/k$.

   b. In particular, the distance between P_0 and any other attribute P_j is: $d_{j,0} = |j|/k$.

(17-3)   For any j, $\mathscr{C}(H_j \,|\, E_0) = C_j(\mathbf{s}_0^0) = \gamma_j \eta_{j0}$ (from T16-1e) $= \eta_{j0}/k$ (from (1b)).

In figure 17-1, the intermittent horizontal line at height 1 represents the $\mathscr{C}$-density on $\mathbf{Z}$ (and hence the $\mathscr{M}$-density). For example, the $\mathscr{C}$-value for H_j on $\mathbf{Z}$ is represented by the rectangle over the j-th interval (shaded in figure 17-1) with the area $\gamma_j = 1/k$. The bell-shaped curve represents the $\mathscr{C}$-density on E_0. For any interval X_j, which represents the attribute P_j, the area over X_j and below the curve (cross-shaded in figure 17-1) represents the value $\mathscr{C}(H_j \mid E_0) = \gamma_j \eta_{j0}/k$ (3). Since the length of the interval is $\gamma_j = 1/k$, the mean height of the curve over the interval is η_{j0}. This holds not only for the intervals of the partition F, but for all intervals, including those of the partitions F' and F'' indicated in figure 17-1, and in particular for arbitrarily small intervals. Thus the height of the curve for any point x of the total space $\mathbf{U}$ indicates the quotient $\mathscr{C}/\delta$ for any small interval of length δ around x, in other words, the η-value at x (with respect to P_0). Therefore we call the curve the $\mathscr{C}$-density curve or the η-curve. According to the principle of self-similarity P16-1 (in §16C), the curve has its maximum for a point of the evidence interval, in our example the interval X_0. This maximum value (or, more exactly, the mean value of the η-curve for X_0) is η_{00} which is >1 (T16-1j). If the intervals are small enough, then the curve will be above the 1-line also for some other intervals near to X_0 (in figure 17-1, this is the case for X_{-2}, X_{-1}, X_1, X_2). Thus here we have, for some $j \neq 0$, $\eta_{j0} > 1$.

(17-4) *Results in the example* (see figure 17-1) for the family F.
    a. In F we have $C_{-1}(\mathbf{s}_0^0) > C_{-1}(\mathbf{s}_0)$; hence $\gamma_{-1}\eta_{-1,0} > \gamma_{-1}$; hence $\eta_{-1,0} > 1$.

According to the sum principle, $\sum_j C_j(\mathbf{s}_0^0) = 1$; therefore the total area under the η-curve must be 1. Since the part near to X_0 is above the the 1-line, other parts must be below it (see T16-1k). According to R16-3e, the curve is monotone decreasing with increasing distance from its maximum to the right, and likewise to the left. (If we accept only the weak η-rule (16-9), the curve is monotone nondecreasing.) Thus:

    b. In F we have, for $j < l < 0$ (or $0 < l < j$): $\eta_{j0} < \eta_{l0} < \eta_\infty$. (If we take the weak rule (16-9), we have $\eta_{l0} \leqq \eta_{j0} \leqq \eta_{00}$)

The situation is different for the partition F'. The interval X_0' for P_0' is the union $\bigcup_{j=-2}^{2} X_j$ of those five intervals in F for which the

η-curve is above the 1-line. Therefore:

(17-5) For F', for every $j \neq 0$, $\eta'_{j0} < 1$.

[Incidentally, the η-curve for F' is not exactly the same as that for F; it must be determined from the latter with the help of the theorems (16-6) and (16-7) for derived η-values. However, the difference between the two curves is sufficiently small to be neglected in our present considerations. The η-curve for another partition is exactly the same as that for F, if the evidence interval in F (in figure 17-1, X_0) is identical with an interval in the other partition (e.g., $X_0 = X''_0$ in F'').]

Now we consider the partition F''. Here, X''_0 is the same as X_0 in F. In contrast, X''_1 contains a considerable number, say n, of the original intervals in F. Therefore, $\gamma''_1 = n\eta''_0$. Then, under suitable conditions (as in figure 17-1) the area of the η-curve over X''_1 is larger than that over X''_0. Thus we have:

(17-6) In F'', $C''_1(s^0_0) > C''_0(s^0_0)$.

Since at the present time we have no exact rules for determining η-values, the following statements are based merely on the preceding informal considerations. Thus they are not part of our formal theory of $\mathscr{C}$-functions. Their purpose is rather to guide us in attempts, to be made later, toward the construction of exact rules. Each of the following statements (7), (8), and (9) states the possibility of a certain case with respect to η-values. In each case, (a) specifies the case; (b) and (c) follow immediately from (a).

(17-7) For the two distinct attributes P_j and P_l of a family, with basic regions X_j and X_l, respectively, the following can occur (viz., if X_j and X_l are sufficiently small and their distance is sufficiently small, comp. (4)(a)):
    a. $\eta_{jl} > 1$.
    b. $C_j(s^l_0) > \gamma_j$. (From (a).)
    c. $P_l a_1$ is positively relevant for $P_j a_2$. (From (b).)

(17-8) On the other hand, it may occur that for a given l, for *every* $j \neq l$ the following holds (viz., if γ_l is sufficiently large, comp. (5)):
    a. $\eta_{jl} < 1$.
    b. $C_j(s^l_0) < \gamma_j$.
    c. $P_l a_1$ is negatively relevant for $P_j a_2$.

(17-9) It may occur that for some distinct attributes P_j and P_l the following holds (viz., if γ_j is sufficiently small and γ_l sufficiently large, and the two regions are sufficiently near to each other, comp. (6)):

a. $C_j(\mathbf{s}_0^j) < C_l(\mathbf{s}_0^j)$.
b. $\gamma_j\eta_{jj} < \gamma_l\eta_{lj}$.

With respect to (9)(a), see the earlier remark following T16-6.

We shall now give, for convenient reference, *four diagrams* which visualize the relations of relative magnitude among the $\mathscr{C}$-values for $s = 0$ and $s = 1$, involving two distinct basic attributes P_j and P_l. We distinguish two cases for γ_j and γ_l: (a_1) they are equal; (a_2) the first is smaller; likewise two cases for η_{jl}: (b_1) it is <1, (b_2) it is >1. [We omit the rare special case that $\eta_{jl} = 1$; here $\gamma\eta_{jl} = \gamma$, hence in figures 17-2 and 17-3, the lowest point would coincide with the one directly above it, and in figures 17-4 and 17-5, each of the two lowest points would coincide with the one straight above it.]

(17-10) Assumptions $(a_1)\gamma_j = \gamma_l = \gamma$.
$\qquad\qquad\quad (b_1)\eta_{jl} < 1$.

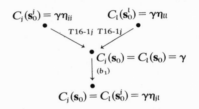

Fig. 17-2.

(17-11) Assumptions: $(a_1)\gamma_j = \gamma_l = \gamma$.
$\qquad\qquad\qquad (b_2)\eta_{jl} > 1$.

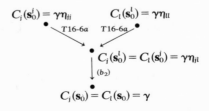

Fig. 17-3.

(17-12) Assumptions: $(a_2)\gamma_j > \gamma_l.$
$\qquad\qquad\qquad (b_1)\eta_{jl} < 1.$

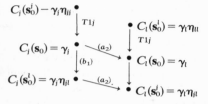

Fig. 17-4.

(17-13) Assumptions $(a_2)\gamma_j > \gamma_l.$
$\qquad\qquad\qquad (b_2)\eta_{jl} > 1.$

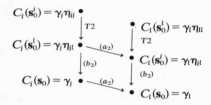

Fig. 17-5.

Each diagram deals with one of the four combinations. Each point in a diagram represents a $\mathscr{C}$-value or two equal $\mathscr{C}$-values. Each $\mathscr{C}$-value is expressed in two forms, in terms of the C_j-function and in terms of γ and η. An arrow running from one point to another signifies the fact that, in the case in question, the first $\mathscr{C}$-value must be greater than the second. Beside each arrow, a reference is given to one of the assumptions or to a theorem. If between two points no greater-relation is indicated either by one arrow or by a pair or a triple of arrows in series, then for the corresponding $\mathscr{C}$-values all three relations are possible, i.e., the first value may be greater or smaller than the second, or equal to it. (However, if for one such pair of values one of the three relations is chosen, then thereby the possibilities for another such pair may be restricted.)

It is at present not yet possible to specify the exact shape of the η-curve. Therefore we have to leave some features of the curve to the subjective judgment. On the other hand, it seems to me, we can give for the choice of some other features at least reasons of plausibility, though not compelling reasons. We shall now consider the questions point by point.

When we study the situation with respect to a certain evidence attribute P_e with interval X_e (in the example of figure 17-1, P_0 with X_0), then we take as origin of the coordinate system the center of this interval X_e. The abscissa x is then the distance from this center, measured by the normalized distance function (D14-4). (The use of the normalized function has the advantage that it enables us to choose one general η-function applicable to any one-dimensional attribute space.) The normalized width of the whole space $\mathbf{U}$ is 1. Hence, if the right-hand end point is at $x = b$, where $b < 1$, the left-hand end point is at $b - 1$, which is negative. In order to avoid certain complications which would otherwise arise, we shall here usually assume that the evidence interval X_e is not marginal, that is, near to one of the two end points. More specifically, we shall assume that both b and $1 - b$ are larger than a certain parameter d^* (which will presently be introduced, and for which we shall choose the numerical value $1/6$).

I. The range of the similarity influence. In the earlier example of figure 16-1 (near the beginning of §16B), we had a one-dimensional space of nine attributes, and considered the similarity influence only between two neighboring attributes. In figure 16-2 we took into consideration various distances, and thereupon laid down the rule R16-3e to the effect that the influence should decrease with growing distance. For any j, let $C_j(\mathbf{s}_0) = c_j$; this is $\gamma_j \eta_{jl}$, hence here, with constant $\gamma_j = \gamma = 1/k$:

(17-14) $c_{jl} = \eta_{jl}/k.$

The probability of H_l, that is, $P_l a_2$, before the first observation yielded the result $E_1 = P_j a_1$, was $\gamma = 1/k$; after that observation it changed to $\gamma \eta_{jl}$. For an attribute near to P_0, say P_{-1}, the probability increased; hence $c_{-1,0} > \gamma$; thus $\eta_{-1,0} > 1$. In figure 17-1, we assumed that it is also increased for P_{-2}, hence $\eta_{-2,0} > 1$. But for certain attributes, the probability must decrease, and hence $\eta_{j0} < 1$, since $\sum_j c_{j0} = 1$.

It seems plausible to assume that the similarity influence has a noticeable effect only within a certain region around the origin as its center. Let this range of influence be the interval $[-d^*, d^*]$. Outside of this interval, η has practically the same value for any attribute; let this value be η^*. Now we have to decide which numerical values to give to the parameters d^* and η^*.

The choice of d^* seems to be, at lest at the present time, a matter of subjective attitude. In the example of figure 16-1, we took into consideration only the effect of contiguous intervals (on P_3 and on P_8) in a space of nine intervals, thus effects at distances of 1/9. We might have considered also the effect of attributes two steps apart, thus at a distance of 2/9. I do not know whether, in a space of nine attributes, anybody would care to extend the influence to three steps, thus at a distance of 1/3. If a space is partitioned into a larger number of attribute regions, say $k = 60$ or 100, the choice of $d^* = 1/3$ would seem to me very generous. I would be inclined to take for d^* something like 1/6. But the choice of 1/8 or even 1/10, or, on the other side, of 1/4 or even 1/3 would also seem acceptable to me. [To give some examples of numerical values of distances, let us take a look at a two-dimensional space we considered earlier, the circular area A represented in figure 14-2, a cross-section of the three-dimensional color space. The (normalized) width of the area A, which is $r^2\pi$, must be 1; hence $r = 1/\sqrt{\pi} = 0.564$. Then the (mean) distance between two adjoining sectors (of the six sectors in figure 14-2) is roughly $2r/3 = 0.38$. Let the marked dots R_1 etc. on the circumference represent very small regions (of a finer partition). Examples of distances: $d(R_1, R_2) = 0.19$; $d(R_2, V_1) = 0.20$; $d(V_1, V_2) = 0.17$.]

II. The η-value η^* for large distances. Once we have chosen d^*, we have to choose the value η^*, to be applied to distances $x > d^*$ (exactly speaking, η^* is the value toward which $\eta(x)$ approaches asymptotically, but to which it is very near for $x < -d^*$ and for $x > d^*$). The problem of the choice of η^* is closely connected with the problem of the choice of a numerical value for another parameter λ, which will be introduced later (in §19). This parameter is applied in the case of certain families, called the λ-families, which are characterized by certain conditions. The main condition is η-equality, that is, the equality of the η-values for all pairs of distinct attributes of the family. This condition is (at least practically) fulfilled, in particular, if for any two distinct attributes in the family the distance exceeds d^*. (This is, for example, the case in the family of the six colors represented by the above mentioned six sectors in figure 14-2, even for $d^* = 1/3$, the largest of the examples of acceptable values of d^* mentioned above.) We shall see that, if a value for λ has been chosen, say λ^*, then the corresponding η-value η^* is uniquely determined:

(17-15) $\eta^* = \lambda^*/(\lambda^* + 1).$

Furthermore, λ should certainly be positive; and it will appear as plausible that it should not be greater than 3. An integer value might seem preferable. If we accept the plausibility arguments, which do not claim to be compelling, we have for λ the choice among the numbers 1, 2, and 3, and hence for η^* 1/2, 2/3, and 3/4. I have myself used mostly $\lambda = 1$ in recent years when I wanted to study a numerical example; therefore I would choose $\eta^* = 1/2$.

III. The form of the η-curve. We wish the curve C for the η-function to be as simple and smooth as it is possible with proper regard to the essential requirements. (This is the reason for (a) and (b) in (16).)

(17-16) *Requirements* for the η-curve C.

    a. C does not have singular points, with a possible exception at 0.

    b. C is symmetric with respect to the origin; the η-function is an even function.

    c. Since $\eta(x)$ is intended to be a probability density function, it must be *normalized* on **U**; that is $\int_{b-1}^{b} \eta(x) \, dx = 1$.

Since $\eta(x)$ converges in both directions asymptotically toward η^*, it seems convenient to represent it as the sum of two functions, the first being constantly η^*, and the second converging both ways toward 0. Therefore we take the following form; then we have a good chance of finding for h either a familiar function or a simple modification of such a function.

(17-17) $\eta(x) =_{\mathrm{Df}} \eta^* + (1 - \eta^*)h(x).$

Thus, if we choose for h a normalized function (16c), then the function η is likewise normalized.

Outside the interval $[-d^*, d^*]$, the curve C is practically horizontal (with value near η^*). Now we shall study the possibilities for the curve inside the interval. For $x < -d^*$, the first derivative h' of h is (either exactly or at least practically) 0; and hence the second derivative is likewise. But to the right of $-d^*$, the curve ascends, first slowly, then more and more steeply. Thus in this first part of the interval, h' and h'' are positive, and hence the curve is concave up. For the shape of the curve at $x = 0$, (13a) allows the choice between two possibilities: either there is no singular point at 0, or there is one. In the *first case*, h, h', and h'' are continuous at 0. Then, because the curve is symmetric with respect to 0, the tangent to the curve must here be horizontal; hence $h' = 0$. Since earlier h' was positive, it has decreased, hence h'' has been negative; the curve is convex up, like a rounded hilltop. Earlier, near $-d^*$, h'' was positive; therefore it must have been 0 at some point, a point of inflection. Thus the curve within the interval is bell-shaped.

In the *second case*, the curve has a singular point at 0. In this case, we *may* let h'' remain positive up to the origin (and then, for simplicity, we *should* do it, in order to avoid a point of inflection). Thus the curve remains concave up all the way to 0, and it is again concave up between 0 and d^*. But at 0 there is a discontinuity. We exclude the case that, as x approaches 0, h tends toward infinity. But we leave open the following two possibilities. Either h' tends to infinity when x approaches 0; then the curve has a *cusp*. Or h' has a finite positive value v on the left side of the origin; then on the right side $h' = -v$. In this case the two tangents of the curve at 0 form a *positive angle* α, and we have $\cot(\alpha/2) = v$.

We shall now investigate in subsection B a specific function f to play the role of h. Its curve is bell-shaped; thus it represents the first case. I have also studied a function g whose curve has at 0 two tangents with a positive angle; thus it represents the second possibility of the second case.

Once we have constructed an η-function $\eta(x)$ of one kind or another, that seems plausible to us, we may apply it in the following ways. First, for any two very small *basic regions* X_j and X_l, whose centers have the distance d_{jl}, we may determine the η-value $\eta_{jl} = \eta(d_{jl})$. With the help of such η-values for small basic regions we can determine the η-value for two *admissible regions* $Y_{j'}$ and $Y_{l'}$ of any size and shape according to T16-3. Furthermore, as far as I can see the situation at present, there is no objection against using essentially the same η-function (but with a suitable adjustment of the normalization factor) also for a two- or more-dimensional attribute space. In the case of two disjoint admissible regions in such a space, for example in the two-dimensional area A in the color space, or in the three-dimensional color space itself, we divide each of the two regions into small basic regions and then determine the η-value again according to T16-3. By the way, in an n-dimensional space ($n \geq 1$), we may go with the width of the basic regions involved to the limit $w(X) \to 0$ and then use the analogue to the formula in T16-3, but with n-fold integrals taking the places of each of the two sums.

B. THE NORMAL FUNCTION f

We shall now study a particular function f to take the place of h in the definition (17) of the η-function. We take here a function

belonging to the first of the two kinds which were just discussed at
the end of §17A, namely the bell-shaped curves. Outside a certain
interval the η-function is practically 0. There are not many functions among those frequently considered in mathematics that have
these two properties. It seems to me that the most natural choice is
the so-called normal (or Gauss-Laplace) probability function. It is
also convenient to use, since the numerical values of the function
itself and of its derivatives and its integral are to be found in easily
accessible tables.

First we define the genral normal function (compare [1950 p.
153], D40-4a and table T40-20):

D17-1 $\phi(u) =_{\mathrm{Df}} \dfrac{1}{\sqrt{2\pi}} e^{-u^2/2}.$

Now we shall define in D2a the special normal function f_σ involving
the parameter σ, the standard deviation, whose value remains to be
chosen; and on the basis of this function f_σ, we shall define in D2b
our present version of the η-function, η_f, in accordance with the
general schema (17).

D17-2. a. $f_\sigma(x) =_{\mathrm{Df}} \dfrac{1}{\sigma} \phi(x/\sigma).$

b. $\eta_f(x) =_{\mathrm{Df}} \eta^* + (1-\eta^*)f_\sigma(x).$

Here we have:

T17-1 $f_\sigma(x) = \dfrac{1}{\sigma\sqrt{2\pi}} e^{-x^2/2\sigma^2}$

This function f_σ was already used in the earlier figure 17-1. We shall
mostly write simply 'f' instead of 'f_σ'. But we must keep in mind
that the function is only defined when we specifiy a value for σ
which will soon be done.

We shall use a convenient notation for definite integrals of our
functions:

D17-3. a. $I\phi(u_1, u_2) =_{\mathrm{Df}} \displaystyle\int_{u_1}^{u_2} \phi(u)du.$

b. $If_\sigma(x_1, x_2) =_{\mathrm{Df}} \displaystyle\int_{x_1}^{x_2} f_\sigma(x)dx.$

T17-2.   For any given pair of values x_1 and x_2 of x, let $u_1 = x_1/\sigma$ and
$u_2 = x_2/\sigma$. Then the following holds.
a. $If(x_1, x_2) = I\phi(u_1, u_2).$

Proof. We take $u = x/\sigma$; hence $dx = \sigma\, du$. Then

$$If(x_1, x_2) = \int_{x_1}^{x_2} f(x)\, dx = \int_{x_1}^{x_2} \frac{1}{\sigma} \phi(x/\sigma)\, dx = \int_{u_1}^{u_2} \frac{1}{\sigma} \phi(u)\sigma\, du$$

$$= \int_{u_1}^{u_2} \phi(u)\, du = I\phi(u_1, u_2). \quad \blacksquare$$

b. As is well known, the function ϕ is normalized on the total **R**: $I\phi(-\infty, \infty) = 1$.

c. f is likewise normalized on **R**: $If(-\infty, \infty) = 1$. (From (a) and (b).)

Strictly speaking, we are here concerned, not with the total space **R**, but with the attribute space **U**, which is the interval $[b-1, b]$ (1f). However, we shall see that, on the basis of our choice of σ, $If(b-1, b)$ and $If(-\infty, \infty)$ are practically equal. Hence f is practically normalized also on **U**.

The choice of σ. We have chosen earlier (in §17AI) a value for d^*. We saw that the choice of d^* may vary considerably from subject to subject. We can easily see that the choice of σ must depend on the choice of d^*. We meant by d^* that distance from the region of the evidence attribute P_e (P_0 in our example) at which the similarity influence practically vanishes. Therefore we must choose σ such that the function f_σ practically vanishes for $x = d^*$ (for the chosen value of d^*, whatever that may be). We shall presently make a suggestion, not directly for σ but for σ/d^*. For our considerations here, it will be convenient to have some numerical values at hand. The following table T3 gives a few values of ϕ and the "tail end" of ϕ that is, $I\phi(u, \infty)$. [By T2b, $I\phi(u, \infty) = 1 - I\phi(-\infty, u)$; published tables are usually given for $I\phi(-\infty, u)$, which is called the "probability integral"; see in [1950, P. 153f.] the definition D40-4b for $\Phi(u)$ (which is $I\phi(-\infty, u)$) and the table T40-20.]

T17-3.

(1) u $(= x/\sigma)$	(2) $\phi(u)$	(3) $I\phi(u, \infty)$ (tail end)
0	.3989	.5000
1	.2420	.1587
2	.0540	.0118
3	.00443	.00135
10/3(d^*)	.00154	.00041
4	.000134	.00003

We see that the value of the normal function ϕ, which gives a measure for the similarity influence, is rather small at $u = 3$ and hence negligible for many practical purposes, and at $u = 4$ for about all purposes. Now d^* is a value of x at which the similarity influence practically vanishes. Therefore it seems plausible to choose σ in such a way that the u-value corresponding to $x = d^*$, that is, $u = d^*/\sigma$, is in the interval $(3, 4)$. I state now my subjective choice in (18a):

(17-18)   **a.** We choose $d^*/\sigma = 10/3$; hence $\sigma = 3d^*/10$.
           b. Since we have chosen $d^* = 1/6$ (in §17A, under (I)), we obtain: $\sigma = 1/20$.

On this basis we can now determine the values in the following table T4; first the same values of u as in T3(1); then $x = \sigma u = u/20$; then by D2: $f(x) = (1/\sigma)\phi(u) = 20\phi(u)$, where the values of $\phi(u)$ are taken from T3; and finally $If(x, \infty)$. This is (by T2a) equal to $I\phi(u, \infty)$ (with $u = x/\sigma$), which is given in T3.

T17-4.

Table for function f (with $\sigma = 1/20$)

(1) u (x/σ)	(2) x (σu)	(3) $f(x)$	(4) $If(x, \infty)$ (tail end)
0	0	7.978	.5000
1	.05	4.840	.1587
2	.1	1.080	.0118
3	.15	.0886	.00135
10/3	1/6(d^*)	.0308	.00041
4	.2	.00268	.00003

We are now in a position to *determine numerical η-values for pairs of attributes* on the basis of the chosen function f. For simplicity, we write:

(17-19) $\eta_j =_{Df} \eta_{j0}$.

Then we have:

(17-20)   For any j, n, $\eta_{n+j,n} = \eta_{n-j,n} = \eta_j$ (provided the subscripts occur as attribute indices).

(17-21)   We use again our earlier numerical values (see (18b), and for η^* the remark at the end of 17AII) and we define 'δ' for convenience in such a way that the length of each attribute interval is 2δ:

   (a) $d^* = 1/6$;
   (b) $\sigma = 1/20$;
   (c) $u = x/\sigma = 20x$;
   (d) $\eta^* = 1/2$;
   (e) $k = 30$;
   (f) $\delta = 1/(2k) = 1/60$.

As in figure 17-1 with family F, we take X_0 as the evidence interval. In terms of the x-coordinate, this interval is $[-\delta, \delta]$; X_1 is $[\delta, 3\delta]$; and generally for $j > 0$, $X_j = [(2j-1)\delta, (2j+1)\delta]$. Therefore it is convenient to use the transformed coordinate $m = x/\delta = 60x$; by (19) η_j is the mean of the η-function over the interval X_j. In the subsequent table T6, the values of η_j are determined in the following way. Column (1) gives the integer values of m ($= 60x$) from -1 to 13. Column (2) gives the values of j (the attribute index) as one half of the even values of m. In (3) we indicate the attribute intervals X_j for $j = 0$ to 6; the end points of these intervals are the odd values of m, from -1 to 13. In (4) we give the values of $x = m/30$, and in (5) those of $u = x/\sigma = 20x = m/3$.

We define now the probability integral $\Phi(u)$ (as in [1950] p. 153, D40-4b) and the analogous function $F(x)$ as follows:

D17-4.   **a.** $\qquad\qquad \Phi(u) =_{\mathrm{Df}} I\phi(-\infty, u).$
   b. $\qquad\qquad F(x) =_{\mathrm{Df}} If(-\infty, x).$

Then the following holds:

T17-5.   For any x, $F(x) = \Phi(x/\sigma) = \Phi(u)$. F and Φ for corresponding arguments x and u ($= x/\sigma$) are equal. (From T2a.)

(17-22)   We define (for the present discussion only) the following notations:
   a. u_j is the u-coordinate of the center of X_j:

$$u_j =_{\mathrm{Df}} 2j/3$$

   b. Similarly for the x-coordinate:

$$x_j =_{\mathrm{Df}} j/30.$$

c. $I\phi_j$ is the integral of ϕ over X_j:

$$I\phi_j =_{Df} I\phi(u_j - 1/3, u_j + 1/3).$$

d. Analogously for f:

$$If_j =_{Df} If(x_j - 1/60, x_j + 1/60).$$

Now the following holds:

(17-23) $If_j = I\phi_j.$ (From T2a.)

We continue with table T6. In column (6) we list from published tables the values of $\Phi(u)$ for the end points of the intervals Xj (the positive odd values of m). According to T5, these are also the values of $F(x)$ for the same points. In column (7) we give the values of $I\phi_j$ for the intervals X_0 to X_6. For $j > 0$, each value is determined as the difference of two values of F in column (6) for the end points of X_j. The given values of $I\phi_j$ are by (23) also the value of If_j for the same intervals.

In column (8) we give the values of $\bar{f}_j$, the mean of the function f for the interval X_j. The mean of a function over an interval is its integral over the interval, divided by the length of the interval measured by the argument of the function. Therefore we must distinguish between the length $\Delta x = 1/k = 1/30$ (see column (4)) and the length $\Delta u = 2/3$ (see column (5)). Thus we obtain

(17-24)   **a.** $\bar{f}_j = If_j/\Delta x = 30 If_j.$
              b. $\bar{\phi}_j = I\phi_j/\Delta u = (3/2)I\phi_j.$

Thus here, for the means $\bar{f}_j$ and $\bar{\phi}_j$, we have no equality analogous to that for F and Φ in T5 and that for If_j and $I\phi_j$ in (23).

With the help of $\bar{f}_j$, we can now determine η_j, which is η_{j0} (19). By D2b,

(17-25) $\eta_j = \eta^* + (1 - \eta^*)\bar{f}_j.$

With our chosen value $\eta^* = 1/2$ (21d):

(17-26) $\eta_j = (\bar{f}_j + 1)/2.$

This yields the values stated in column (9). For $j > 6$, η_j is practically $1/2$. Thus all η values for pairs in our example situation are now determined.

T17-6.

(1) $m=60x$	(2) i	(3) X_i	(4) $x=m/60$	(5) $u=20x$	(6) $\Phi(u)=F(x)$	(7) $If_i=I\phi_i$	(8) $\bar{f}_i$	(9) η_i
-1			-1/60	-1/3	.3694			
0	0	X_0				.2612	7.836	4.418
1			1/60	1/3	.6306			
2	1	X_1				.2107	6.321	3.661
3			3/60	1	.8413			
4	2	X_2				.1109	3.327	2.164
5			5/60	5/3	.95221			
6	3	X_3				.03791	1.1373	1.0686
7			7/60	7/3	.99012			
8	4	X_4				.00853	.2559	.6280
9			9/60	3	.99865			
10	5	X_5				.00123	.0369	.5184
11			11/60	11/3	.99988			
12	6	X_6				.000106	.00318	.5015
13			13/16	13/3	.9999926			

Procedure for a convenient approximation. We have just given exact formulas for η_j, which is $\eta_{l,m}$ for any pair of attributes P_l and P_m such that $|l-m|=j$. We shall now propose a magnitude η_j', which may sometimes be taken as a convenient approximation for η_j. We define η_j' as follows:

(17-27) $\eta_j' =_{Df} \eta(x_j)$, where x_j is the x-coordinate of the center of the interval X_j.

We shall now give in T7 the values of η_j' for our example of the family F of k attributes based upon a partition of the one-dimensional attribute space **U** into k equal intervals. For the numerical calculations we use again the values chosen earlier: $k = 30$, $d^* = 1/6$, $\sigma = 1/20$, and $\eta^* = 1/2$.

The values in the table are determined as follows. We have in column (1) the j-values from 0 to 6 as in table T6, column (2). In column (2) we give as values of x_j those values of x which correspond in T6 column (4) to values of j. Similarly, we give in column (3) for u_j the corresponding u-values in T6, column (5). In column (4), the values of $\phi(u_j)$ have been taken from published tables. The values of $f(x_j)$ in column (5) are obtained, according to D2a, from those of $\phi(u_j)$ by multiplying with $1/\sigma$, which is 20. Finally, the values of η_j' are determined as follows:

(17-28) $\eta_j' = (f(x_j)+1)/2$, in analogy to (26), but with the center value $f(x_j)$ instead of the mean value $\bar{f}_j$.

I have purposely used here the same example family as earlier. The approximate values η_j' have, of course, no practical interest for us, since we are in possession of the more exact values η_j. But we may use the latter for judging the accuracy of the approximation procedure with η_j'. Therefore we list here in column (7) the former values of η_j; furthermore in (8) the difference $\Delta = \eta_j' - \eta_j$, which is the error of the approximation, and in (9) the relative error Δ/η_j. We find that the absolute value of the latter does not exceed 3%. This may be regarded as quite satisfactory in view of the fact that the similarity influence, which is represented by the parameter η, is only a secondary factor in the determination of $\mathscr{C}$-values.

In this subsection 17B we have dealt with the problem of developing rules for the determination of numerical values of the parameter η for any pair of attributes, on the basis of the distance between their regions. Our method combined subjective and objective elements; this is typical for many methods in the construction

T17-7 Calculation of example values of η'_i

(1) j	(2) x_j	(3) u_j	(4) $\phi(u_j)$	(5) $f(x_j)$	(6) η'_i	(7) η_i (for comparison)	(8) error Δ $(\eta'_i - \eta_i)$	(9) relative error $\dfrac{\Delta}{\eta_i}$
0	0	0	.39894	7.9788	4.4894	4.418	.071	0.016
1	$\frac{1}{30}$	$\frac{2}{3}$	.31945	6.3890	3.6945	3.661	.034	0.009
2	$\frac{2}{30}$	$\frac{4}{3}$	.16401	3.2802	2.1401	2.164	−0.024	−0.011
3	$\frac{3}{30}$	2	.05399	1.0798	1.0399	1.0686	−0.0287	−0.027
4	$\frac{4}{30}$	$\frac{8}{3}$	.01140	0.2280	0.6140	.6280	−0.0140	−0.022
5	$\frac{5}{30}$	$\frac{10}{3}$	.001542	0.03084	0.51542	.5184	−0.0030	−0.006
6	$\frac{6}{30}$	4	.000134	0.00268	0.50134	.50159	−0.00025	−0.0005

of a system of IL. The subjective component was conspicuous in the choice of numerical values for some of the parameters, for example d^*, the distance at which the similarity influence disappears either completely or at least practically. This holds also for η^*, the value of η for distances beyond the effective region of the similarity influence. But η^* is closely connected with another parameter λ; when a value for λ has been chosen, then the value of η^* is thereby uniquely determined. Later (in Part II), in the section on the λ-system, we shall discuss in detail various factors that seem to be relevant for the choice of a λ-value. The problem of determining values for η is more complicated and more difficult than that of values for γ. As was shown in §16, it seems quite plausible and almost inevitable to take the value of γ_j for the attribute P_j as being proportional to the size of the region X_j of P_j in the attribute space. The problem of the constant of proportionality solves itself since the sum of the γ's for all attributes of a family must be 1. Thus, once we have a metric and thereby a normalized width function w, it is clear that we must take $\gamma_j = w(X_j)$, as we did in rule R16-1d. So far our path is relatively clear, and hence objective. However, in the construction of a metric for a given attribute space U, that is, in the introduction of a normalized distance function d, we have again a combination of subjective and objective factors. This construction belongs to applied IL, and is the task of psychologists. But even here, there seems to be a strong objective component, indicated by the fact that the psychologists seem to find a remarkable degree of intersubjective agreement in the judgment of subjects concerning equality of distances in an attribute space. Once a distance function is chosen, certain properties of the η-function seem to be indisputable and may therefore be regarded as objective; examples are the requirement that η should be nondecreasing and, in general, increasing with increasing distance, and the requirement that the integral of the η-function with a given evidence point or interval, taken over the whole attribute space, should be one. But choosing a particular function among those fulfilling the objective requirements, seems to be subjective to a high degree.

C. THE PROXIMITY INFLUENCE

We have discussed in detail the first kind of analogy influence, the similarity influence. Now I shall make some brief remarks about the second kind, the *proximity influence*. In those languages that are dealt with in this article, the proximity influence does not occur. In these languages, the indices 1, 2, 3, etc., of the individuals a_1, a_2, a_3, etc., do not indicate the positions of the individuals in a spatial or temporal order, but constitute an arbitrary enumeration and indicate merely identity and distinctness. Therefore in these languages the individual indices are treated as inductively irrelevant, and hence symmetric $\mathscr{C}$-functions are applied. In later articles, however, we shall discuss also languages in which the indices indicate the positions of the individuals in a basic spatial or temporal order. The order may either be merely topological, or metric. In a discrete temporal order of certain events (e.g., the state of the weather at a given place on successive days) for any i, a_{i+1} is the event which occurs in the series next after the event a_i. In a set of objects or events with a one-dimensional spatial order (e.g., a series of books on a shelf, or a series of houses on a street) a_{i+1} is the next individual after a_i in the fixed order. If in a given temporal or spatial series the distance between any two successive individuals a_i and a_{i+1} is everywhere the same, say of (spatial or temporal) length δ, then the indices indicate not only a topological order but a metric. In this case, provided that the elementary distance δ is known, the distance between any two individuals is determined by their indices; e.g., the distance between a_i and a_{i+n} is $n\delta$. The index number of an individual in a metric order (sometimes also that in a merely topographical order) is called the *coordinate* of the individual. A language of this kind is called a *coordinate language* (comp. [1950, §15B] and pp. 73 f., and [1956, §18]).

Let $\mathscr{L}$ be a language of the kind described with a basic (topological or metric) order of the individuals, represented by their indices. We consider a series of atomic propositions with the same attribute, say P_3, but with successive individuals, beginning with an arbitrary individual, say a_2. Let A_i^j be the atomic proposition $P_j a_i$. Then these propositions are: A_2^3, A_3^3, A_4^3, etc. Now we take the first of these propositions as our fixed evidence; we are interested in the $\mathscr{C}$-values for the other propositions as hypotheses. Let the value of $\mathscr{C}(A_{2+n}^3 \mid A_2^3)$ be x_n. In other words, our evidence says that the object a_2 has the attribute P_3, and we consider the probabilities x_n for other individuals a_{2+n} to have the same attribute. It seems plausible to assume that this probability should be higher for the object a_3, which is near to the observed object a_2, than for a remote one, say a_{100}; and similarly, the probability for a_4 should be lower than that for a_3, but higher than that for a_{100}. This means that $x_1 > x_2 > x_{100}$. Since we certainly have $x_0 = 1$ and $x_1 < 1$, it seems natural to make the rules for $\mathscr{C}$ such that $x_0 > x_1 > x_2 > x_3$, etc., at least for small values of n. For large numbers n, the values of x_n and x_{n+1} should be practically equal. We might make them actually equal for every $n \geqq n^*$, where n^* is chosen as a fixed threshold value. Alternatively, we might let x_n always decrease with increasing n. In the latter case, let $\lim_{n \to \infty} x_n = x_\infty$. By the principle of instantial relevance (P13-1), for any n, $x_n > \mathcal{M}(A_2^3)$. But for any i, $\mathcal{M}(A_i^3) = \gamma_3 > 0$; therefore all x_n and x_∞ are positive. The essential point in the choice of a $\mathscr{C}$-function for the described situation is this: do we wish to make $\mathscr{C}$ such that $x_1 > x_2$? If and only if $\mathscr{C}$ is made this way, shall we say that $\mathscr{C}$ *shows the proximity influence*; this term is chosen because our reason for making $\mathscr{C}$ higher at a_3 than at a_4 is the fact that a_3 is nearer than a_4 to the observed individual a_2. A $\mathscr{C}$ of this kind is obviously not symmetric, and the individual indices are no longer inductively irrelevant.

As with the similarity influence, the amount of the proximity influence is usually small and can therefore be disregarded in many cases.

Let us now briefly compare the two kinds of analogy influence. Let $\mathscr{L}$ be a language with one finite family F of k basic attributes, which form a series, i.e., a one-dimensional similarity order $P_1, P_2, \ldots, P_k$ (as in §17A and B). Let $\mathscr{L}$ be a coordinate language, the individuals having a basic one-dimensional order (temporal or spatial) indicated by their indices. We arrange the atomic propositions of $\mathscr{L}$ in a two-dimensional array (see figure 17-6). The j-th column corresponds to the attribute P_j; the i-th row corresponds to the individual a_i. Let us take as the fixed evidence for both kinds of analogy influence an arbitrary atomic proposition, say A_2^3. For the *proximity* influence we consider the *column* of this evidence; thus

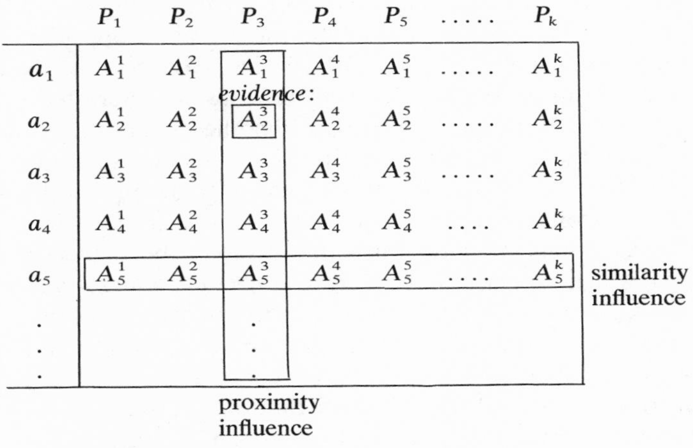

Fig. 17-6. Similarity influence and proximity influence

we keep the attribute fixed and vary the individual. The $\mathscr{C}$-value for A_2^3 is 1; that for A_3^3 (and the same for A_1^3) is smaller; then, by the proximity influence, the $\mathscr{C}$-value decreases step for step when we take as the hypothesis A_4^3, A_5^3, etc. For the *similarity influence* we consider a *row different* from that of the evidence; in the diagram, it is the row of a_5. [In the row of the evidence, the $\mathscr{C}$-value for the evidence itself is 1, while that for any other atomic proposition of the row is 0.] By the similarity influence, the $\mathscr{C}$-value in the row of a_5 is highest for A_5^3 (the case of self-similarity). Then it decreases step for step as we go to farther propositions, either to the right or to the left. There is one essential difference between the two situations. The propositions in any row are disjoint; they form a partition of **Z**. Therefore the $\mathscr{C}$-values considered for the similarity influence sum up to 1. In contrast, the propositions of a column are compatible; even the infinite class of all of them is consistent, i.e., the intersection $A^3 = \bigcap_{i=1}^{\infty} A_i^3$ is non-empty. [A^3 contains exactly one model, viz., the constant function Z such that, for every i, $Z(i) = 3$; A^3 is the universal proposition $(x)P_3(x)$.]

Both kinds of analogy influence will be discussed in greater detail in later articles. Many points in this area are today not yet sufficiently clear and need further investigation.

18
Some Special Kinds of Families

Suppose we have chosen a fixed $\mathscr{C}$-function $\mathscr{C}$, which we intend to apply to many different families of attributes. $\mathscr{C}$ may be defined for a language $\mathscr{L}$ containing all the families in which we are interested. We shall now consider some special kinds of families. These kinds will be defined in terms of the values of $\mathscr{C}$ for propositions involving only the family in question (D3-5b). Therefore, in the case of a family F^m, we shall consider only the sublanguage $\mathscr{L}^m$ of $\mathscr{L}$, restricted to F^m. This is sufficient because, according to the rule of sublanguages (R6-1), any proposition in $\mathscr{L}^m$ has the same $\mathscr{C}$-value as the corresponding proposition in $\mathscr{L}$.

D18-1. Let F be a family of attributes, with index set I_F. Let $\mathscr{C}$ be a $\mathscr{C}$-function for F (among other families). Let γ- and η-values be defined (as in D16-1) on the basis of values of $\mathscr{C}$.

    a. F has γ-*equality* (or: F is a γ-*family*) with respect to $\mathscr{C} =_{\mathrm{Df}}$ for any $j, l \in I_F$, $\gamma_j = \gamma_l$.

    b. F has η-*equality* (or: F is an η-*family*) with respect to $\mathscr{C} =_{\mathrm{Df}}$ for any $j, l, m, n \in I_F$ ($j \neq l$, $m \neq n$), $\eta_{jl} = \eta_{mn}$.

    c. F has $\gamma - \eta$-*equality* (or: F is a $\gamma - \eta$-*family*) with respect to $\mathscr{C} =_{\mathrm{Df}} F$ has γ-*equality* and η-equality with respect to $\mathscr{C}$.

Note that these definitions (and likewise those later in this section) refer only to $\mathscr{C}$-values, not to concepts like width or distance. The condition for γ-equality is merely the equality of the γ-values, in other words, of the values of $C_j(\mathbf{s}_0)$ (or of $\mathrm{MI}(\mathbf{s}_0^j)$) or of $\mathscr{C}(P_j a_i \mid \mathbf{Z})$). For the question of γ-equality it does not matter whether in our construction of the function $\mathscr{C}$ we decided to make these values equal in view of the equality of the widths of the attributes (in accordance with R16-1) or whether we did it for other reasons, good or bad ones, or for no reason.

Strictly speaking, the concept of γ-equality is not a property of F, but a relation between F and $\mathscr{C}$. Any given family F has γ-equality with respect to some $\mathscr{C}$-function, and γ-inequality with respect to another. However, in our present discussions, we treat γ-equality (and likewise the other concepts) as a property of F. We imagine that a fixed function $\mathscr{C}$ has been chosen or is somehow given. Therefore we shall often omit the phrase "with respect to $\mathscr{C}$." We shall further assume tacitly, as in earlier sections, that the given $\mathscr{C}$ is symmetric and regular, unless the contrary is stated.

The following theorem states consequences of γ-equality. We shall apply the concept of γ-equality *to finite families only*. If F is a denumerable family, then, because of the sum theorem (T16-1c), γ-equality involves difficulties. If we wish $\mathcal{M}$ be to σ-additive (D1-8), γ-equality is impossible, unless we give up the normalization of $\mathcal{M}$ (D1-7). If we are willing to give up σ-additivity, an infinite family can have γ-equality; but then every $\gamma_j = 0$, and hence for every atomic proposition, $\mathcal{M} = 0$, which would violate regularity.

T18-1. Let the finite family F of k attributes have γ-*equality* (with respect to $\mathscr{C}$). Let C be the representative function for $\mathscr{C}$. The following holds for any j and l (not necessarily distinct) in I_F ($= \mathbf{N}_k$).

    a. $C_j(\mathbf{s}_0) = \mathrm{MI}(\mathbf{s}_0^j) = \gamma_j = 1/k$. (From T16-1a.)

    b. $C_j^1(\mathbf{s}_0^l) = C_l^1(\mathbf{s}_0^j) = \dfrac{1}{k}\, \eta_{jl}$. (From T16-1e.)

    c. $0 < \eta_{jl} < k$. (From T16-1f.)

    d. For any given l, $\dfrac{1}{k}\sum_j \eta_{jl} = 1$. (From T16-1g.)

    e. If $\mathscr{C}$ satisfies the principle of instantial relevance (P13-1), then $1 < \eta_{jj} < k$. (From T16-1j.)

    f. $\mathrm{MI}(\mathbf{s}_0^{jl}) = \dfrac{1}{k^2}\, \eta_{jl}$. (From T16-1l.)

    g. $\mathrm{MI}(\mathbf{s}_0^{jj}) = \dfrac{1}{k^2}\, \eta_{jj}$. (From T16-1m.)

The following theorem gives results about η-equality. We shall apply η-equality to *finite families only*. In a metrical attribute space, η-equality corresponds to the equality of the distances (for basic attributes, R16-3d and f). For a finite number k, this requires a dimension number of at least $k - 1$ for the attribute space. An infinite family would require an infinite dimension number.

Note that any family with $k = 2$ is trivially an η-family (by T16-1d).

T18-2. Let the family F of k attributes have η-*equality* (with respect to $\mathscr{C}$). We shall designate the common η-value for all pairs of two distinct attributes by 'η'. The following holds for any j, l, m, n in $\mathbf{N}_k$ ($j \neq l$, $j \neq n$, $m \neq n$).

    a. $C_j(\mathbf{s}_0^l) = \gamma_j \eta$. (From T16-1e.)
    b. $C_j(\mathbf{s}_0^l) = C_j(\mathbf{s}_0^n)$. (From (a).)
    c. $\dfrac{C_j(\mathbf{s}_0^l)}{C_m(\mathbf{s}_0^n)} = \dfrac{\gamma_j}{\gamma_m}$. (From (a).)
    d. $C_j(\mathbf{s}_0^j) = 1 - \eta(1 - \gamma_j)$.

Proof. From the sum condition for C_j:

$$C_j(s_0^i) = 1 - \sum_{m(\neq j)} C_m(s_0^i);$$

hence by (a):

$$= 1 - \eta \sum_{m(\neq j)} \gamma_m;$$
$$= 1 - \eta(1 - \gamma_j). \quad \blacksquare$$

e. If $\mathscr{C}$ satisfies the principle of instantial relevance (P13-1), then $0 < \eta < 1$. (From T16-1e and k.)

f. $\eta_{jj} = \dfrac{1}{\gamma_j}[1 - \eta(1 - \gamma_j)]$. (From (d) and T16-1i.)

g. $\eta_{jj} = \eta + \dfrac{1 - \eta}{\gamma_j}$. (From (f).)

h. If $\mathscr{C}$ satisfies the principle of instantial relevance, then
$0 < \eta < 1 < \eta_{jj} < \dfrac{1}{\gamma_j}$. (From (e) and T16-1j.)

Note that T2h yields $\eta_{jj} > \eta$ by presupposing merely the principle of instantial relevance, without the use of P16-1 and without restriction to basic attributes.

The following theorem gives some consequences of $\gamma - \eta$-equality, based on T1a and parts of T2.

T18-3. Let the family F of k attributes have $\gamma - \eta$-*equality* (with respect to $\mathscr{C}$). Let j and m be any two distinct attribute indices. We take again $\eta = \eta_{jm}$.

a. $C_j(s_0^m) = \dfrac{1}{k}\eta$. (From T2a.)

b. $C_j(s_0^j) = 1 - \eta\dfrac{k-1}{k}$. (From T2d.)

c. $C_j(s_0^j) = \dfrac{1}{k}\eta_{jj}$. (From T16-1i.)

d. η_{jj} has the same value for every index j; let this value be η': $\eta_{jj} = \eta' = k - (k-1)\eta$. (From (b) and (c).)

e. $C_j(s_0^j) = \dfrac{1}{k}\eta'$. (From (c) and (d).)

f. $\mathrm{MI}(s_0^{jm}) = \dfrac{1}{k^2}\eta$. (From T1f.)

g. $\mathrm{MI}(s_0^{jj}) = \dfrac{1}{k^2}\eta'$. (From T1g.)

h. If $\mathscr{C}$ satisfies the principle of instantial relevance, then $1 < \eta' < k$. (From T16-1j.)

i. $k - \eta' = (k-1)\eta$. (From (d).)

j. $\eta = \dfrac{k - \eta'}{k - 1}$. (From (i).)

k. $\eta' - \eta = k(1 - \eta)$. (From (i).)

l. $\eta' - 1 = (k-1)(1-\eta)$. (From (k).)

The results become plausible in the following way. In the case of γ-equality, we have (by T1d):

$$\sum_j \eta_{jl} = k;$$

hence:

$$\eta_{ll} + \sum_{j(\neq l)} \eta_{jl} = k.$$

Then, if also η-equality holds, each of the $k-1$ terms of the latter sum is η:

$$\eta' + (k-1)\eta = k. \quad \text{(This is the same as T3d or T3i.)}$$

If we choose a value for η, then the corresponding value for η' is uniquely determined. The following diagram (figure 18-1) shows the relation.

We see that, the nearer η comes to 1 from below, the nearer η' comes to 1 from above. More specifically, η divides the segment $(0, 1)$ in the same ratio as η' divides the segment $(k, 1)$ (taken in the descending direction).

From now on, whenever η-equality holds, we shall write 'η' for the common value of η_{jl} for all pairs of distinct j, l; and, if furthermore γ-equality holds, we take 'η'' for the common value of η_{jj} for any index j.

Previously we considered the concept of symmetry with respect to individuals (§9). Now we shall introduce a similar but somewhat

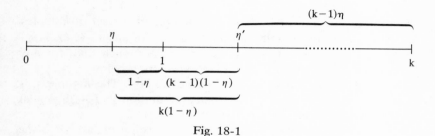

Fig. 18-1

more complicated concept, the symmetry with respect to the attributes of a family, or briefly *attribute symmetry*. Earlier we called a function $\mathscr{C}$ or $\mathscr{M}$ symmetric (with respect to individuals) if it is invariant under a transposition of any two individuals. One might consider similarly to call a function $\mathscr{C}$ or $\mathscr{M}$ attribute-symmetric if it is invariant under any permutation of the attributes of any family. However, a definition of this kind would not be appropriate. While a language usually refers to only one set of individuals, it may refer to several families of attributes. In this case it may well occur that we wish our $\mathscr{C}$-function to be invariant under any permutation of the attributes of the family F but not invariant under a permutation of the attributes of another family F' (e.g., if among the attributes of F' different widths or different distances occur). Therefore we shall ascribe the property of attribute symmetry not to a $\mathscr{C}$-function but to a family. [Strictly speaking, when applying the concept of attribute symmetry, we should refer both to a family and a $\mathscr{C}$-function. But this would be rather cumbersome. Therefore we shall usually refer explicitly to the family only and presuppose tacitly the reference to the $\mathscr{C}$-function; in the formal definition the latter reference is also given, but included in parentheses.]

In analogy to the earlier definition of individual symmetry, we shall give the definition of the attribute symmetry of a family F in terms of permutations of the index set of F. As in the case of γ-equality and η-equality (both of which are L-implied by attribute symmetry, as we shall see, T4f and h), we shall assume that F contains a finite number k of attributes; hence the index set is $\mathbf{N}_k$.

The following definitions are analogous to those in D9-2.

D18-2. Let F be a finite family of k attributes. Let ψ be a permutation for F (i.e., of the index set $\mathbf{N}_k$ of F).

    a. ψ' is *the mapping of* $\mathbf{Z}$ *onto* $\mathbf{Z}$ *induced by* $\psi =_{\mathrm{Df}}$ for any $Z \in \mathbf{Z}$, $\psi'(Z)$ is the model $Z' \in \mathbf{Z}$ defined as follows: for any individual index i, $Z'(i) = \psi(Z(i))$.

    b. Let $Z, Z' \in \mathbf{Z}$. The *model* Z' is *attribute-isomorphic* to Z with respect to $F =_{\mathrm{Df}}$ for some permutation ψ for F, $Z' = \psi'(Z)$.

    c. For any $s \geqq 0$, ψ'_s is the mapping of the set of k-tuples $\mathbf{N}^{k,s}$ (see (3-7a)) onto itself, induced by $\psi =_{\mathrm{Df}}$ for any $\mathbf{s} = \langle s_1, \ldots, s_k \rangle$ in $\mathbf{N}^{k,s}$, $\psi'_s(\mathbf{s})$ is the k-tuple $\langle s'_1, \ldots, s'_k \rangle$ in $\mathbf{N}^{k,s}$ such that, for any index j, $s_j = s'_{j'}$, where $j' = \psi(j)$. (See explanation below.)

    d. Let $\mathbf{s}$ and $\mathbf{s}'$ be any k-tuples in $\mathbf{N}^{k,s}$. The k-tuple $\mathbf{s}'$ is *attribute-isomorphic* to $\mathbf{s} =_{\mathrm{Df}}$ for some permutation χ of $\mathbf{N}_k$, $\mathbf{s}' = \chi'_s(\mathbf{s})$ (where χ'_s is induced by χ in the sense of (c)).

    e. Let ψ' be induced by ψ (in the sense of (a)). ψ'' is *the* *mapping of* $\mathscr{E}$ *onto* $\mathscr{E}$, induced by $\psi =_{\mathrm{Df}}$ for any $B \in \mathscr{E}$, $\psi''(B) =$ $\{Z':$ for some $Z \in B$, $Z' = \psi'(Z)\}$.

    f. Let $B, B' \in \mathscr{E}$. The proposition B' is *attribute-isomorphic* to $B =_{\mathrm{Df}}$ for some permutation χ of $\mathbf{N}_k$, if χ'' is induced by χ in the sense of (e), $B' = \chi''(B)$.

[Explanation to D2c. If an expression for the k-tuple $\mathbf{s}$ is given as a sequence of k numerals (see (3-7b)), then an expression for $\mathbf{s}' = \psi'_s(\mathbf{s})$ is formed by a rearranging of the numerals as follows: for every index j, the jth numeral is shifted to the position $j' = \psi(j)$. Example for $k = 4$: Let $\psi = \begin{pmatrix} 1 & 2 & 3 & 4 \\ 4 & 3 & 1 & 2 \end{pmatrix}$; i.e., $\psi(1) = 4, \ldots, \psi(4) = 2$. Suppose that $\mathbf{s} = \langle 4, 0, 7, 6 \rangle$, with $s = 17$. Then $\mathbf{s}' = \psi'_s(\mathbf{s}) = \langle 7, 6, 0, 4 \rangle$. $j' = \psi(j)$; e.g., for $j = 4$, $4' = \psi(4) = 2$, hence $s'_2 = s_4 = 6$. Suppose that the initial 17-sample has in the model Z the k-tuple $\mathbf{s}$. Then it has in $Z' = \psi'(Z)$ the k-tuple $\mathbf{s}' = \psi'_s(\mathbf{s})$.]

[As in most of our discussions since §10, we have presupposed in D2 a language which contains F as the only family. For a language $\mathscr{L}$ containing several families we can apply the same definitions to a family F^m of $\mathscr{L}$, with the following modifications. We replace 'F' throughout by 'F^m'. In D2a, we define Z' as follows: For any individual index i, (1) $Z'(m, i) =_{\mathrm{Df}} \psi(Z(m, i))$; (2) for any family index p $(p \neq m)$, $Z'(p, i) = Z(p, i)$. In D2f, before the symbol of definition, we insert "with respect to F^m".]

D18-3. Let F be a finite family of k attributes. F has *attribute symmetry* or, for short, F is a *symmetric family* (with respect to $\mathscr{C}$) $=_{\mathrm{Df}}$ for every $s \geq 0$, for every $\mathbf{s} \in \mathbf{N}^{k,s}$, for every permutation ψ for F, $\mathrm{MI}(\mathbf{s}) = \mathrm{MI}(\psi'_s(\mathbf{s}))$, where MI is representative of the function $\mathscr{M}$ related to $\mathscr{C}$.

The definition of attribute symmetry with respect to $\mathscr{C}$ refers only to values of $\mathscr{C}$, not to those of the distance function d or the width function w (although, according to the rules R16-1 and R16-3, the values of w and d may influence those of γ and η, respectively, and hence those of $\mathscr{C}$). Therefore it would, in principle, be admissible to lay down an axiom requiring attribute symmetry for all families. But I prefer now to define it merely as a possible condition for a family with respect to a $\mathscr{C}$-function, because I wish to admit also families and $\mathscr{C}$-functions for which the condition is not fulfilled. This depends on the nature of the family and should therefore be regulated by suitable rules. I shall soon come back to this question (after T8, under III). The same holds for the λ-condition, which will be explained in the next section. In earlier publications I required both properties by axioms or conventions (attribute symmetry by convention C8 in [1952a, §4] and as Axiom NA8 in [1959, Anhang B]; the λ-condition (for $k > 2$) as convention C9 and as Axiom NA14 at the same places). In the present article I introduce by axioms those properties which I wish to require for all or most of the language forms which I plan to consider here or later. Thus I state axioms for the symmetry with respect to individuals (in §9) and for Kolmogoroff's continuity (in §20 below), because in most language forms I wish to apply them generally, i.e., for all possible families, although in some particular language forms I shall not apply them. On the other hand, properties like γ-equality, η-equality, attribute symmetry, or the λ-condition, are here not required by axioms but merely defined as possible conditions, because even in a simple language form (e.g., a language with a finite number of finite families of monadic predicates) each of these properties seems inadequate for certain kinds of families. The foregoing remarks are merely intended as an indication of the way in which the term "axiom" is used in this article; they are not meant as a recommendation. There is another way of formulation for which I have still some liking, though I do not apply it in this article. This is the way I used in the formal system in [1950], chapters V–VIII. There I did not state any axioms, but merely definitions of kinds of $\mathscr{C}$-functions (e.g., regularity and symmetry). Today I would add definitions of kinds of families (with respect to $\mathscr{C}$-functions). I have chosen here the formulation in terms of axioms (modified by the separation of what I call possible conditions) chiefly for the reason that it seems closer to what is customary today.

The following theorem states some consequences of attribute symmetry. The theorem refers only to the case that $k > 2$. In the case that $k = 2$, η-equality holds trivially; and F is symmetric if-if it has γ-equality.

T18-4.   Let F be a *symmetric family* (with respect to $\mathscr{C}$) containing k attributes ($k > 2$). Let j, m, n be three distinct attribute indices. Let $s \geq 0$. Let $\mathbf{s}$ be a k-tuple in $\mathbf{N}^{k,s}$. Let ψ be a permutation for F. Let $\mathbf{s}' = \psi_s'(\mathbf{s})$. Let $m' = \psi(m)$. For any $H, E \in \mathscr{E}$, let $H'' = \psi''(H)$ and $E'' = \psi''(E)$.

> **a.** $\mathrm{MI}(\mathbf{s}) = \mathrm{MI}(\mathbf{s}')$.
> **b.** $\psi_{s+1}'(\mathbf{s}^m) = \mathbf{s}'^{m'}$.

Proof.   Since $\psi(m) = m'$ and $\psi_s'(\mathbf{s}) = \mathbf{s}'$, we have by D2c: s_m (in $\mathbf{s}$) $= s_{m'}'$ (in $\mathbf{s}'$). $\mathbf{s}^m$ is like $\mathbf{s}$, except with $s_m + 1$ instead of s_m. Therefore $\psi_{s+1}'(\mathbf{s}^m)$ is like $\mathbf{s}'$, except with $s_{m'}' + 1$ instead of $s_{m'}'$; hence it is $\mathbf{s}'^{m'}$.   ∎

    c. $\text{MI}(\mathbf{s}^m) = \text{MI}(\mathbf{s}'^{m'})$. (From (b).)

    d. $\psi_0'(\mathbf{s}_0) = \mathbf{s}_0$.

    e. $\text{MI}(\mathbf{s}_0^m) = \text{MI}(\mathbf{s}_0^{m'})$. (From (c) and (d).)

  +f. $\gamma_m = \gamma_{m'}$. (From (e) and T16-1a.) Thus F has γ-*equality*.

    g. Let ψ be such that $\psi(j) = j$; hence $j = m'$. Then $\text{MI}(\mathbf{s}_0^{jm}) = \text{MI}(\mathbf{s}_0^{jm'})$. (From (c).)

  +h. $\eta_{jm} = \eta_{jm'}$. (From (g) and T1f.) Hence F has η-*equality*.

    i. $C_m(\mathbf{s}) = C_{m'}(\mathbf{s}')$.

Proof. By T12-1j, $C_m(\mathbf{s}) = \text{MI}(\mathbf{s}^m)/\text{MI}(\mathbf{s})$. Likewise $C_{m'}(\mathbf{s}') = \text{MI}(\mathbf{s}'^{m'})/\text{MI}(\mathbf{s}')$. Hence the assertion by (a) and (c). ∎

  +j. $\mathcal{M}(H) = \mathcal{M}(H'')$.

Proof. Let n be such that for any individual index i involved in H, $i \leq n$. Let $\mathscr{B}_H^{(n)}$ be defined as in D3-6e. Then by T3-4i, with $\sum\limits_{A}$ covering all $A \in \mathscr{B}_H^{(n)}$:

(1) $\mathcal{M}(H) = \sum\limits_{A} \mathcal{M}(A)$.

    For any $A \in \mathscr{B}_H^{(n)}$, let $A'' = \psi''(A)$, let A have the k-tuple $\mathbf{s}$ and A'' the k-tuple $\mathbf{s}''$, hence $\mathbf{s}'' = \psi_n'(\mathbf{s})$. Therefore, for any $A \in \mathscr{B}_H^{(n)}$, $\text{MI}(\mathbf{s}) = \text{MI}(\mathbf{s}'')$ (by (a)), and $\mathcal{M}(A) = \mathcal{M}(A'')$. Now we have:

(2) $\mathcal{M}(H'') = \sum\limits_{A''} \mathcal{M}(A'')$, with $\sum\limits_{A''}$ covering all $A'' \in \mathscr{B}_{H''}^{(n)}$. Hence the assertion. ∎

  +k. $\mathscr{C}(H \mid E) = \mathscr{C}(H'' \mid E'')$. (From (j).)

We shall now define (D4) a condition which is similar to, but weaker than attribute symmetry; it does not imply γ-equality. We shall call this condition, which will not be used frequently, "*weak attribute symmetry*". We shall later find that this condition together with γ-equality is equivalent to attribute symmetry (T7).

D18-4. Let F be a family of k attributes, with $k > 2$. F has *weak attribute symmetry* (or: F is a weakly symmetric family) (with respect to $\mathscr{C}$) $=_{\text{Df}}$ for every $s \geq 0$, for every $\mathbf{s} \in \mathbf{N}^{k,s}$, for any given index j, for every permutation ψ for F such that, for the given j, $\psi(j) = j$,

$$C_j^s(\mathbf{s}) = C_j^s(\psi_s'(\mathbf{s})).$$

It is easily seen that, in the special case $s = 0$, the condition is always trivially fulfilled; and in the case $s = 1$, the condition is the same as η-equality. The definition is restricted to families with $k > 2$. For $k = 2$, ψ can only be the identity, and hence the condition would always be trivially fulfilled.

T18-5. If the family F is symmetric, then F is weakly symmetric. (From T4i and D4.)

T18-6. Let $\mathscr{C}$ satisfy the following condition with respect to a family F of k attributes $(k > 2)$. For any $s > 0$, for any k-tuple $\mathbf{s} = \langle s_1, \ldots, s_k \rangle$ in $\mathbf{N}^{k,s}$, for any three distinct attribute indices j, m, n, $C_j(\mathbf{s}) = C_j(\mathbf{s}_{(m,n)})$, where $\mathbf{s}(m, n)$ is formed from $\mathbf{s}$ by interchanging s_m and s_n. Then $\mathscr{C}$ has *weak attribute symmetry* with respect to F.

Proof. Let $\mathscr{C}$ satisfy the condition stated. Let ψ be any permutation of $\mathbf{N}_k$ such that, for the given j, $\psi(j) = j$. ψ can be split up into a finite number of transpositions (i.e., interchanges of two elements). By supposition, C_j is invariant with respect to any of these transpositions, and therefore also with respect to ψ. Hence $\mathscr{C}$ has weak attribute symmetry. ∎

T18-7. Let F (with $k > 2$) be a *weakly symmetric family* (with respect to $\mathscr{C}$). Let j, m, n be three distinct attribute indices. Let $s \geqq 0$. Let $\mathbf{s} \in \mathbf{N}^{k,s}$. Let ψ be a permutation for F such that, for the given j, $\psi(j) = j$. Let $\mathbf{s}' = \psi'_s(\mathbf{s})$. Let $m' = \psi(m)$. Then the following holds.

  a. $C_j^s(\mathbf{s}) = C_j^s(\mathbf{s}')$. (From D4.)

  b. $\dfrac{MI^{s+1}(\mathbf{s}^j)}{MI^{s+1}(\mathbf{s}'^j)} = \dfrac{MI^s(\mathbf{s})}{MI^s(\mathbf{s}')}$. (From (a).)

  c. $\dfrac{MI^{s+p}(\mathbf{s}^{j^p})}{MI^{s+p}(\mathbf{s}'^{j^p})} = \dfrac{MI^s(\mathbf{s})}{MI^s(\mathbf{s}')}$.

   (From (b), by mathematical induction with respect to p.)

  +d. F has η-*equality*. (The proof is analogous to that of T4g and h.)

  e. If F has moreover γ-equality, then F has attribute symmetry.

Proof. For any given s, let D_s be the definiens in D4. We must show that for every s D_s holds.

(1) D_0 holds trivially; because of the γ-equality, D_1 holds.

  We shall show that:

(2) For a given s, suppose that D_s holds; then D_{s+1} holds too.

Let s^* be a k-tuple in $N^{k,s+1}$. There must be some attribute index m such that the mth number in s^* is positive; let this number be $s_m + 1$. Let s be like s^*, except with s_m instead of $s_m + 1$. Hence $s^* = s^m$. On the basis of m and s, let ψ, s', m' be as in T4. According to the supposition in (2), D_s holds. Hence by T4a and c, $MI^s(s) = MI^s(s')$, and $MI^{s+1}(s^m) = MI^{s+1}(s'^{m'})$. Now $s'^{m'} = \psi'_{s+1}(s^m)$ (T4b) and $s^m = s^*$. Hence $MI^{s+1}(s^*) = MI^{s+1}(\psi'_{s+1}(s^*))$. Since this is the case for an arbitrary s^*, D_{s+1} holds. Thus (2) is proved. The assertion follows from (1) and (2) by mathematical induction with respect to s. ∎

+T18-8. Let F be a family of k attributes, with $k > 2$. F has attribute symmetry if-if F has weak attribute symmetry and γ-equality.

Proof. 1. Let F have weak attribute symmetry and γ-equality. Then F has attribute symmetry, by T7e.
2. Suppose that F has attribute symmetry. Then F has γ-equality (by T4f) and weak attribute symmetry (by T5). ∎

Let us now consider for each of the properties of families defined in this section, the condition which the region representing the attributes of a family F must satisfy in order to ensure that property.

I. γ-equality. Obviously F has this property if either the condition in rule R16-1a holds for each pair of distinct attributes in F, or if, on the basis of a quantitative width function, all attributes of F have the same width according to R16-1c or d.

II. η-equality. For the question of η-equality with respect to basic attributes, the situation is similar on the basis of rules R16-3a,b,d. The η-values for nonbasic attributes must be determined from those for basic attributes with the help of T16-3. In accordance with our considerations on the η-function in §17, we may assume that the η-curve outside of its central hill-shaped part is practically horizontal. More specifically, according to (17-17), beyond a certain value d^* of the distance, η has a practically constant value η^*. If in a family F the distance between any two of the attribute regions is not less than d^*, we might call F a *"long-distance family"*. Since in this case the η-values are practically equal, we shall usually treat a family of this kind as an η-family. [In §17A, under I, we chose for d^* the numerical value 1/6. In the example of the circular area A in figure 14-2, which is a cross-section of the color-space, we found the distance between any two adjacent ones of the six sectors representing the six colors in our color family to be 0.38, thus considerably higher than d^*. Thus this is a long-distance family; and we take it as an η-family. In a case like this, where we assign equal η-values in spite of considerable differences among the distances, we must, of course, use the *weak η-rule* (16-9), since R16-3e is not satisfied.]

III. *Attribute symmetry*. This question involves a new problem. The first step is simple. Since $\gamma - \eta$-equality is a necessary condition for attribute symmetry, the conditions for γ-equality and η-equality must certainly be satisfied. But $\gamma - \eta$-equality is not sufficient. [An example of a symmetric and regular function MI for which $\gamma - \eta$-equality holds, but not attribute symmetry, can be constructed with the help of concepts to be introduced later. Such an MI can be defined as a convex combination of several suitably chosen MI-functions of the λ-system, which will be explained in the next section.] Thus the question is: should we require for attribute symmetry more than $\gamma - \eta$-equality? And if so, what?

One might perhaps consider laying down a rule of the following kind:

(18-1) If the family F has $\gamma - \eta$-equality and, moreover, is such that all inductively relevant properties of attributes and relations among attributes hold (or do not hold) for all attributes in the same way, then F shall be treated as a symmetric family.

But this formulation is not suitable as a rule because it is too vague. It fails to specify just which properties and relations of attributes are inductively relevant. We have earlier stated a conjecture (C15-3) to the effect that for basic attributes only widths and distances are relevant. If we were certain of the correctness of this conjecture, we might be inclined to think that for attribute symmetry with respect to basic attributes nothing more should be required than equality of widths and equality of distances. But then we need not state a rule referring to distances and width. We could formulate the requirements in terms of inductive logic referring to $\mathscr{C}$-values, since the equality of widths is expressible as γ-equality, and the equality of distances as η-equality. Thus we might formulate the following rule of inductive logic:

(18-2) If a family F of basic attributes has $\gamma - \eta$-equality, we shall treat F as a symmetric family.

An alternative formulation would be as an axiom for $\mathscr{C}$:

(18-3) If $\mathscr{C}$ has $\gamma - \eta$-equality for a family F of basic attributes, then $\mathscr{C}$ has also attribute symmetry for F.

This is, of course, not meant as asserting that attribute symmetry follows logically from $\gamma - \eta$-equality (on the basis of our earlier axioms). If (18-3) were accepted, it would be a new axiom. Its acceptance would express our decision to exclude those $\mathscr{C}$-functions which, for a given family F of basic attributes, have $\gamma - \eta$-equality but not attribute symmetry.

We might also consider taking as an axiom the following statement which is somewhat stronger than (18-3):

(18-4) If $\mathscr{C}$ has η-equality for a family F of basic attributes, then $\mathscr{C}$ has also weak attribute symmetry.

(18-3) follows from (18-4) by T7e.

At the present moment, at least (18-3) seems to me rather plausible. However, before we decide to accept (18-3) or even (18-4) as a general axiom, it seems advisable to wait for further investigation of the question whether these statements do not lead to undesirable consequences. However, in constructing a particular $\mathscr{C}$-function for a given family, after deciding to give it $\gamma - \eta$-equality no matter whether this is done on the basis of the strong or the weak η-rule), we shall often decide to give it attribute symmetry too.

19
Lambda-families

Suppose we investigate the C-function of a person X, either by observing the bets he is willing to accept or by asking whether certain C-values are equal or not. We are interested in his C-function for a family of more than two attributes. As an example, we consider the family $F = \{\text{Red, Blue, Yellow}\}$ for balls drawn from an urn. Suppose that to our questions he tells us that for his C-function the following values are equal: $C_1(5, 6, 9)$, $C_1(5, 2, 13)$, $C_1(5, 13, 2)$. If he gives many examples of this kind, we shall presume that his C-function is always in accord with the following principle:

(19-1) *λ-principle:* For any $\mathbf{s} = \langle s_1, \ldots, s_k \rangle$, $C_j(\mathbf{s})$ depends only on s_j and s, but is independent of the other $k - 1$ numbers in $\mathbf{s}$.

It seems that most people follow this principle, whether explicitly formulated or not. This includes also the majority of those who work in mathematical statistics. Although they usually reject any nonfrequency concept of probability, they still are interested in estimating the relative frequency (*rf*) of an attribute P_j in a future sample K, based on an observed sample proposition E with the k-tuple $\mathbf{s}$. If a statistician accepts such an estimator function est $(rf, P_j, K \mid E)$ and is willing to regard its values as indicating fair betting quotients, then we may represent his function *est* by that C-function which has the same values:

(19-2) $$C_j(\mathbf{s}) = \text{est } (rf, P_j, K \mid E).$$

In earlier publications I took (1) or an equivalent principle as a general axiom (C9 in [1952*a*] p. 14 and NA14 in [1959] p. 246). Later I recognized that it is better not to require this for all $\mathscr{C}$-functions, but rather to regard it as a condition fulfilled by some but not by all $\mathscr{C}$-functions. (An exact formulation of this condition will be given in D1a; (1) is meant merely as a preliminary, informal statement of the condition.) The $\mathscr{C}$-functions fulfilling the condition will be called $\lambda - \mathscr{C}$-functions. The families to which we apply these $\mathscr{C}$-functions are called λ-families. They include most of the usual run of families; excluded are those special cases in which the similarity influence must be taken into consideration.

The λ-$\mathscr{C}$-functions are of fundamental importance, both theoretically and practically, for the whole of inductive logic, for all forms of languages. First, for a language of the simplest form, with one family of attributes, very often the natural choice of a $\mathscr{C}$-function will be that of a λ-$\mathscr{C}$-function; if so, the determination of the values of the representative λ-$\mathscr{C}$-function is especially simple. And in the case of more complicated languages, where the λ-$\mathscr{C}$-functions are not directly applicable, they still serve as a basis for the construction of other $\mathscr{C}$-functions suitable for these languages. This is the case, for example, for a language with a single family F for which a λ-$\mathscr{C}$-function is unsuitable (because in F there are considerable differences between the distances, and therefore different η-values are required) or for a language with several families, or for a language with one or more dyadic relations, or with quantitative physical magnitudes.

Suppose that the function $\mathscr{C}$ for a family of k attributes ($k > 2$), has η-equality and that the k γ-values and η are given. We have seen earlier that hereby all values of C for $s = 0$ and $s = 1$ are uniquely determined, but the C-values for larger s are in general not determined. However, we shall find that, if $\mathscr{C}$ is moreover a λ-$\mathscr{C}$-function (all λ-$\mathscr{C}$-functions have η-equality), then all C-values for any s, and thus all values of $\mathscr{C}$ are determined.

I said above that the great majority of gamblers and of statisticians accept implicitly the λ-principle. It seems, in fact, that they would choose one particular function of this kind, which is characterized by what I call "the straight rule" (it is called "the proportional rule" in Carnap–Stegmüller [1959].) This rule occurs in two related forms. The first refers to the C-function which I denote by "^0C"; the second refers to the estimator function ^{0}est (represented by ^0C in the sense of (2)).

(19-3)   *The straight rule* for $\mathscr{C}$:

$$^0C_j(\mathbf{s}) =_{\mathrm{Df}} s_j/s.$$

(19-4)   *The straight rule for estimating the relative frequency* of the attribute P_j in any future sample K or in the rest of the population on the basis of the sample description E:

$$^0\mathrm{est}\,(rf,\,P_j,\,K \mid E) = s_j/s.$$

The straight rule in either of the two forms has serious disadvantages. If $s_j = 0$, then both ^0C_j and the estimate vanish. Thus ^0C is not regular, and hence not strictly coherent (T8-6). Therefore some bets in accordance with ^0C—and likewise with ^{0}est, if the estimate is intended to provide a fair betting quotient—are unreasonable.

From a common sense point of view, many values of ^0C and ^{0}est seem quite acceptable, e.g., if $0 < s_i < s$ and hence the value of the functions is neither 0 nor 1. But even the values $C_2(20, 0, 0) = 0$ and $C_1(20, 0, 0) = 1$ might to some not appear as very disturbing, since we would expect in the first case, if not 0, certainly a small value; and in the second case a large value. In contrast, in the following examples, the values of $^0\mathscr{C}$ differ widely from those intuitively required. Suppose that balls are drawn from an urn containing one hundred thousand balls; each ball has one of the five colors: Red, Orange, Yellow, Green, Blue.

(19-5) In this situation, on the basis of the observation that the first ball was red, $^0\mathscr{C}$ has the value 1 for each of the following predictions:

 (a) The next ten balls to be drawn will be red.
 (b) The next one thousand balls will be red.
 (c) All the one hundred thousand balls in the urn will be seen to be red.

Now we consider values of $^0\mathscr{M}$, the $\mathscr{M}$-function related to $^0\mathscr{C}$. They are initial probabilities, i.e., assigned before any ball is drawn.

(19-6) $^0\mathscr{M}$ has the value 1 for each of the following propositions:

 (a) Among the five colors, there are four (it is not specified which they are) which will not occur among the first ten balls.
 (b) Likewise for the first one thousand balls.
 (c) Likewise for all the one hundred thousand balls.

It seems to me that, judged intuitively, the values for the two propositions (a) in (5) and (6) should not be near 1, and the values for (b) and (c) in both (5) and (6) should even be near to 0. Therefore the straight rule is theoretically quite unacceptable. Nevertheless, the values of ^0C and ^{0}est (not those of $^0\mathscr{C}$ in general or those of $^0\mathscr{M}$) may often be used as convenient approximations in practical work, if s is sufficiently large. [This is analogous to the use of $\pi = 22/7$ or 3.1416 or 3.1415926, although theoretically false, as convenient approximations by the craftsman, the engineer, or the astronomer, respectively.]

We have seen that the λ-principle is widely accepted implicitly, though mostly in the questionable special form of the straight rule, which lacks regularity. It will now be our task to study the *regular* λ-$\mathscr{C}$-functions.

In my earlier expositions of λ-$\mathscr{C}$-functions, I did assume attribute symmetry ([1952a] §4, C8] and [1959] NA8, p. 244), and hence γ-equality. But I have found that it is possible to develop the essential features of the λ-$\mathscr{C}$-functions without this assumption. This procedure is more general, by admitting also $\mathscr{C}$-functions without γ-equality. The λ-$\mathscr{C}$-functions with γ-equality will later be dealt with as a special case.

I shall now state the formal definition of the λ-condition, in a form somewhat different from (19-1). We shall see (T2c) that the two formulations are equivalent. At present we presuppose that the family F has *at least three attributes*; families with two attributes will be dealt with later. We restrict the definition to finite families, as we did for η-equality, which is implied by the λ-condition, as we shall see soon (T1a).

D19-1. Let F be a finite family of k attributes, with $k > 2$.
   a. F fulfills the λ-*condition* (with respect to $\mathscr{C}$ or C) $=_{Df}$ for any $s \geq 0$, for any $\mathbf{s} \in {}^0\mathbf{N}^{k,s}$, for any three distinct attribute indices j, m, n, $C_j(\mathbf{s}^m) = C_j(\mathbf{s}^n)$.
   b. F fulfills the λ-γ-*condition* (with respect to $\mathscr{C}$ or C) $=_{Df}$ F fulfills the λ-condition and has γ-equality.

Suppose we have chosen a $\mathscr{C}$-function $\mathscr{C}$ with representation C. If a family F fulfills the λ-condition (with respect to $\mathscr{C}$ or C), we say also that F is a λ-*family* (with respect to $\mathscr{C}$), and $\mathscr{C}$ is a λ-$\mathscr{C}$-*function* (for F), and that C is a λ-C-function (for F). In the case of the λ-γ-condition, we use similarly the terms "λ-γ-*family*", "λ-γ-$\mathscr{C}$-function", and "λ-γ-C-function". For an $\mathscr{M}$-function which is related to a λ-$\mathscr{C}$-function, we use the terms "λ-$\mathscr{M}$-function", "λ-γ-$\mathscr{M}$-function", and similarly for MI-functions and MS-functions.

We shall first investigate λ-families in general, and later λ-γ-families.

T19-1. Let F be a λ-*family* (with respect to $\mathscr{C}$), with $k > 2$. For any $s \geq 0$, any $\mathbf{s} \in {}^0\mathbf{N}^{k,s}$, any three distinct indices j, m, n, the following holds.
   +a. F has η-*equality*.

Proof. By D1a: $C_j(\mathbf{s}_0^m) = C_j(\mathbf{s}_0^n)$. Hence with T16-1e: $\eta_{jm} = \eta_{jn}$ (1). We have to show that also the η's for two arbitrary pairs of distinct indices are equal, say $\eta_{jm} = \eta_{nl}$, where l is an arbitrary index distinct from j, m, n. From (1) by substitution: $\eta_{nj} = \eta_{nl}$ (2). By T16-1d, $\eta_{jn} = \eta_{nj}$. Hence with (1): $\eta_{jm} = \eta_{nj}$; and with (2): $\eta_{jm} = \eta_{nl}$. ∎

+b. Let $\mathbf{s}' = \langle s_1', \ldots, s_k' \rangle$ and $\mathbf{s}'' = \langle s_1'', \ldots, s_k'' \rangle$ be two k-tuples in $^0\mathbf{N}^{k,s+1}$ which, for a given j, agree in the jth number: $s_j' = s''$. Then $C_j(\mathbf{s}') = C_j(\mathbf{s}'')$.

Proof. We can form a sequence of n k-tuples $\mathbf{s}_{(1)}, \ldots, \mathbf{s}_{(n)}$ in $^0\mathbf{N}^{k,s+1}$ ($n \leq s + 2$), where for $p = 1, 2, \ldots, n$, $\mathbf{s}_{(p)} = (s_1^{(p)}, \ldots, s_k^{(p)})$ such that (1) $\mathbf{s}_{(1)} = \mathbf{s}'$, (2) $\mathbf{s}_{(n)} = \mathbf{s}''$, and (3) for any p ($p = 1, \ldots, n-1$), $\mathbf{s}_{(p+1)}$ is formed from $\mathbf{s}_{(p)}$ as follows. Let m_p be the smallest number $\leq k$ such that $s_{m_p}^{(p)} < s_{m_p}$, and n_p the smallest such that $s_{n_p}^{(p)} > s_{n_p}''$. Then we take for $\mathbf{s}_{(p+1)}$: $s_{m_p}^{(p+1)} = s_{m_p}^{(p)} + 1$, and $s_{n_p}^{(p+1)} = s_{n_p}^{(p)} - 1$, while for every l distinct from m_p and n_p, $s_l^{(p+1)} = s_l^{(p)}$. Here m_p, n_p, and j are distinct. Therefore $s_j^{(p+1)} = s_j^{(p)}$; and, by D1a, $C_j(\mathbf{s}_{(p)}) = C_j(\mathbf{s}_{(p+1)})$. [This is seen as follows. Let $\mathbf{s}$ be like $\mathbf{s}_{(p)}$, except with $s_{n_p}^{(p)} - 1$ instead of $s_{n_p}^{(p)}$. Then $\mathbf{s}_{(p)} = \mathbf{s}^{n_p}$, and $\mathbf{s}_{(p+1)} = \mathbf{s}^{m_p}$.] Hence the assertion by mathematical induction with respect to p. ∎

+c. F has weak attribute symmetry (D18-4). (From (b).)

We shall now introduce *G-functions*, defined in terms of C_j-functions. We shall see (T2a) that, in the case of a λ-family, these G-functions can be taken as representative functions for $\mathscr{C}$. The definition itself is, however, not restricted to λ-families.

D19-2. Let F be a family of k attributes. Let $\mathscr{C}$ be any $\mathscr{C}$-function and C be its representative function. The *G-function for $\mathscr{C}$* (and for C) is defined as follows: for any $s \geq 0$, any $n \in {}^0\mathbf{N}_s$, any $j \in \mathbf{N}_k$,

$$G_j^s(n) =_{\mathrm{Df}} C_j^s(\mathbf{s}),$$

where $\mathbf{s} = \langle s_1, \ldots, s_k \rangle$ is as follows: $s_j = n$; if j' is the smallest positive integer distinct from j, $s_{j'} = s - n$; and for any l distinct from j and j', $s_l = 0$. (Thus $\mathbf{s} \in {}^0\mathbf{N}^{k,s}$.)

[The essential point in the specification of $\mathbf{s}$ in this definition is the condition that $s_j = n$. The other conditions have been chosen arbitrarily, since in the case of a λ-family the other members of $\mathbf{s}$ are irrelevant for $C_j(\mathbf{s})$.]

T19-2. Let F be a λ-*family* (with respect to $\mathscr{C}$) with $k > 2$. Let G be the G-function for $\mathscr{C}$. Then the following holds for any $s \geq 0$, any $\mathbf{s} = \langle s_1, \ldots, s_k \rangle$ in $^0\mathbf{N}^{k,s}$, and any three distinct indices j, m, n.

   +a. $C_j^s(\mathbf{s}) = G_j^s(s_j)$. (From D2 and T1b.)
   b. $C_j(\mathbf{s}^m) = C_j(\mathbf{s}^n) = G_j^{s+1}(s_j)$. (From (a) and D1a.)
   +c. $G_j^0(0) = \gamma_j$. (From (a) with $s = 0$, D16-1a.)
   +d. $G_j^1(0) = \gamma_j\eta$. (From T1a, T18-2a.)
   +e. $G_j^1(1) = 1 - \eta(1 - \gamma_j)$. (From T1a, T18-2d.)

T2a is of special importance. It shows that, in the case of a λ-family, all values of the C-function are represented by values of the corresponding G-function. Thus, for a λ-$\mathscr{C}$-function, the corresponding G-function can be taken as a *representative function*. This function G has the advantage of being much simpler than the C-function. [Note that in "$G_j^s(n)$", in contrast to "$C_j^s(\mathbf{s})$", the reference to s is essential, since s is not otherwise determined.]

T19-3. Let C be a *symmetric* C-function for k-tuples (D12-3a). Let G be defined for C as in D2. Then the following holds.

a. The following three conditions are satisfied for any $s \geq 0$ (by D12-3a).

(1) *Sum condition.* For any $\mathbf{s} = \langle s_1, \ldots, s_k \rangle$ in ${}^0\mathbf{N}^{k,s}$,

$$\sum_{j=1}^{k} G_j^s(s_j) = 1.$$

(2) *Product condition.* For any distinct j and l in $\mathbf{N}_k$, and any m, n in $\mathbf{N}_s$ such that $m + n \leq s$ (if $k > 2$) or $m + n = s$ (if $k = 2$):

$$G_j^s(m)G_l^{s+1}(n) = G_l^s(n)G_j^{s+1}(m).$$

(3) For any s, j, m ($m \leq s$), $G_j^s(m) \geq 0$.

b. Let C be, moreover, *regular*. Then the above conditions (1) and (2) are satisfied and, instead of (3), the following stronger condition:

(3′) For any s, j, m, $G_j^s(m) > 0$.

Here under (b) we can take, instead of the product condition (2), either of the following two forms of the *quotient condition:*

(2′) $$\frac{G_l^{s+1}(n)}{G_j^{s+1}(m)} = \frac{G_l^s(n)}{G_j^s(m)}; \quad \text{or:}$$

(2″) $$\frac{G_l^{s+1}(n)}{G_l^s(n)} = \frac{G_j^{s+1}(m)}{G_j^s(m)}.$$

c. Let C be symmetric and *semi-regular* (i.e., for any $\mathbf{s}$ such that $s_j > 0$, $C_j(\mathbf{s}) > 0$; see D7-2. Then the conditions (1), (2), and (3) in (a) are satisfied, and also the following condition (weaker than (3′)):

(3″) For any s, j, m, if $m > 0$, then $G_j^s(m) > 0$.

We shall now prove some important properties of G-functions.

T19-4. Let C be a regular, symmetric C-function for k-tuples $(k>2)$. Let G be defined for C as in D2. Let $\gamma_1, \ldots, \gamma_k$, and η be given.

      a. All values of G^0 and G^1 are determined. (From T2c, d, e.)

   +b. For any $s>0$, if all values of G^s are given, then all values of G^{s+1} are uniquely determined.

Proof. From T3b(2'), with $n = m = 0$:

$$\frac{G_l^{s+1}(0)}{G_j^{s+1}(0)} = \frac{G_i^s(0)}{G_j^s(0)}.\tag{1}$$

[Note that for (1) the condition that $k>2$ is essential. If $k=2$, T3a(2) and T3b(2') and (2'') hold only if $s = m + n$; therefore (1) here would hold only for $s = 0$.]

$$\frac{G_i^s(0)}{G_j^s(0)} = \frac{\gamma_l}{\gamma_j}.\tag{2}$$

(This holds for $s = 0$ by T2c. If it holds for a given s, then by (1) also for $s+1$. Thus (2) holds by mathematical induction with respect to s.) From T3a(1), with $s_j = s$, and all other $s_l = 0$:

$$G_j^s(s) + \sum_{l(\neq j)} G_l^s(0) = 1.$$

By (2), the latter sum is $\dfrac{G_j^s(0)}{\gamma_j} \displaystyle\sum_{l(\neq j)} \gamma_l$; and this last sum is $1 - \gamma_j$. Hence

$$G_j^s(s) + G_j^s(0) \frac{1-\gamma_j}{\gamma_j} = 1.$$
$$G_j^s(s) = 1 - G_j^s(0) \frac{1-\gamma_j}{\gamma_j}.\tag{3}$$

Hence with $s+1$ for s:

$$G_j^{s+1}(s+1) = 1 - G_j^{s+1}(0) \frac{1-\gamma_j}{\gamma_j}.\tag{4}$$

From T3b(2'), for $n \leq s$, $j \neq l$:

$$\frac{G_l^{s+1}(n)}{G_j^{s+1}(0)} = \frac{G_l^s(n)}{G_j^s(0)}.\tag{5}$$

For $n \leq s$, $j = l$:

$$\frac{G_l^s(n)}{G_j^s(0)} = \frac{G_l^n(n)}{G_j^n(0)}.$$

(1. This hold identically for $s = n$. 2. If it holds for $s = m$, then by (5) also for $s = m + 1$. Thus the assertion holds for any $s \geq n$, by mathematical induction with respect to s.)

Hence with (3):

$$\frac{G_l^s(n)}{G_j^s(0)} = \frac{1}{G_j^n(0)}\left[1 - G_l^n(0)\frac{1-\gamma_l}{\gamma_l}\right],$$

$$= \frac{1}{G_j^n(0)} - \frac{G_l^n(0)}{G_j^n(0)} \cdot \frac{1-\gamma_l}{\gamma_l};$$

hence with (2):

$$= \frac{1}{G_j^n(0)} - \frac{1-\gamma_l}{\gamma_j};$$

thus:

$$G_l^s(n) = G_j^s(0)\left[\frac{1}{G_j^n(0)} - \frac{1-\gamma_l}{\gamma_j}\right]. \qquad (6)$$

By T3a(1), with $s_i = n$, $s_l = s - n$, all others 0:

$$G_i^s(n) + G_l^s(s-n) + \sum_{m(\neq i,l)} G_m^s(0) = 1.$$

Here we replace the first two G-terms by their equivalents according to (6):

$$G_j^s(0)\left[\frac{1}{G_j^n(0)} - \frac{1-\gamma_i}{\gamma_j} + \frac{1}{G_j^{s-n}(0)} - \frac{1-\gamma_l}{\gamma_j}\right] + \sum_{m(\neq i,l)} G_m^s(0) = 1.$$

By (2), the last sum is $G_j^s(0) \cdot \dfrac{1}{\gamma_j} \sum_{m(\neq i,l)} \gamma_m$ and the latter sum is $1 - \gamma_i - \gamma_l$. Thus:

$$G_j^s(0)\left[\frac{1}{G_j^n(0)} + \frac{1}{G_j^{s-n}(0)} - \frac{1}{\gamma_j}\right] = 1.$$

Hence with $s + 1$ for s and 1 for n:

$$G_j^{s+1}(0)\left[\frac{1}{G_j^1(0)} + \frac{1}{G_j^s(0)} - \frac{1}{\gamma_j}\right] = 1.$$

Since $G_j^1(0) = \gamma_j \eta$ (by T2d),

$$G_j^{s+1}(0) \cdot \frac{G_j^s(0) + \gamma_j \eta - \eta G_j^s(0)}{G_j^s(0) \cdot \gamma_j \eta} = 1.$$

$$G_j^{s+1}(0) = \frac{G_j^s(0) - \gamma \eta}{G_j^s(0) \cdot (1 - \eta) + \gamma_j \eta}. \tag{7}$$

Thus (b) is proved. If all values of G^s are given, $G_j^{s+1}(0)$ is determined by (7); then, for any n ($n = 1, \ldots, s$), $G_l^{s+1}(n)$ is determined by (5); and $G_j^{s+1}(s+1)$ by (4). ∎

c. $G_j^s(0) = \dfrac{\gamma_j \eta}{(1 - \eta)s + \eta}.$

Proof. Let the right-hand side be $f(s)$.—1. That $G_j^0(0) = f(0) = \gamma_j$, is seen by T2c.—2. It can easily be shown by (7) (in the preceding proof) that if $G_j^s(0) = f(s)$, then $G_j^{s+1}(0) = f(s+1)$.—The assertion follows by mathematical induction with respect to s. ∎

+d. For any $s \geq 0$, and $n \in {}^0\mathbf{N}_s$, and any $j \in \mathbf{N}_k$,

$$G_j^s(n) = \frac{n(1 - \eta) + \gamma_j \eta}{s(1 - \eta) + \eta}.$$

Proof. For a given s, let the right-hand side be $g(n)$.—1. By (c), $G_j^s(0) = g(0)$.—2. Let us assume that, for $n < s$,

$$G_j^s(n) = g(n). \tag{i}$$

We shall show that

$$G_j^s(n+1) = g(n+1). \tag{*}$$

We have by (6), in the proof for (b), with j and l exchanged, for $n < s$, with $n + 1$ for n:

$$G_j^s(n+1) = G_l^s(0) \left[\frac{1}{G_l^{n+1}(0)} - \frac{1 - \gamma_j}{\gamma_l} \right]. \tag{ii}$$

From (c) we obtain these two results:

$$G_l^{n+1}(0) = \frac{\gamma_l \eta}{(1 - \eta)(n + 1) + \eta},$$

and

$$G_l^s(0) = \frac{\gamma_l \eta}{(1 - \eta)s + \eta}.$$

We substitute these in (ii):

$$G_j^s(n+1) = \frac{\gamma_i \eta}{(1-\eta)s+\eta}\left[\frac{(1-\eta)(n+1)+\eta}{\gamma_i \eta} - \frac{1-\gamma_i}{\gamma_i}\right],$$

$$= \frac{(1-\eta)(n+1)+\gamma_j \eta}{(1-\eta)s+\eta}.$$

The right-hand side is $g(n+1)$. Thus we have derived (*) from (i).—3. (d) follows from (1) and (2) by mathematical induction with respect to n. ■

T4d is an important result. It gives an explicit formula for the determination of all values of G in terms of $\gamma_1, \ldots, \gamma_k$, and η; in other words, in terms of the values of G^0 and G^1. [The results stated in T4, but restricted to the case of γ-equality, were proved by Kemeny; see the remarks following T12.]

Another form of the formula in T4d:

$$G_j^s(n) = \frac{n + \gamma_j \dfrac{\eta}{1-\eta}}{s + \dfrac{\eta}{1-\eta}}.$$

This form suggests the idea of using instead of η another parameter defined by $\eta/(1-\eta)$. This will indeed turn out to be convenient, especially in formulas for C and MI. We shall use for this parameter the letter 'λ':

D19-3. $\lambda =_{\text{Df}} \dfrac{\eta}{1-\eta}$.

From now on, we shall use λ as the main parameter, instead of η. I have used the parameter λ since 1947, while the idea of η and its dependence on distance in the attribute space came up much later. The parameter λ gave the name to the λ-system, the system of the λ-$\mathscr{C}$-functions, which was represented in [1952a]. The parameter η corresponds to the parameter λ''', which I mentioned in [1952a, p. 51] as an alternative to λ, defined by $\lambda/(\lambda+1)$ (comp. T5a below), but which I did not use further on.

If a particular value of the parameter λ is chosen, then we shall affix a numeral for this value as a left-hand superscript to the letters '$\mathscr{C}$', 'C', etc. Thus, e.g., the functions $^2\mathscr{C}$, ^2C, ^2G, $^2\mathscr{M}$, etc. are characterized by $\lambda = 2$. In the following we write 'λ' as a superscript; but it is to be kept in mind that in each concrete case 'λ' is to be replaced by a numeral.

In the following T5, the items after (a) are obtained from earlier theorems by replacing η in accordance with (a).

T19-5.   Let F, $\mathscr{C}$, k, G, s, $\mathbf{s}$, j, m, n be as in T2.

a. $\eta = \dfrac{\lambda}{\lambda + 1}$. (From D3.)

b. $^\lambda G_j^1(0) = \dfrac{\gamma_j \lambda}{\lambda + 1}$. (From T2d.)

c. $^\lambda G_j^1(1) = \dfrac{1 + \lambda \gamma_j}{1 + \lambda}$. (From T2e.)

d. If $\mathscr{C}$ satisfies the principle of instantial relevance (P13-1), then $0 < \lambda < \infty$. (From T18-2e.)

+e. $^\lambda G_j^s(n) = \dfrac{n + \lambda \gamma_j}{s + \lambda}$. (From T4d.)

+f. If $\mathbf{s} = \langle s_1, \ldots, s_k \rangle$, $^\lambda C_j^s(\mathbf{s}) = \dfrac{s_j + \lambda \gamma_j}{s + \lambda}$. (From (e) and T2a.)

g. $^\lambda C_j^s(\mathbf{s})$ is the weighted mean of the observed relative frequency s_j/s and the initial C_j-value γ_j, with the weights s and λ, respectively. (From (f).)

h. Let $r_j =_{\mathrm{Df}} s_j/s$.
   (1) If $r_j = \gamma_j$, then $^\lambda C_j^s(\mathbf{s}) = r_j = \gamma_j$.
   (2) If $r_j < \gamma_j$, then $r_j < {}^\lambda C_j^s(\mathbf{s}) < \gamma_j$.
   (3) If $\gamma_j < r_j$, then $\gamma_j < {}^\lambda C_j^s(\mathbf{s}) < r_j$.
   Thus, if r_j and γ_j are equal, $^\lambda C_j^s(\mathbf{s})$ coincides with them; if they are unequal, $^\lambda C_j^s(\mathbf{s})$ lies between them. (From (g).)

T5f gives the basic formula for the theory of λ-$\mathscr{C}$-functions. Of this theory, only a few elementary results will be given in this section. An extended treatment will be given in a later article of this series.

According to T5d, we exclude the two extreme cases $\lambda = 0$ and $\lambda = \infty$. The functions $^0\mathscr{C}$ and $^\infty\mathscr{C}$ characterized by these values will not be considered as functions of the λ-system. However, in view of the fact that each of these two functions has been recommended by well-known authors, we shall at least discuss them. $^0\mathscr{C}$ was discussed earlier, as representing the straight rule (see (3)ff.); $^\infty\mathscr{C}$ was discussed, under the symbol 'c†' in [1950, pp. 564f.] We call $^0\mathscr{C}$ and $^\infty\mathscr{C}$ "improper" λ-$\mathscr{C}$-functions. We may regard $^\lambda C$ for any finite positive value of λ as determined by T5. Hence it seems natural to define ^0C

and $^{\infty}C$ as follows (where 'λ' is taken as a variable ranging over the positive (finite) real numbers, and $^{\lambda}C_j^s(\mathbf{s})$ as a function of λ, for given s, $\mathbf{s}$, and j):

D19-4.   **a.** $^{0}C_j^s(\mathbf{s}) =_{\text{Df}} \lim\limits_{\lambda \to 0} {}^{\lambda}C_j^s(\mathbf{s}).$

        b. $^{\infty}C_j^s(\mathbf{s}) =_{\text{Df}} \lim\limits_{\lambda \to \infty} {}^{\lambda}C_j^s(\mathbf{s}).$

Then we obtain from T5f the following results.

T19-6.   **a.** For $s = 0$, $^{0}C_j(\mathbf{s}_0) = \gamma_j$.
        b. For $s > 0$, $^{0}C_j(\mathbf{s}) = s_j/s$.
        c. For $s \geqq 0$, $^{\infty}C_j(\mathbf{s}) = \gamma_j$.

We see from T6b, that for $s > 0$ ^{0}C corresponds to the straight rule (3) (for $s = 0$ the straight rule does not define any value). Therefore our objections against the straight rule apply likewise to ^{0}C; this function violates the axiom of regularity and hence the requirement of strict coherence. But the straight rule is often applied; and even more frequently the corresponding estimate function ^{0}est (see (4)). (I have discussed the functions ^{0}C and ^{0}est, under the symbols 'c_0' and 'e_0', respectively, in [1952a, §14].)

We see from T6c that the value of $^{\infty}C_j$ is independent of s. Thus a person who takes $^{\infty}C$ as his credibility function, refuses to learn anything from experience. $^{\infty}C$ violates the principle of instantial relevance (P13-1), and also Reichenbach's axiom of convergence, which will be stated in the next section. For these reasons we reject $^{\infty}\mathscr{C}$. Surprisingly, this function has been adopted by a number of authors; among them not only Wittgenstein, who makes merely some brief remarks on probability, but also some who have given much careful thought to problems of probability, like Charles S. Peirce and John M. Keynes, a fact that seems surprising and hard to explain. (For references and further discussions of the function $^{\infty}\mathscr{C}$ see [1950, p. 565], where it is denoted by '$c\dagger$', and [1952a, §13], where the symbol 'c_∞' is used; von Wright [1951, p. 373] mentions also Bernard Bolzano and Moses Mendelssohn as advocating the same function.)

The basic formulas for MI and MS will now be stated. $\left('\prod\limits_{j}' \text{ is}\right.$ always short for '$\prod\limits_{j=1}^{k}$'.$\left.\right)$ But in T7, $\prod\limits_{j}$ need range only over those indices j for which $s_j > 0$. (Any product of an empty set of numbers is 1; for any n, $\begin{bmatrix} n \\ 0 \end{bmatrix} = \begin{pmatrix} n \\ 0 \end{pmatrix} = 1$.)

T19-7. Let $^{\lambda}\mathscr{C}$ be a λ-$\mathscr{C}$-function for $k > 2$. Let $^{\lambda}\mathscr{M}$ be related to $^{\lambda}\mathscr{C}$. Hence $^{\lambda}\mathscr{M}$ is a λ-$\mathscr{M}$-function. Let $^{\lambda}$MI (D11-1) and $^{\lambda}$MS (D11-5) be representative functions for $^{\lambda}\mathscr{M}$. Then the following holds for any $s \geq 0$, any $k > 2$, any $\mathbf{s} = \langle s_1, \ldots, s_k \rangle$ in $^{0}\mathbf{N}^{k,s}$. Let m_j be defined as follows: $m_0 = 0$; for $j \geq 1$, $m_j = \sum_{l=1}^{j} s_l$.

    a. $$^{\lambda}\mathrm{MI}(\mathbf{s}) = \prod_{j} \prod_{p=0}^{s_j-1} {}^{\lambda}G_j^{m_j+p}(p).$$

Proof. Let the submodel Z' be like Z'_s (for the given $\mathbf{s}$) in D12-1. Hence in Z', the first s_1 individuals have attribute P_1, the next s_2 have P_2, etc., and the last s_k have P_k. For any $n < s$, let $\mathbf{s}_{(n)}$ be the k-tuple of that submodel of Z' which is restricted to $\mathbf{N}_n$. According to T12-3a, $^{\lambda}C$ and $^{\lambda}$MI satisfy T12-1h:

$$^{\lambda}\mathrm{MI}(\mathbf{s}) = \prod_{i=1}^{s} {}^{\lambda}C_{Z'(i)}^{i-1}(\mathbf{s}_{(i-1)}). \qquad (*)$$

Let X_j be the partial product containing those s_j factors of the above product in $(*)$ for which $Z'(i) = j$; these are the factors with $i = m_j + 1, \ldots, m_j + s_j$. Then, in terms of the G-function, by T2a,

$$X_j = \prod_{p=0}^{s_j-1} {}^{\lambda}G_j^{m_j+p}(p).$$

Hence the assertion. ∎

    b. $$^{\lambda}\mathrm{MI}(\mathbf{s}) = \frac{\prod_{j} \prod_{p=0}^{s_j-1} (p + \lambda\gamma_j)}{\prod_{i=0}^{s-1} (i + \lambda)}.$$

Proof. From (a), by T5e:

$$^{\lambda}\mathrm{MI}(\mathbf{s}) = \prod_{j} \prod_{p=0}^{s_j-1} \frac{p + \lambda\gamma_j}{m_j + p + \lambda}.$$

    The denominators in the total product run from λ to $s - 1 + \lambda$. Hence the assertion. ∎

    +c. $$^{\lambda}\mathrm{MI}(\mathbf{s}) = \frac{\prod_{j} (\lambda\gamma_j)_{s_j}}{(\lambda)_s}.$$

(From (b), with D10-5.)

d. $\quad {}^{\lambda}\text{MI}(\mathbf{s}) = \dfrac{\Gamma(\lambda)}{\prod\limits_{j}\Gamma(\lambda\gamma_j)} \cdot \dfrac{\prod\limits_{j}\Gamma(s_j + \lambda\gamma_j)}{\Gamma(s+\lambda)} .$

(From (c) and T10-5e.)

+e. $\qquad\qquad {}^{\lambda}\text{MS}(\mathbf{s}) = \dfrac{\prod\limits_{j}\left(\dfrac{s_j + \lambda\gamma_j - 1}{s_j}\right)}{\left(\dfrac{s+\lambda-1}{s}\right)} .$

(From (c), D11-5a.)

We have defined the λ-condition (D1) only for a family of more than two attributes. Thus our theorems on λ-families were likewise restricted. Now we shall consider *a family F of two attributes* P_1 *and* P_2, with γ_1 and $\gamma_2 = 1 - \gamma_1$, respectively. If we were to formulate the λ-condition without the restriction to $k > 2$, which was imposed in D1, it would say the following:

(19-7)   For any $k \geqq 2$, for any $s > 0$, for any $\mathbf{s} = \langle s_1, \ldots, s_k \rangle$ in ${}^{0}\mathbf{N}^{k,s}$, $C_j^s(\mathbf{s})$ depends merely on s and s_j; in other words, if $\mathbf{s}' = \langle s_1', \ldots, s_k' \rangle$ in ${}^{0}\mathbf{N}^{k,s}$ such that, for the given j, $s_j = s_j'$, then $C_j^s(\mathbf{s}) = C_j^s(\mathbf{s}')$. (Compare T1b.)

But for $k = 2$, (7) is always fulfilled trivially; for, if $s_1 = s_1'$, then $\mathbf{s}' = (s_1, s - s_1) = \mathbf{s}$. Therefore we might be tempted to assume that all the results which we have derived from the λ-condition would likewise hold for our family F with $k = 2$. But this is not the case, as we shall see. First let us state some results which hold also for $k = 2$; most of them are obvious. Since F has η-equality (D18-1b), we take $\eta = \eta_{12} = \eta_{21}$; then we can define λ as in D3. We define G as in D2; T3 was not restricted and thus holds here too.

T19-8.   Let F be a family with $k = 2$. For any $s \geqq 0$, and any $\mathbf{s} = \langle s_1, s_2 \rangle$, where $s_2 = s - s_1$, the following holds.

    a. F has η-equality. (By T16-1d, $\eta_{12} = \eta_{21}$.)

    b. F has weak attribute symmetry. (See the remarks following D18-4.)

    c. (1) $G_1^s(n) = C_1^s(n, s - n)$; (2) $G_2^s(n) = G_2^s(s - n, n)$. (From D2.)

    d. $C_j^s(\mathbf{s}) = G_j^s(s_j)$. (From (c).) Thus G is a representative function for C.

    e. $G_j^0(0) = \gamma_j$.

f. $G_j^1(0) = \gamma_i \eta$.

g. $G_j^1(1) = 1 - \eta(1 - \gamma_i)$. (From (a) and T18-2d.)

h. $\eta = \dfrac{\lambda}{\lambda + 1}$. (From D3.)

i. $G_j^1(0) = \dfrac{\lambda \gamma_j}{1 + \lambda}$. (From (f) and (h).)

j. $G_j^1(1) = \dfrac{1 + \lambda \gamma_j}{1 + \lambda}$. (From (g) and (h).)

k. If C satisfies the principle of instantial relevance, $0 < \lambda < \infty$. (From T17-2e.)

The important results for the λ-system are contained in T4, especially parts (b) and (d). The proofs of these results made use of the condition that $k > 2$ (see the remark on (1) in the proof of T4b). The results cannot be proved for the case $k = 2$ without additional assumptions.

On the other hand, it would certainly seem desirable to obtain for $k = 2$ results corresponding to T4d and T5f, if this is possible on the basis of plausible additional assumptions. We might just decide to assume that T4d or T5f holds also for $k = 2$. It seems, however, preferable to choose instead an assumption which is less specific and hence less dubious. We shall take the following one:

(19-8) *Principle of linearity.* Let $\mathscr{C}$ be a $\mathscr{C}$-function for a family F of *two attributes.* Let G be defined by D2. Let γ_1 and η (or λ) be given. (Hence the G-values for $s = 0$ and $s = 1$ are determined.) Then, if any $s > 0$ and any j ($= 1, 2$) are given, $G_j^s(n)$ is a linear function of n.

This principle seems rather plausible. Since for every $k > 2$, $G_j^s(n)$ is a linear function of n (T5e), it would be strange if it were nonlinear for $k = 2$.

We shall now show that this principle leads to the desired results.

T19-9. Let F be a family with $k = 2$. Let $\eta = \eta_{12} = \eta_{21}$, and let λ be defined as in D3. Let G satisfy the principle of linearity (8); hence for every $s > 0$, there are two constants A_s and B_s such that for any n

$$G_1^s(n) = A_s n + B_s \qquad (n = 0, \ldots, s). \tag{*}$$

Then the following holds.

      a. If, for some $s > 0$, A_s and B_s are given, then A_{s+1} and

B_{s+1} are determined as follows:

$$A_{s+1} = A_s/(A_s + 1); \qquad B_{s+1} = B_s/(A_s + 1).$$

Proof.   I. From T3a(1) (sum condition):

$$G_1^s(n) + G_2^s(s - n) = 1, \tag{1}$$

and:

$$G_1^{s+1}(n + 1) + G_2^{s+1}(s - n) = 1. \tag{2}$$

From T3a(2) (product condition):

$$G_1^s(n) \cdot G_2^{s+1}(s - n) = G_2^s(s - n) \cdot G_1^{s+1}(n).$$

Hence with (2) and (1):

$$G_1^s(n)[1 - G_1^{s+1}(n + 1)] = [1 - G_1^s(n)]G_1^{s+1}(n). \tag{3}$$

Hence for $n = 0$:

$$G_1^s(0)[1 - G_1^{s+1}(1)] = [1 - G_1^s(0)]G_1^{s+1}(0).$$

Hence according to our assumption(*):

$$B_s[1 - A_{s+1} - B_{s+1}] = [1 - B_s]B_{s+1},$$
$$B_s[1 - A_{s+1}] = B_{s+1}. \tag{4}$$

From (3) with $n = s$:

$$G_1^s(s)[1 - G_1^{s+1}(s + 1] = [1 - G_1^s(s)]G_1^{s+1}(s).$$

Hence by (*):

$$(A_s s + B_s)[1 - A_{s+1}(s + 1) - B_{s+1}] = [1 - A_s s - B_s](A_{s+1} s + B_{s+1}).$$

By replacing 'B_{s+1}' in accordance with (4) and simplifying, we obtain:

$$A_{s+1}(A_s + 1) = A_s.$$

Hence:

$$A_{s+1} = A_s/(A_s + 1). \tag{5}$$

This is the first assertion of (a).

II. From (4), by replacing 'A_{s+1}' in accordance with (5), we obtain:

$$B_{s+1} = B_s/(A_s + 1). \tag{6}$$

This is the second assertion of (a).   ∎

b. $A_s = 1/(s + \lambda); \; B_s = \lambda \gamma_1/(s + \lambda).$

Proof. (A). By (*): $G_1^1(n) = A_1 n + B_1$. Hence with T8i: $B_1 = \lambda\gamma_1/(1+\lambda)$; hence with T8j: $A_1 = 1/(1+\lambda)$. Thus the assertions hold for $s = 1$.

(B). Suppose that the assertions hold for a given s; that is:

$$A_s = 1/(s+\lambda); \qquad \text{let this be } f_1(s). \tag{7}$$

$$B_s = \lambda\gamma_1/(s+\lambda); \qquad \text{let this be } f_2(s). \tag{8}$$

We shall now show that then the assertions hold also for $s+1$. From (7):

$$A_s + 1 = (s+\lambda+1)/(s+\lambda). \tag{9}$$

We had in (a):

$$A_{s+1} = A_s/(A_s + 1),$$
$$= 1/(s+\lambda+1).$$

This is $f_1(s+1)$. Again in (a):

$$B_{s+1} = B_s/(A_s + 1);$$

with (9):

$$= B_s(s+\lambda)/(s+\lambda+1);$$

with (8):

$$= \lambda\gamma_1/(s+1+\lambda).$$

This is $f_2(s+1)$.

(C). The two assertions in (b) follow from (A) and (B) by mathematical induction with respect to s. ∎

c. $G_1^s(n) = \dfrac{n+\lambda\gamma_1}{s+\lambda}$. (From (*) and (b).)

d. $G_2^s(n) = \dfrac{n+\lambda\gamma_2}{s+\lambda}$.

Proof. From (1): $G_2^s(n) = 1 - G_1^s(s-n)$. Hence with (c):

$$G_2^s(n) = 1 - \frac{s-n+\lambda\gamma_1}{s+\lambda} = \frac{n+\lambda(1-\gamma_1)}{s+\lambda}.$$

Hence the assertion. ∎

e. For any $\mathbf{s} = \langle s_1, s_2 \rangle$ in ${}^0\mathbf{N}^{2,s}$,

$$C_j^s(\mathbf{s}) = G_j^s(s_j) = \frac{s_j + \lambda\gamma_j}{s+\lambda}.$$

(From (c) and (d).)

We shall from now on accept the principle of linearity (8). Then, according to T9e, the formulas for $C_i^s(\mathbf{s})$ and $G_i^s(n)$, which were previously proved for any $k > 2$ (T5e and f) hold also for $k = 2$. The same holds obviously also for the earlier formulas for $MI(\mathbf{s})$ and $MS(\mathbf{s})$ (T7c and e). Thus here also the functions $\mathscr{C}$ and $\mathscr{M}$, and likewise their representative functions G, C, MI, etc., are uniquely determined once a value for the parameter λ is chosen. We attach here likewise a numeral for the chosen λ-value as a left-hand superscript, and write in general "$^{\lambda}\mathscr{C}$", "$^{\lambda}C$", etc.

Now we extend the definition D1 to the case $k = 2$.

D19-5. Let F be a family of two attributes. For a given $\mathscr{C}$, let γ_1, γ_2, η_{12} be defined as earlier (D16-1) on the basis of the values of C_i^0 and C_i^1. Let λ be defined on the basis of η_{12} as earlier (D3).

   a. F fulfills the λ-*condition* (with respect to $\mathscr{C}$ or C) $=_{Df}$
   for any $s > 0$, for any $\mathbf{s} = \langle s_1, s_2 \rangle$ in $^0\mathbf{N}^{2,s}$,

$$C_i^s(\mathbf{s}) = \frac{s_i + \lambda \gamma_i}{s + \lambda}.$$

   b. F fulfills the λ-γ-*condition* (with respect to $\mathscr{C}$ or C) $=_{Df}$ F fulfills the λ-condition and has γ-equality.

If the conditions of the definition are fulfilled, we shall apply, as previously, also the terms "λ-family", "λ-γ-family", "λ-$\mathscr{C}$-function", etc.

T19-10. Let F be a family of two attributes. With respect to a given function $\mathscr{C}$, F fulfills the λ-condition if-if F fulfills the principle of linearity (8).

Proof. The λ-condition (D5a) follows from the linearity by T9e. The inverse implication is obvious. ∎

We have two quite different presuppositions for λ-$\mathscr{C}$-functions. For the case $k > 2$ we took the λ-condition in D1, which requires that $C_i(\mathbf{s}^m) = C_i(\mathbf{s}^n)$, or the equivalent condition in T1b. In contrast, for the case $k = 2$ we have the principle of linearity. (In earlier expositions of the λ-system, I took these two conditions as axioms, e.g., in [1959, NA14, p. 246, and NA15, p. 249].) It would be desirable to have a single assumption applicable to any $k \geq 2$, one that would yield the same results as our present two assumptions together. It would further be desirable for the single assumption to have at least a fair plausibility. If we were to take a generalized assumption of linearity for any $k \geqq 2$, this would be equivalent to our two present assumptions; but it would be less plausible. Our assumption for $k > 2$ in the form stated in T1b is quite plausible; it is indeed often implicitly used in common sense considerations. The plausibility of our linearity assumption for $k = 2$ is by no means immediate but merely derivative on the basis of the proved linearity for $k > 2$.

Henceforth we shall use the terms "λ-family", "λ-condition", "λ-$\mathscr{C}$-function", etc. in the unrestricted sense applying to both $k > 2$ and $k = 2$. And we shall simply refer to the earlier theorems (although they were restricted to $k > 2$), since we have now shown that they hold for any $k \geqq 2$.

So far we have considered λ-families in general. Now we shall consider an important special kind of λ-families, the λ-γ-families. These are those λ-families which have γ-equality (D1b). Theorems for them are derived from the earlier general theorems by simply taking, for any j, $\gamma_j = 1/k$. We state the theorems generally, for any $k \geqq 2$.

T19-11. Let F be a λ-γ-family (with respect to $\mathscr{C}$) of k attributes ($k \geqq 2$). For any $s \geqq 0$, any $\mathbf{s} = \langle s_1, \ldots, s_k \rangle$ in $^0\mathbf{N}^{k,s}$, and any three distinct indices j, m, n, the following holds:

    a. F has γ-equality (D1b); hence $\gamma_j = 1/k$.

    +b. F has attribute symmetry. (From T1c, T18-6.)

    c. $^\lambda G_j^0(0) = 1/k$. (From T2c.)

    d. $^\lambda G_j^1(0) = \dfrac{\lambda}{(\lambda + 1)k}$. (From T5b.)

    e. $^\lambda G_j^1(1) = \dfrac{1 + \lambda/k}{1 + \lambda}$. (T5c.)

    +f. $^\lambda G_j^s(n) = \dfrac{n + \lambda/k}{s + \lambda}$. (T5e.)

    +g. $^\lambda C_j^s(\mathbf{s}) = \dfrac{s_j + \lambda/k}{s + \lambda}$. (From T5f.)

    h. $^\lambda C_j^s(\mathbf{s})$ is the weighted mean of s_j/s and $1/k$, with the weights s and λ, respectively. (From T5g.)

    i. Let $r_j =_{\text{Df}} s_j/s$.

        (1) If $r_j = 1/k$, then $^\lambda C_j^s(\mathbf{s}) = r_j = 1/k$.

        (2) If $r_j < 1/k$, then $r_j < {}^\lambda C_j^s(\mathbf{s}) < 1/k$.

        (3) If $1/k < r_j$, then $1/k < {}^\lambda C_j^s(\mathbf{s}) < r_j$. (From T5h.)

We give now some formulas for $^\lambda$MI and $^\lambda$MS, derived from T7. $\left(\text{For '}\prod_j\text{', see the remark preceding T7.}\right)$

T19-12. Let $^\lambda\mathscr{C}$, $^\lambda\mathscr{M}$, $^\lambda$MI, and $^\lambda$MS be as in T7, but with γ-equality and for any $k \geqq 2$. Then the following holds for any $s \geqq 0$ and any $\mathbf{s} = \langle s_1, \ldots, s_k \rangle$ in $^0\mathbf{N}^{k,s}$.

$$\mathbf{a.} \quad {}^\lambda\text{MI}(\mathbf{s}) = \frac{\prod\limits_{j} \prod\limits_{p=0}^{s_j-1} (p + \lambda/k)}{\prod\limits_{i=0}^{s-1} (i + \lambda)}.$$

$$\mathbf{+b.} \quad {}^\lambda\text{MI}(\mathbf{s}) = \frac{\prod\limits_{j} (\lambda/k)_{s_j}}{(\lambda)_s}$$

$$\mathbf{c.} \quad {}^\lambda\text{MI}(\mathbf{s}) = \frac{\Gamma(\lambda)}{\prod\limits_{j} \Gamma(\lambda/k)} \cdot \frac{\prod\limits_{j} \Gamma(s_j + \lambda/k)}{\Gamma(s + \lambda)}.$$

$$\mathbf{+d.} \quad {}^\lambda\text{MS}(\mathbf{s}) = \frac{\prod\limits_{j} \binom{s_j + \lambda/k - 1}{s_j}}{\binom{s + \lambda - 1}{s}}.$$

In the original form of the λ-system, published in 1952 in [1952a], I assumed attribute symmetry. Thus the system was restricted to those families and $\mathscr{C}$-functions which, in my present terminology, fulfill the λ-γ-condition. In the original system I accepted as axioms (there called "conventions") among others the following: (i) attribute symmetry, (ii) a λ-axiom similar to the λ-principle (1), (iii) an interval axiom corresponding to T11i, and (iv) the condition that the value of the parameter λ is not dependent on s or s_j (and hence, for a given family with a given k, λ is a constant). (These four assumptions were stated as the conventions C8, C9, C10, and C11 in [1952a, pp. 14, 26, 29].) John G. Kemeny found in 1952 that axioms (iii) and (iv) are redundant. He proved on the basis of the other axioms (for $k > 2$ and with γ-equality) that, when a value of λ is chosen and the values of $^\lambda G^s$ are given, all values of $^\lambda G^{s+1}$ are determined; hence, since the values of $^\lambda G^0$ and $^\lambda G^1$ are known (as in T11c, d, e), all values of $^\lambda G$ for any s are determined. (Kemeny's proof is published in his [1964, §4], the ms of which was written and delivered in 1954; and in Carnap–Stegmüller [1959, p. 247].) This elimination of the assumptions (iii) and (iv) was an essential improvement in the foundations of the λ-system. Then I proposed as a solution for the case $k = 2$ the assumption (v) of the linearity of G (as in (8)). (The assumptions (i), (ii), and (v) are given as the axioms NA8, NA14, and NA15 in Carnap–Stegmüller [1959, pp. 244, 246, 249].) Finally, I worked out the generalized form of the λ-system which permits different γ-values of the attributes. (This form is published here for the first time; my proof of the result that all values of $^\lambda G$ are determined when the γ's and η (or λ) are given (T4d, T5e) is analogous to Kemeny's proof but somewhat more complicated.)

In our discussion of certain kinds of families in the preceding section we raised also the question of methodological rules for these kinds; and more specifically the following question: which conditions must the regions representing the attributes of a family F in the attribute space fulfill to make it appropriate to treat F (with respect to $\mathscr{C}$) as a family of the kind in question? Let us first consider the question of conditions for λ-γ-families. Since we found that λ-γ-families are symmetric (T11b), we have to supplement our previous considerations only by an answer to the question: which additional conditions must a symmetric family fulfill in order to qualify for being treated as a λ-γ-family? Considerations analogous to those which led us, at the end of the preceding section, to (18-1) and (18-2), make it appear not implausible to assume that for basic attributes we need not require any additional conditions. If we were certain of this, we would accept the following rule of inductive logic:

(19-9) If a family F of basic attributes is symmetric, we shall treat F as a λ-γ-family.

The following is an alternative formulation, which we might consider as an axiom for $\mathscr{C}$ (analogous to (18-3)):

(19-10) If $\mathscr{C}$ has attribute symmetry for a family F of basic attributes, then $\mathscr{C}$ is a λ-γ-$\mathscr{C}$-function.

We might also consider taking as an axiom the following statement (analogous to (18-4)), which is somewhat stronger than (10):

(19-11) If, for a family of basic attributes, $\mathscr{C}$ has weak attribute symmetry, then $\mathscr{C}$ is a λ-$\mathscr{C}$-function.

(19-10) follows from (19-11) by T18-7.

Like their analogues in §18, the last two statements seem to me fairly plausible. But before accepting them as axioms, it would seem advisable to study their consequences more thoroughly.

The following statement is obviously a consequence of (18-3) and (19-10):

(19-12) If, for a family of basic attributes, $\mathscr{C}$ has γ-η-equality, then $\mathscr{C}$ is a λ-γ-$\mathscr{C}$-function.

Similarly, the next statement follows from (18-4) and (19-11):

(19-13) If, for a family of basic attributes, $\mathscr{C}$ has η-equality, then $\mathscr{C}$ is a λ-$\mathscr{C}$-function.

Although we do, at the present time, not yet accept these statements as general axioms, we shall often in the choice of a $\mathscr{C}$-function for a given family F proceed as follows. When we judge (presumably on the basis of the methodological rule (R16-2) that for F a $\mathscr{C}$ with η-equality is suitable, then we shall decide to choose a λ-$\mathscr{C}$-function. We do this not only in the case of basic attributes, but usually also for other attributes, unless we see a particular reason (say, with respect to the shapes of the regions) against the choice of a λ-$\mathscr{C}$-function. In particular, we shall usually take a family of two attributes as a λ-family, since it has trivially η-equality.

We have earlier discussed some possible forms of a *principle of analogy* (16-10ff). The following theorem states relations between weaker versions of the principle and some of the statements just discussed.

T19-13. Let $\mathscr{C}$ be a symmetric $\mathscr{C}$-function for the family F of k basic attributes.

   a. If $\mathscr{C}$ has η-equality, it has weak attribute symmetry.

Proof. Let $\mathbf{s} = \langle s_1, \ldots, s_k \rangle$ be an arbitrary k-tuple in ${}^0\mathbf{N}^{k,s}$. Let j, m, n be three arbitrary distinct indices. Let $p = s_m - s_n$. We assume that $p > 0$ (for $p < 0$ the proof is analogous with s_m and s_n exchanged; for $p = 0$ the result is trivial). Hence $s_m = s_n + p > s_n$. Let $\mathbf{s}^*$ be like $\mathbf{s}$, except that the mth number is s_n instead of $s_m = s_n + p$. Thus $\mathbf{s}^*$ fulfills condition B$_3$; the mth and nth numbers are equal. $\mathbf{s}^* \in {}^0\mathbf{N}^{k,s-p}$; $\mathbf{s} = \mathbf{s}^{*mp}$. Let $\mathbf{s}' = \mathbf{s}^{*np}$; hence $\mathbf{s}' \in {}^0\mathbf{N}^{k,s}$. Suppose that $\mathscr{C}$ has η-equality; hence $\eta_{jm} = \eta_{jn}$ and thus $C_j(\mathbf{s}) = C_j(\mathbf{s}')$. Since $\mathbf{s}$ and the triple j, m, n were arbitrary, this shows that, for any j, C_j is invariant under any transposition with respect to two indices distinct from j. Thus $\mathscr{C}$ has weak attribute symmetry.

   b. If $\mathscr{C}$ has η-equality, then $\mathscr{C}$ is a λ-$\mathscr{C}$-function.

Proof. Suppose that $\mathscr{C}$ has η-equality. Hence, for any three distinct indices j, m, n, $\eta_{jm} = \eta_{jn}$. Thus, for any $\mathbf{s}$, $C_j(\mathbf{s}^m) = C_j(\mathbf{s}^n)$. Hence, by D1a, $\mathscr{C}$ is a λ-$\mathscr{C}$-function. ■

The person X wishes to assign rational credence values to unknown propositions on the basis of the observations he has made. It is the purpose of inductive logic to help him do this in a rational way; or, more precisely, to give him some general rules, each of which warns him against certain unreasonable steps. The rules do not, in general, lead him to specific values; they leave some freedom for choice within certain limits. What he chooses is not a credence value for a given proposition, but rather certain features of a general policy for determining credence values. In order to recognize the role of our present topic, the λ-system, let us suppose that X asks for advice how to proceed with propositions involving a family F of k attributes $P_1, \ldots, P_k$. He wishes to choose a $\mathscr{C}$-function for F; he is satisfied if we help him to find a suitable C-function, since he knows how to compute $\mathscr{C}$-values from C-values. We suppose that X has sound common sense in probability matters, and that this has led him to accept some general principles, say the basic axioms and those of regularity and symmetry, and the principle of instantial relevance. He is not yet in a position to determine specific C-values. But he is able to make comparative judgments in certain simple situations, either with the help of the axioms or directly by common sense. In order to be able to determine specific C-values, he wishes to learn about the λ-system. For this purpose we shall help him now in taking the following steps: (1) to determine the γ-values; (2) to decide whether to use the λ-method; (3) to determine the range of admissible λ-values; and (4) to choose a λ-value.

1. *Determination of the γ-values.* Let $k = 3$. We ask X whether or not he takes the three values of $C_j(0, 0, 0)$ ($j = 1, 2, 3$) as equal. (If he is unwilling to assign $\mathscr{C}$-values on empty evidence, we ask about $C_j(1, 1, 1)$ or $C_j(2, 2, 2)$.) If he takes the three values as equal, we show him that each is $1/3$. If he is unable to see any reason for taking one value as higher than another, we advise him to take γ-equality. If he says that the values are unequal, e.g., that in the cases mentioned $C_1 > C_2 > C_3$, it is more difficult to help him to obtain numerical values. We may try an *objective method*. For example, if the attributes are colors, we might ask him to indicate in a color atlas the boundaries of the three regions, and then we determine their widths on the basis of a suitable metric (e.g., Ostwald's). Or we use a *subjective procedure*, by determining his subjective γ-values from his preferences among certain offers of bets or the like in an assumed simple situation, characterized by $(0, 0, 0)$ or $(1, 1, 1)$ or $(2, 2, 2)$. (If he has already some experience with the objects in question, it will usually not be of this simple form. In this case we must ask him to disregard the experience and to imagine how he would react in such a simple situation.)

2. *The decision to use or not to use the λ-method.* In some cases, where we have a quantitative distance function for the attribute space, we can apply an *objective procedure.* We determine the distances of the attributes in the attribute space, in our example, the color space. According to our earlier considerations about the dependence of the η-values on the distances, we are for practical purposes entitled to choose a $\mathscr{C}$-function with η-equality not only if the distances are equal or approximately equal, but also if none of the distances is below a certain threshold value (say, as a rule of thumb, $1/6$). In these cases, we shall advise X to use not only η-equality, but, more specifically, the λ-method, i.e., to restrict his choice to λ-$\mathscr{C}$-functions.

If we have no metric and are even incapable of a comparative judgment about the threshold criterion just mentioned, we shall be satisfied with using a *subjective procedure.* We ask X for a comparative judgment of equality or inequality with respect to certain pairs of C-values which are equal for λ-C-functions, e.g., $C_1(2, 5, 0)$ and $C_1(2, 0, 5)$, and analogous pairs for C_2 and for C_3. Most people would in most cases of this kind vote for equality. If X does so or if at least he says that he is not aware of any reason for judging one value in such a pair to be higher than the other, we advise him to choose a λ-$\mathscr{C}$-function.

On the other hand, if either the objective situation in the attribute space or X's subjective judgments of inequality point clearly in the direction of the inequality of η-values, then a $\mathscr{C}$-function outside of the λ-system must be taken. (Various kinds of such $\mathscr{C}$-functions for various situations will be dealt with in later articles.)

3. *The range of admissible λ-values.* Let us now suppose that we have decided to advise X to use for the given family F a λ-$\mathscr{C}$-function. Then only one other decision is to be made, the choice of the value of λ. Once a value is chosen, all C-values are uniquely determined, and thereby all values of $\mathscr{C}$ and $\mathscr{M}$. We have earlier given reasons for the exclusion of 0 and ∞; thus only finite, positive real numbers remain as possible λ-values. But this is a very comprehensive range. It would be desirable to find reasons for narrower boundaries. First let us look at an example to see how the values of $^\lambda C$ vary with the change of λ. We consider a family F of $k = 4$ attributes with γ-equality. We have $C_1(s) = \dfrac{s_1 + \lambda/4}{s + \lambda}$. For $\lambda = \infty$, this is $1/4$ (by T6c); and for $\lambda = 0$, it is $s_1/s = r_1$. Let us take $s = 5$, $s_1 = 3$; then $r_1 = .6$. Thus the difference between the C-values for the two extreme (improper) λ-values is considerable. We give, in addition, the values of C_1 for some proper λ-values:

(19-14) $^\lambda C_1$-values for various λ's with $k = 4$, $s = 5$, $s_1 = 3$:

λ	$= 0$	.01	.25	1	2	4	100	∞
$^\lambda C_1(s) =$	.600	.599	.583	.542	.500	.444	.267	.250

As I have said earlier [1952a, p. 53], it seems advisable to exclude not only the extreme values 0 and ∞ for λ, but also those positive finite values which are either very large or very small. I will state here briefly the results (so far unpublished, except for Shimony's) of considerations in these two directions. I plan to discuss them in detail in a later article in this series.

First let us examine *large* λ-*values*. While $^\infty\mathscr{C}$ disregards experience entirely, λ-$\mathscr{C}$-functions with finite but high λ do take account of experience, but give it too little influence. The first step was made by Abner Shimony who showed that λ-values of the order of magnitude of a million lead to unacceptable $\mathscr{C}$-values (J. Symb. Logic, 19, 1954, 300f.). I made then investigations with the help of examples somewhat similar to Shimony's, which led to the exclusion of far lower λ-values, for example:

(19-15) For a family with $k = 4$ and γ-equality, it seems plausible that λ should not be higher than 10. (The boundary of 10 here is taken somewhat arbitrarily.)

Later (in 1957) I found a plausible requirement which leads to a further exclusion of large λ-values. For a λ-γ-family F of k attributes, for any $s > k$, let us compare two samples. Let E_1 be a sample description (s.d.) for the first sample, in which the k numbers are equal (if s is divisible by k) or differ at most by one; let E_2 be an s.d. for the second sample, in which all s individuals have the first attribute. The degree of order (or uniformity, compare [1952a, p. 66]) of E_1 is the minimum for the given k and s; that of E_2 is the maximum. Therefore in inductive logic the second sample should certainly be given a preferential status in comparison to the first. This is indeed the case in the λ-system, inasmuch as here $\mathcal{M}(E_2) > \mathcal{M}(E_1)$. This can easily be shown with the help of the following theorem.

(19-16)   Suppose that in s we have $s_m > s_n$. Then $\mathrm{MI}(s^m) > \mathrm{MI}(s^n)$.

Proof. $\mathrm{MI}(s^m) = \mathrm{MI}(s) \cdot C_m(s) > \mathrm{MI}(s) \cdot C_n(s)$
(by T11g) $= \mathrm{MI}(s^n)$.

This says in effect the following. Suppose that in an s.d. E (with k-tuple s^n) the number of P_n is positive but does not exceed that of P_m. Suppose that E' is formed from E by shifting one individual from P_n to P_m. (Thus E' has the k-tuple s^m.) Then, according to (16), $\mathcal{M}(E') > \mathcal{M}(E)$. It follows that $\mathcal{M}(E_2) > \mathcal{M}(E_1)$, since E_2 can be formed from E_1 by a series of steps each of which is analogous to the step from E to E' (for some m and n).

Now it seems not implausible to require that the preferential treatment of the second sample should go still further, to the effect that of the following two requirements (a) and (b) at least the first should be fulfilled, and perhaps also the second:

(19-17)   Let S_1 be the structure proposition (§10) of the first sample, and S_2 that of the second. It is required that
   (a) $\mathcal{M}(S_2)$ be not smaller than $\mathcal{M}(S_1)$.
   (b) $\mathcal{M}(S_2)$ be not equal to $\mathcal{M}(S_1)$.

Now in the λ-system the following three results can easily be shown:

(19-18)   Let $\mathcal{M}$ be the function $^\lambda\mathcal{M}$ with a given λ-value. Then the following holds for the λ-γ-family F.
   (a) If $\lambda = k$, then $\mathcal{M}$ has the same value for all structures (for the given k and s). (This $^k\mathcal{M}$ is the function $^*\mathcal{M}$, discussed under the symbol 'm^*' in [1950, §110, see (1)b, p. 563] and in [1952a, §15].)
   (b) If $\lambda < k$, then $\mathcal{M}(S_2) > \mathcal{M}(S_1)$.
   (c) If $\lambda > k$, then $\mathcal{M}(S_2) < \mathcal{M}(S_1)$.

Therefore, if someone accepts in requirement (17) either the weak version (a) or the strong one consisting of (a) and (b) together, he must accept the corresponding version of the following require-ment:

(19-19)   For any λ-γ-family of k attributes ($k \geq 2$), we must have:
    (a) $\lambda \leq k$,
    (b) $\lambda \neq k$.

As with (17), so here, at least part (a) seems to me plausible.

Originally, in [1950, §110], I regarded the function $\mathcal{M}^*$, charac-terized by $\lambda = k$, as preferable. If we accept the strong version of (19), $\mathcal{M}^*$ would be excluded. Other considerations, which I shall discuss elsewhere, seem to show that for large k, λ should be considerably less than k.

Now we shall consider the question of the exclusion of *small* λ-*values*. Using the $\mathcal{C}$-function with $\lambda = 0$ means disregarding the logical factor in the situation and, in particular, the widths of the attributes. A $\mathcal{C}$ with a positive but very small λ takes account of the widths, but insufficiently. Usually we have good intuitive judgment about C-values. However, for the present purpose they are not very suitable because they do not change much with changing λ. Now, in order to show the serious disadvantages of the straight rule, I used in the examples of (5) and (6) above, propositions of a special nonatomic form, because for them the values of $^0\mathcal{M}$ differ widely from intuitively acceptable values. One might expect that for small positive λ-values the same holds, though to a lesser degree. We shall see that this is indeed the case.

As in the earlier examples, let F be a λ-γ-family with $k = 5$. For any $s > 0$ and any attribute index j, let $B_{s,j}$ be the homogeneous s.d. for the initial s-sample, in which all individuals have the attribute P_j. Let $B_s =_{\mathrm{Df}} \bigcup_{j=1}^{k} B_{s,j}$; hence B_s says that the first s individuals are alike (with respect to F). Thus the earlier example (5)(a) is $B_{10,1}$, and (6)(a) is B_{10}. We have from T7c:

(19-20)   **(a)** $^\lambda\mathcal{M}(B_{s,j}) = \dfrac{(\lambda/k)_s}{(\lambda)_s}$

    (b) $^\lambda\mathcal{M}(B_s) = k\,^\lambda\mathcal{M}(B_{s,j})$.
    (c) $^\lambda\mathcal{M}(B_{1,j}) = 1/k$. (From (a).)
    (d) $^\lambda\mathcal{M}(B_1) = 1$. (From (b) and (c).)
    (e) $^\lambda\mathcal{C}(B_{s,j} \mid B_{1,j}) = {}^\lambda\mathcal{C}(B_s \mid B_1)$, (from (b)),

$$= {}^\lambda\mathcal{M}(B_s). \text{ (From (d).)}$$

The following numerical values are obtained by (20)(a).

(19-21) Values of $^\lambda \mathcal{M}(B_s)$ for $k = 5$; $s = 10$ and 20; and various values of λ.

s	$\lambda = 0$	.1	.25	.5	.75	1.
10	1.	.868	.685	.436	.263	.144
20	1.	.820	.580	.327	.171	.083

If X chooses one of the six λ-values mentioned in the heading of the table, then X must accept the corresponding $\mathcal{M}$-value (listed on the line for $s = 10$) as the initial probability of the prediction B_{10} that the first ten balls will have the same color. (According to (20)(e), this is also the conditional probability of the prediction that the subsequent nine balls will be red, given that the first ball is red.) Now it seems to me that, from a common sense point of view, the proposition B_{10} is not something to be expected easily; if the event occurred we would find it startling. Therefore its initial probability should definitely be less than 1/2 and, in my feeling, considerably less. Therefore I regard the $\mathcal{M}$-value .685 as entirely unacceptable and the value .436 as rather questionable. Accordingly, for a family with $k = 5$, $\lambda = 1/4$ is unacceptable, and even $\lambda = 1/2$ should be excluded.

In earlier years the λ-system was sometimes criticized for the reason that it admits an enormous range of $\mathcal{C}$-functions with greatly different values. But in the course of the years the range of admitted λ-values has been more and more narrowed down. At present, it is, roughly speaking, the interval from 1/2 to k; here the difference between the values of two C-functions with different λ's are rather small, except for very small s. Some ways for further reduction of the range are under investigation.

4. *The choice of a λ-value.* Even though the range of admitted λ-values, originally infinite, was soon reduced to a finite size and later to a small one, there still remains the necessity of choosing one out of an infinity of possible values. There are several points of view from which we might look at this problem.

Let us first consider the view that, although certain boundaries for λ can be determined objectively by the consideration of rationality requirements, within these limits everyone is free to make his choice as he pleases. We might call this a (modified) *subjectivist point of view*. (A similar view, but without acceptance of objective limits, might be called a purely subjectivist view.) In situations where we have a free choice, it seems often natural to let the choice be guided by considerations of simplicity. Therefore we shall usually consider in the first place integers as λ-values. My earlier preference for the function $\mathcal{M}^*$ ($\lambda = k$, (18a)) was motivated by the fact that for this function the formulas for MI and MS have an especially simple form (simpler than for any other admitted λ, after the exclusion of $\lambda = 0$ and $\lambda = \infty$). Later I found that, at least for large k, a λ-value equal to or near k would be too high. At present it is not yet clear whether λ should at all depend on k. Some considerations, which I shall soon discuss, seem to indicate that it might be better to use the same λ-value for all families, irrespective of k, or at least for all long-distance families (i.e., those in which all distances between attributes are large enough to disregard the similarity influence). If we do this, then, on the basis of the weak requirement (19a), the choice is only between 1 and 2. And if we accept the stronger requirement (19b), we shall take $\lambda = 1$. (In recent years, when considering numerical examples, I have usually taken $\lambda = 1$.) If we take $\lambda = 1$ for all long-distance families, we have (by T5a) $\eta = 1/2$.

From another, but closely related point of view, we might regard X's choice of a λ-value (and likewise his decisions in other respects in the process of constructing a $\mathscr{C}$-function for some form of language) as determined by, and therefore symptomatic of, certain features of X's personality. We may call this the "*personalist point of view*". (I do not mean to imply that this is the same as Savage's conception which he calls "personalistic" [1954, pp. 3, 56 ff.].) This is similar to what I called earlier the subjectivist point of view; or it may perhaps be regarded as a special case of the latter. When the subjectivist asserts that X is free in his choice (say, of the λ-value of similar matters) and that two different persons X and Y may make different choices without either of them violating standards of rationality, the personalist would agree; but he would add the remark that X's choice should not be regarded as arbitrary or unpredictable in the sense that a person of X's nature could just as well have made another choice; X's choice is rather regarded as determined or at least influenced by his personality.

In order to see which particular personality trait may be regarded as determining the choice of a λ-value, let us analyse the influence which the choice of a smaller or a larger λ-value has on the resulting values of ${}^{\lambda}\mathscr{C}$. Let us consider a sequence of s.d.'s. E_l ($l = 1, 2, \ldots$) such that, for any l, E_l is an s.d. of a sample of ln

individuals, among them lp individuals with the attribute P_1. Thus in each of these samples, r_1 ($= s_1/s$, the relative frequency of P_1) has the same value p/n. We have (by T5f) for E_l with k-tuple $\mathbf{s}_l$:

(19-22)
$$C_1(\mathbf{s}_l) = \frac{pl + \lambda\gamma_1}{nl + \lambda}.$$

According to T5g, this is the weighted mean between γ_1 and r_1 with the weights λ and $s = nl$ respectively. Thus the weight of γ_1 remains constant, while with increasing l, the weight of r_1 grows with every step, beyond all bounds. The initial value (for the case of the empty sample, $l = 0$) is $C_1(\mathbf{s}_0) = \gamma_1$. Let us suppose that $r_1 > \gamma_1$. Then the further values of $C_1(\mathbf{s}_l)$ for $l = 1, 2, \ldots$, grow more and more and approach r_1 asymptotically. This holds for any proper (i.e., positive finite) value of λ. Now the difference in the effect of various λ-values is this: the larger the λ-value, the slower is the increase of C_1. Metaphorically speaking, while the force of the growing experience, showing the same value r_1 in larger and larger samples, pulls C_1 from the initial point γ_1 higher and higher towards r_1, λ measures the resistance or inertia against this influence of experience. We recognize this effect of λ in the earlier example (14): the larger the λ-value, the closer is C_1 to its initial value γ_1.

We obtain a clearer picture of the motion of C_1 with increasing s but constant r_1 by focusing our attention not on the values of $C_1(\mathbf{s})$ itself (as in (22)), but rather on those of $^\lambda q(s)$, which we define as follows (for the present discussion only):

(19-23) **(a)**
$$^\lambda q(s) =_{Df} \frac{C_1^s(\mathbf{s}) - C_1^0(\mathbf{s})}{r_1 - C_1^0(\mathbf{s})}.$$

(b)
$$^\lambda q(s) = \frac{C_1^s(\mathbf{s}) - \gamma_1}{r_1 - \gamma_1}.$$

With s running from 0 towards ∞, $C_1^s(\mathbf{s})$ moves from γ_1 towards r_1. $^\lambda q(s)$ measures the fraction of the segment (γ_1, r_1) that $C_1^s(\mathbf{s})$ has passed through for a given s. We obtain (from T5f, with $s_1 = r_1 s$):

(19-24)
$$^\lambda q(s) = \frac{s}{s + \lambda} = \frac{s/\lambda}{s/\lambda + 1}.$$

Thus, in comparison with $^\lambda C_1^s(\mathbf{s})$, $^\lambda q(s)$ has the advantage of depending merely on s and λ, and in fact only on s/λ, but is independent of r_1 and γ_1. Suppose that X, using a certain λ-value, has obtained a certain C_1-value on the basis of a sample of size s. Suppose that Y uses a λ-value double that of X. Then Y must, in order to obtain the same C_1-value, proceed in the sequence of increasing samples (with constant r_1) to the sample of size $2s$. We may then say that the inductive inertia of Y is double that of X.

Thus from the personalist point of view it is regarded as possible that rational people use different λ-values for the same family of attributes. The difference may be attributed to their different inductive inertia. In earlier times my thoughts about the choice of a λ-value went mainly in this personalist direction.

In recent years, after the introduction of the η-parameter, I began to look at the problem of the choice of a λ-value from an *objectivist point of view*. I recognized that the value of η_{il} should depend on the distance between the regions of the attributes P_j and P_l in the attribute space. In general (aside from long distances), the smaller the distance, the larger should be the η-value. Our earlier considerations to this effect (in §17) were concerned with the case of different distances within the same family. In contrast, we shall now study, as the first of two examples, the case of two families, each with equality of distances, but the distance in one family differing from that in the other.

As an example, let F be a family based on a partition of the color space U, consisting of a large number of small regions with equal widths. Now we consider, say in the context of an investigation of objects of a certain kind, a subfamily F' of F, which contains only three of the colors in F. Suppose that one belongs to the pure red part of U, the second to the pure yellow part, and the third to the pure blue part, and that the three distances, which in this case are large, are equal. Let another subfamily F'' consist likewise of three of the colors in F; all three belong to the pure red part and are near to each other. Let the three distances again be equal; but in this case they are quite small. Because of the equality of distances in F', we have η-equality, and therefore we decide to take F' as a λ-family. And the same holds for F''. There is, however, a difference; the equal distances in F' are large, but those in F'' are very small. Therefore the common η-value for the pairs of distinct attributes in F', say η', is considerably smaller than the common η-value in F'', say η''. [Let the three attributes in F which were selected for F', be P_1, P_2, P_3; and those selected for F'' be P_4, P_5, P_6. Let the language $\mathscr{L}$ contain only the family F, language $\mathscr{L}'$, the family F', and language $\mathscr{L}''$, F''. $\mathscr{L}'$ and $\mathscr{L}''$ are sublanguages of $\mathscr{L}$. However, sublanguages of this kind, formed by restriction of the attribute space, are essentially different from those to which the axiom of sublanguages refers, and they involve new problems. At present it is not yet known whether an η-value η_{jl} for the attributes P_j and P_l in F should remain unchanged in a sublanguage containing these attributes, so that the common η-value η' in F' should be equal to the value of η_{12} ($=\eta_{23}=\eta_{31}$) in F, and η'' equal to the value of η_{45} ($=\eta_{56}=\eta_{64}$) in F. Nevertheless it seems highly plausible that η' should be considerably smaller than η''.] Now for any λ-family with the common η-value η, we have $\lambda = \eta/(1-\eta)$ (by D3). Thus we obtain for F': $\lambda' = \eta'/(1-\eta')$, and for F'': $\lambda'' = \eta''(1-\eta'')$. Since $\eta' < \eta''$, we have $\lambda' < \lambda''$.

In considering the problems of the choice of a λ-value in earlier times, before the relevance of the distances in the attribute space was discovered, my friends and I often discussed the following questions. Suppose that for a given family F a certain λ-value has been accepted, what effect should this have upon our choice of a λ-value for another family F', (1) if F' has the same size (i.e., number of attributes) as F, and (2) if F' has another size. At that time we considered only families with attribute symmetry and hence with γ-equality, and we gave no attention to the distances between attributes. Therefore we regarded the size as the only trait of a family that might possibly influence the choice of λ. Therefore I laid down a rule which could be formulated in our present terminology like this:

(19-25) For all λ-γ-families of the same size the same λ-value should be used.

(This rule is implied by the axiom of the invariance of $\mathscr{C}$ with respect to any permutation of a set of families (which meant λ-γ-families) of the same size, [1959, NA9, p. 244].) The question whether the rule (25) of the equality of λ-values should be extended to some or even all cases of families of different sizes was left open. Consequently I distinguished two kinds of inductive methods (i.e., general rules for determining $\mathscr{C}$-values for any family); an inductive method of the first kind assigns the same λ-value to all families, irrespective of size, while an inductive method of the second kind takes λ as varying with the size k. (The two kinds of methods are discussed in [1952a, §§11 and 15].) I mentioned then that all historically known methods belong to the first kind (by leading either to the straight rule, which corresponds to $\lambda = 0$, or to Laplace's rule of succession, which corresponds to $\lambda = 2$). Actually my main reason (practically the only one) for introducing the second kind was the fact that the method I had proposed in [1950,

Appendix] belongs to this kind. This is the $\mathcal{M}^*$-method, i.e., the general rule assigning to any family of k attributes the value $\lambda = k$. I have not given serious consideration to any other method of the second kind, nor has any other author as far as I know.

It seems today that a general rule assigning to every family a suitable λ-value cannot be either of the first kind, assigning to all families the same λ, or of the second kind, making λ dependent on k. The recognition of the influence of the attribute distances excludes rule (25) and thereby all methods of the first or the second kind. Our earlier example of a subfamily F' of three colors with large distances and another family F'' of three colors with small distances is a counterexample against rule (25). Since in this example we have $k' = k''$ ($= 3$), rule (25) would require that λ' for F' and λ'' for F'' be equal. But we found it highly plausible to assume that λ' is smaller than λ''.

In the example mentioned we had two families of the same size but with different distances, and we found unequal λ's. This suggests that the distance is more relevant for the λ-value of a family than its size. This impression is strengthened by the following results (26) and (27). They concern special pairs of families with the same (effective) distance but different sizes; and they say that both families of such a pair have the same λ-value. In particular, $\mathcal{L}$ is a language containing the family F of size k ($k > 2$) as the only family; $\mathcal{L}'$, F', and k' are analogous, and likewise $\mathcal{L}^*$, F^*, and k^*. F is a λ-family. $\mathcal{L}'$ and $\mathcal{L}^*$ are sublanguages of $\mathcal{L}$ of the following kind. The three families have the same attribute space $\mathcal{U}$; but F' and F^* are based on coarser partitions of $\mathcal{U}$ than F.

(19-26)   Let F and F' be as described. In particular, let $k' = k - 1$, and let F' be formed from F by leaving $k - 2$ attributes unchanged, but uniting two attributes of F into one attribute of F' (that is to say, the region of the attribute in F' is the union of the regions of the two attributes in F). Let F be a λ-family with the λ-value λ. Then the following holds.

   (a) F' is likewise a λ-family.
   (b) The λ-value λ' for F' must be equal to λ.

Outline for a proof of (a).   According to the axiom of sublanguages (§6), for every proposition in $\mathcal{L}'$ there is a corresponding proposition in $\mathcal{L}$; and, if A corresponds to A' and B to B',

   (i) $\mathcal{M}(A') = \mathcal{M}(A)$; and $\mathcal{C}(A' \mid B') = \mathcal{C}(A \mid B)$.

Since F is a λ-family, it satisfies the λ-condition (D1a):

(ii) For any $s \geqq 0$, for any $\mathbf{s} \in {}^0\mathbf{N}^{k,s}$, for any three distinct attribute indices j, m, n, $C_j(\mathbf{s}^m) = C_j(\mathbf{s}^n)$.

For the purpose of indirect proof, let us assume that (a) is false. Then by D1a:

(iii) For some $s' \geqq 0$, for some $\mathbf{s}' \in {}^0\mathbf{N}^{k',s'}$, for some three distinct indices j', m', n', $C_{j'}(\mathbf{s}'^{m'}) \neq C_{j'}(\mathbf{s}'^{n'})$.

Let us suppose that the attributes $P_1, \ldots, P_{k-2}$ remain unchanged, and that P_{k-1} and P_k are united into the attribute $P'_{k'}$ in F'; i.e., the region $X'_{k'} = X_{k-1} \cup X_k$. (The proof is obviously analogous if instead any other pair of attributes in F is chosen for uniting.) Let E' be an s.d. for the initial s'-sample with k'-tuple s'. Let $A_i'^{l'}$ be the atomic proposition in $\mathscr{L}'$ with the attribute $P'_{l'}$ and the individual a_i.

(iv) The proposition A in $\mathscr{L}$ corresponding to $A_1'^{l'}$ is as follows:
   (a) If $l' < k'$ (and hence $P'_{l'}$ is the same as $P_{l'}$ in F), A is $A_i^{l'}$ (i.e., the atomic proposition in $\mathscr{L}$ with $P_{l'}$ and a_i).
   (b) If $l' = k'$, A is $A_i^{k-1} \cup A_i^k$.

Let E' be an s.d. in $\mathscr{L}'$ for the initial s'-sample with k'-tuple s', with s' and $\mathbf{s}'$ as in (iii). Then we have from (iii):

(v) $\mathscr{C}(A_{s'+2}'^{j'} \mid E' \cap A_{s'+1}'^{m'}) \neq \mathscr{C}(A_{s'+2}'^{j'} \mid E' \cap A_{s'+1}'^{n'})$.

Let $\mathbf{s}' = \langle s'_1, \ldots, s'_{k'} \rangle$. Let $p = s'_{k'}$. Then E' is an intersection of s' atomic propositions; just p of them with attribute $P'_{k'}$. Thus, by (iv), the proposition E corresponding to E' is an intersection of $s' - p$ atomic propositions and p unions of two atomic propositions each. By distribution, the intersection of these p pair-unions is the same as a union of 2^p intersections of p atomic propositions each. Thus E is a union of 2^p s.d.'s of the initial s'-sample. Of the three distinct indices j', m', n' in (iii), at most one can be k'. Consequently, we have to distinguish four cases: (1) $m' = k'$; (2) $n' = k'$; (3) $j' = k'$; (4) none of them is k'. In each case, the propositions corresponding to the three atomic propositions mentioned in (v) are determined by (iv). Thus we obtain from (v) by (i) in each of the four cases an inequality of $\mathscr{C}$-values for propositions in $\mathscr{L}$. Here we will not carry out this lengthy procedure. In each case it can then be shown that the resulting inequality is incompatible with the general statement (ii). Therefore our assumption of the falsity of (a) is impossible.

Proof of (b). We have $k \geqq 3$. 1. First case: $k > 3$. Then $1, 2 < k'$. By D16-1b: $\eta_{12} = C_1(\mathbf{s}_0^2)/C_1(\mathbf{s}_0) = C_1(\mathbf{s}_0'^2)/C_1(\mathbf{s}_0')$ (by (i)) $= \eta'_{12}$. We have in $\mathscr{L}$ (by D3): $\lambda = \eta_{12}/(1 - \eta_{12}) = \eta'_{12}/(1 - \eta'_{12}) = \lambda'$.—2. Second case: $k = 3$; hence $k' = 2$. By (16-7), η'_{12} for F' is a weighted mean of η_{12} and η_{13} for F. But $\eta_{12} = \eta_{13}$ (T1a); hence $\eta'_{12} = \eta_{12}$. Thus again $\lambda' = \lambda$.

Now we can easily prove the following general result, for an arbitrary sublanguage F^* with an arbitrary number k^* of attributes.

(19-27)   As previously, let $\mathscr{L}$ be a language with the λ-family F of size k $(k > 2)$ and λ-value λ. Let $\mathscr{L}^*$ be a sublanguage of $\mathscr{L}$ with a family F^* of size k^* $(2 \leqq k^* < k)$ of such a kind that F^* is based upon a coarser partition of the attribute space than F. Then F^* is likewise a λ-family, and its λ-value λ^* is equal to λ.

Proof.   Let $h = k - k^*$.—1. First case: $h = 1$. F^* is formed from F by uniting two attributes. Therefore the assertions are the same as (26).—2. Second case: $h > 1$. We can form a series of $h + 1$ families $F_0, F_1, \ldots, F_h$ such that F_0 is F and F_h is F^*, and for every n from 0 to $h - 1$, F_{n+1} is formed from F_n by uniting two attributes. Thus, by (27), if F_n is a λ-family, then F_{n+1} is likewise a λ-family and has the same λ-value as F_n. Therefore, by mathematical induction with respect to n, F^* is a λ-family and has the same λ-value as F.

We see from (27) that, if any λ-family F of any size k $(k > 2)$ is given, then we can construct, for any smaller number k^* $(2 \leqq k^* < k)$ a λ-family F^* of size k^* with the same (effective) distance and therefore with the same η-value and the same λ-value. This shows again that the decisive factor for the λ-value of a family is not its size, but the distance between its attributes. And the last example shows, in particular, that the $\mathscr{M}^*$-rule, which prescribes as the λ-value for any family its number of attributes, is untenable as a general rule, since it can be applied to at most one of the two familes F and F^*, and also to at most one of the $h + 1$ families in the series mentioned in the last proof.

The situation with respect to the problem of the choice of a λ-value for a given family, or preferably the choice of a general rule determining the λ-value for any family (or at least for any family in a comprehensive class of families) is certainly in need of further investigation and clarification. At present I am inclined to regard the size of the family as irrelevant and the attribute distance as the most important factor. This means, if we assume the general form of the η-curve proposed in (17-17), that all long-distance families, for any attribute space and for any size of the family, have practically the same λ-value. If we accept the requirement (19)(a), then here the values 1 and 2 come primarly into consideration. I am inclined to take $\lambda = 1$, which is the simplest value in the admitted range. I have lately used this value whenever I wished to calculate a numerical example. The λ-value for a family with a *short* distance will then depend mainly on this distance.

I think there need not be a controversy between the objectivist point of view and the subjectivist or personalist point of view. Both have a legitimate place in the context of our work, that is, the construction of a system of rules for determining probability values with respect to possible evidence. At each step in the construction, a choice is to be made; the choice is not completely free but is restricted by certain boundaries. Basically, there is merely a difference in attitude or emphasis between the subjectivist tendency to emphasize the existing freedom of choice, and the objectivist tendency to stress the existence of limitations. I give more attention to the latter, because in my work I am mainly interested in discovering new rationality requirements which lead to narrower boundaries. I have repeatedly experienced a development of the following kind, similar to that described in this section in connection with the problem of choosing a λ-value. At the beginning of the investigation there is a great number, sometimes even an embarrassing abundance of possibilities to choose from. But then, with the gain of deeper insight into the situation, the range of choice is gradually narrowed down. It seems advisable—especially at the present time, when we are still in the initial phase of the whole construction—to keep an open mind, free of prejudice in the one or the other direction. Suppose that at some point in the context of a given problem, say, the choice of a parameter value, we find that we have a free choice within certain boundaries, and that at the moment we cannot think of any additional reactionality requirement which would constrict the boundaries. Then it would certainly be imprudent to assert that the present range of choice will always remain open. How could we deny the possibility that we shall find tomorrow an additional requirement? But it would also be unwise to regard it as certain that such an additional requirement will be found, or even to predict that by the discovery of further requirements the range will shrink down to one point.

20

The Limit Axioms

[*Editor's Note.* This section is based upon Carnap's unrevised first version, dated May 1965. Almost all of it (and all of part C) appears here essentially as Carnap left it in 1965.

Here are stated two further axioms: a law of large numbers (Reichenbach's axiom, A7), and the usual axiom of σ-additivity, A8. It was seen in Arts. 4 and 5 that in the presence of A1–A6, the Reichenbach axiom implies the principle of instantial relevance, viz., the principle that C_i is an increasing function of its jth argument, when all other arguments are constant. And in §3 of Art. 5, Gaifman expressed the content of the Reichenbach axiom (over and above A1–A6) in terms of the de Finetti representation of symmetric MI-functions:

$$\text{MI}(s_1, \ldots, s_k) = \int_\Delta r_1^{s_1} \cdot \ldots \cdot r_k^{s_k} d\mu(r_1, \ldots, r_k)$$

where Δ is the simplex consisting of points $(r_1, \ldots, r_k)$ with nonnegative coordinates that sum to 1. The condition that Gaifman there states as equivalent to A7 is this:

(*) The complement, with respect to Δ, of the union of all the open subsets of Δ whose μ-measure is 0, is a union of subsimplices of Δ.

Thus if $k = 2$ so that Δ is the line-segment $\{(x, 1-x): 0 \leq x \leq 1\}$, (*) requires that μ assign 0 to the whole interior of Δ if it assigns 0 to any open subinterval of Δ.]

A. THE AXIOM OF CONVERGENCE (REICHENBACH)

The axiom of convergence (20-1) was suggested to me in 1953 by Hilary Putman, who proposed for it the name "Reichenbach's axiom". Here it is formulated first for a language $\mathscr{L}$ with a single family of attributes P_j ($j = i, \ldots, k$). Thus the first argument of '$Z(m, i)$' as in D3-4 is redundant. Here a model will be a function Z of a single argument, where $P_{Z(i)}$ is the attribute true in the model of individual a_i:

$$Z(i) = j \quad \text{if-if} \quad Z \in P_j a_i.$$

Let $E_s(Z)$ be the sample proposition for the initial s-sample $\{a_1, \ldots, a_s\}$ in Z, i.e.,

$$E_s(Z) =_{\text{Df}} \bigcap_{i=1}^{s} P_{Z(i)} a_i.$$

Let $s(Z)$ be the k-tuple for the initial s-sample in Z:

$$s(Z) = \langle s_1(Z), \ldots, s_k(Z) \rangle, \qquad s = \sum_{j=1}^{k} s_j(Z),$$

where $s_j(Z)$ is the number of individuals in the initial s-sample that have the attribute P_j in Z. Let $r_j^s(Z)$ be the relative frequency of P_j in the initial s-sample in Z:

$$r_j^s(Z) = s_j(Z)/s.$$

And let $R_j(Z)$ be the limit (if any) approached by $r_j^s(Z)$ as s increases without bound:

$$R_j(Z) = \lim_s r_j^s(Z).$$

In these terms the axiom proposed by Putnam was:

(20-1) If $R_j(Z)$ exists then $\lim_s \mathscr{C}(P_j a_{s+1} \mid E_s(Z)) = R_j(Z)$.

Here $\lim_s \mathscr{C}(P_j a_{s+1} \mid E_s)$ and R_j are functions defined on subsets of the space $\mathbf{Z}$ of all models. Axiom (20-1) asserts that on the domain of definition of R_j, both functions are defined, and equal.

When I first published the axiom of convergence (in [1964c], p. 976, A13), I expressed some doubts about the suitability of the name, "Reichenbach's axiom," since Reichenbach had rejected any non-frequency concept of probability. However, we might interpret Reichenbach's concept of a *posit* of probability as an *estimate* of probability. As the probability concept that Reichenbach intended was the limit of relative frequency, it is to be represented here by $R_j(*Z)$, where $*Z$ is the model that corresponds to reality in the intended interpretation of $\mathscr{L}$: truth = truth-in-$*Z$. Reichenbach's requirement that the posit be self-correcting means that $\lim_s \text{est}\,(R_j, E_s(Z)) = R_j(Z)$, either on the whole domain of definition of R_j or, perhaps, only on some subset of that domain that we are sure contains $*Z$. If explicated as an expected value, this estimate is equal to the $\mathscr{C}$-value in (20-1): cf. (19-2) and [1950], T106-1c. Then for those who accept $\mathscr{C}$-functions, (20-1) is essentially the same as Reichenbach's requirement.

If we assume (as we usually do) that $\mathscr{C}$ is regular, we can use the representative function C_j in formulating Reichenbach's axiom:

(20-2) On the domain of definition of R_j, $\lim_s C_j(s) = R_j$.

Here the equation is between functions. To the same effect we could have said, "$\lim_s C_j(s(Z)) = R_j(Z)$ wherever $R_j(Z)$ exists."

For the axiom of convergence I shall adopt the following slightly different form, which has the advantage that it refers to *all* models Z, not only to those for which $R_i(Z)$ exists:

A9. Axiom of convergence (Reichenbach). Let $\mathscr{C}$ be a symmetric (not necessarily regular) $\mathscr{C}$-function. Then the function $\lim_s [\mathscr{C}(P_j a_{s+1} \mid E_s) - r_j^s]$ is defined, and vanishes identically, on **Z**.

(In other words: $\lim_s [\mathscr{C}(P_j a_{s+1} \mid E_s(Z)) - r_j^s(Z)]$ exists and is 0 for all Z in **Z**.)

If $\mathscr{C}$ is assumed to be regular, we may use the following form:

A9′. Let $\mathscr{C}$ be a symmetric and regular $\mathscr{C}$-function. Then for every attribute index j, $\lim_s [C_j(\mathbf{s}) - r_j^s]$ exists, and vanishes identically, on **Z**.

We now state two forms of the axiom for $\mathscr{M}$ instead of $\mathscr{C}$, corresponding to A9 and A9′, respectively.

A9$_m$. Let $\mathscr{M}$ be a symmetric (not necessarily regular) $\mathscr{M}$-function. Then for any attribute index j, $\lim_s [\mathscr{M}(E_s \cap P_j a_{s+1}) - \mathscr{M}(E_s) r_j^s]$ exists, and vanishes identically, on **Z**.

A9$_m'$. Let MI be a symmetric (not necessarily regular) MI-function (D11-3a). Then for any attribute index j, $\lim_s (\mathrm{MI}(\mathbf{s}^j) - \mathrm{MI}(\mathbf{s}) r_j^s)$ exists, and vanishes identically, on **Z**.

Note that here, in contrast to A9′, regularity is not assumed.

The effective equivalence of A9 and A9$_m$ is shown in the following theorem.

T20-1 Let $\mathscr{C}$ be a symmetric (not necessarily regular) $\mathscr{C}$-function, and let $\mathscr{M}$ be related to $\mathscr{C}$ (D1-11).
    a. If $\mathscr{C}$ satisfies axiom A9, then $\mathscr{M}$ satisfies A9$_m$.

Proof. 1. Suppose that, for some s, $\mathscr{M}(E_s(Z)) = 0$. Then for that Z, both $\mathscr{M}$-values in the formula in A9$_m$ are 0, and the same holds also for any $s' > s$. Hence the limit is 0. —2. Suppose that, for every s, $\mathscr{M}(E_s(Z)) > 0$. Then we have from A9: $\lim_s [\mathscr{M}(E_s(Z) \cap P_j a_{s+1}) / \mathscr{M}(E_s(Z)) - r_j^s(Z)] = 0$. Hence, multiplying by $\mathscr{M}(E_s(Z))$, we have A9$_m$. ∎

b. If $\mathcal{M}$ satisfies A9$_m$ and is regular, then $\mathcal{C}$ satisfies A9.

Proof. If $\mathcal{M}$ is regular, $\mathcal{M}(E_s(Z)) > 0$. Then we obtain A9 from A9$_m$ by dividing through by $\mathcal{M}(E_s(Z))$. ■

The following theorem shows which $\mathcal{C}$-functions of the (extended) λ-system satisfy axiom A9, and which violate it.

T20-2 Let $\mathcal{C}$ be a λ-$\mathcal{C}$-function.
    a. $\mathcal{C}$ satisfies A9 whenever λ is a positive real number.

Proof. From T19-5g,

$$^{\lambda}C_j^s(\mathbf{s}(Z)) - r_j^s(Z) = \frac{sr_j^s(Z) + \lambda\gamma_j}{s + \lambda} - r_j^s(Z)$$

$$= \frac{\lambda}{s + \lambda}(\gamma_j - r_j^s(Z)).$$

The limit of this last difference is $\gamma_j - R_j(Z)$, which is finite. The limit of $\lambda/(s+\lambda)$ is 0; hence likewise the limit of the left-hand side. Thus A9′ is satisfied. ■

    b. If $\mathcal{C}$ is the (improper) λ-$\mathcal{C}$-function with $\lambda = 0$, then $\mathcal{C}$ satisfies A9.

Proof. From T-19-6b, $\lim ({}^0C_j(\mathbf{s}) - r_j^s)$ exists and vanishes identically on **Z**. Thus A9′ is satisfied. ■

    c. The (improper) λ-$\mathcal{C}$-function with $\lambda = \infty$ (D19-4b) violates A9.

Proof. From T19-6c: for any s and Z, $^{\infty}C_j^s(\mathbf{s}(Z)) = \gamma_j$. Now let Z_0 be a model in which no individual has the attribute P_j; hence for any $s > 0$, $r_j^s(Z_0) = 0$. Then we have $\lim_s [^{\infty}C_j^s(\mathbf{s}(Z_0)) - r_j^s(Z_0))] = \gamma_j > 0$. Thus A9′ is violated. ■

It seems that, up to the present time, the Reichenbach axiom has been used only for two important results. The first (T2c) is the exclusion of the function $^{\infty}\mathcal{C}$, which seems clearly unacceptable but has been advocated by some prominent authors (see §19, remarks on T19-6c). The second result is the derivation of the principle of instantial relevance, particularly its second part (P13-1b) (see the paragraph following P13-1). It would be of interest to prove additional theorems with the help of the axiom.

B. THE AXIOM OF σ-ADDITIVITY.

Our second limit axiom asserts σ-additivity (or countable additivity or complete additivity, D1-8) of $\mathcal{M}$:

A8. $\mathcal{M}$ is σ-additive.

Here we do not need separate forms for $\mathcal{C}$ and $\mathcal{M}$. As a statement about $\mathcal{C}$, A8 says that $\mathcal{C}(H\,|\,Z)$ as a function of H $(H\in\mathcal{C})$ is σ-additive.

D20-1. Let f be a probability measure on a σ-field $\mathcal{A}$. f has *Kolmogorov continuity* $=_{\mathrm{Df}} \lim_{n} f(B_n) = 0$ for every denumerable sequence $\mathcal{B} = \{B_1, B_2, \ldots\} \subset A$ for which we have $\bigcap \mathcal{B} = \varnothing$, $B_{n+1} \subset B_n$, and $B_{n+1} \neq B_n$ for all n.

Kolmogorov [1933, chap. II, §1] states this property of probability measures in his "axiom of continuity".

T20-3. For probability measures on σ-fields, the properties of Kolmogorov continuity and σ-additivity are coextensive.

(For a proof, see Kolmogorov, ibid., or Loève [1960, p. 84].)

The following theorem states some consequences of A8. The items (a)–(e) are well known; the rest are immediate consequences for our languages.

T20-4 Let $\mathcal{C}$ be a symmetric (not necessarily regular) $\mathcal{C}$-function, and let $\mathcal{M}$ be related to $\mathcal{C}$ and satisfy A8. Let $\mathcal{A} = \{A_1, A_2, \ldots\}$ be a denumerable sequence of propositions. For any $m > 0$, let $B_m = \bigcup\limits_{n=1}^{m} A_n$, and let $B = \bigcup \mathcal{A}$. Then the following hold.

a. $\mathcal{M}(B) = \lim\limits_{m} \mathcal{M}(B_m)$.

b. If $\mathcal{A}$ is, moreover, disjoint, then $\mathcal{M}(B) = \sum\limits_{n=1}^{\infty} \mathcal{M}(A_n)$.

c. For any E in $\mathcal{C}$ such that $\mathcal{M}(E) > 0$, $\mathcal{C}(B\,|\,E) = \lim\limits_{m} \mathcal{C}(B_m\,|\,E)$. If $\mathcal{A}$ is disjoint, then $\mathcal{C}(B\,|\,E) = \sum\limits_{n=1}^{\infty} \mathcal{C}(A_n\,|\,E)$. Thus, for the given E, the measure function $\mathcal{C}(\cdot\,|\,E)$ is σ-additive.

d. Let $D_0 = Z$, and for any $m > 0$, $D_m = \sum\limits_{n=1}^{m} A_n$. Let $D = \bigcap \mathscr{A}$. Then $\mathcal{M}(D) = \prod\limits_{m=0}^{\infty} \mathscr{C}(A_{m+1} \mid D_m)$. ($\mathscr{C}$ has "complete multiplicativity", Good [1962. p. 328].)

e. If the values of $\mathcal{M}$ on a field $\mathscr{F}$ are given, then the values of $\mathcal{M}$ on the σ-field generated by $\mathscr{F}$ are uniquely determined. (From the Extension theorem [Art. 3, (7-1)].)

f. Special case of (e), for a monadic predicate language. If the values of $\mathcal{M}$ on $\mathscr{C}^{\text{mol}}$ are given, then the values of $\mathcal{M}$ on $\mathscr{C}$ are uniquely determined.

g. Special case for language $\mathscr{L}_{1,1}$ with one family of k attributes. Let MI be representative of $\mathcal{M}$. If all values of MI are given (for all finite k-tuples), then all values of $\mathcal{M}$ on $\mathscr{C}$ are uniquely determined. Thus MI is indeed representative of the whole function $\mathcal{M}$.

h. (For $\mathscr{L}_{1,1}$.) Let MI be representative of $\mathcal{M}$. If all values of MI are given, then all values of $\mathscr{C}(H \mid E)$ are uniquely determined for pairs H, E in $\mathscr{C}$ such that $\mathcal{M}(E) > 0$. (From (g).)

Thus, in virtue of A8, the following holds: for any $\mathcal{M}$-function on $\mathscr{C}^{\text{mol}}$, there is exactly one $\mathcal{M}$-function that is its extension on $\mathscr{C}$. (By "$\mathcal{M}$-function", we mean here always an admissible $\mathcal{M}$ function, i.e., one that satisfies our axioms.) Suppose we have chosen a particular function $\mathcal{M}'$ on $\mathscr{C}^{\text{mol}}$; then we shall decide to take on $\mathscr{C}$ that function $\mathcal{M}$ which is the unique extension of $\mathcal{M}'$. The principle underlying this decision is usually applied tacitly. We shall soon formulate it explicitly in a more general form as the methodological rule MR1.

C. EXTENSION OF $\mathcal{M}$ AND $\mathscr{C}$.

First let us define some terms that will be convenient for our discussions. (They correspond to the terms "almost L-true," "almost L-false," and "almost L-equivalent" for sentences, see [1950, D58-1].)

D20-2. The following definitions hold for any A, B in $\mathscr{C}$, any field $\mathscr{B}$ ($\mathscr{B} \subset \mathscr{C}$), with respect to a given $\mathcal{M}$-function.

    a. A is *almost empty* (or: almost impossible) $=_{\text{Df}} A \neq \varnothing$, but $\mathcal{M}(A) = 0$.

    b. A is *almost necessary* $=_{\text{Df}} -A$ is almost empty (hence $A \neq Z$, but $\mathcal{M}(A) = 1$).

c. A almost $\subset B =_{\text{DF}} A \cap -B$ is almost empty.

d. A almost $= B$ (or: A and B almost coincide) $=_{\text{Df}} A$ almost $\subset B$, and B almost $\subset A$.

e. $\mathscr{B}^{\text{poss}} =_{\text{Df}} \mathscr{B} - \{\varnothing\}$. ($\mathscr{B}^{\text{poss}}$ contains the possible (non-empty) propositions of $\mathscr{B}$.)

f. $\mathscr{B}^0 =_{\text{Df}}$ the class of the almost empty propositions in $\mathscr{B}$.

g. $\mathscr{B}^+ =_{\text{Df}} \mathscr{B}^{\text{poss}} - \mathscr{B}^0$. (The propositions in $\mathscr{B}$ with positive $\mathscr{M}$.)

If $\mathscr{M}$ is regular, the concepts defined in D2a, b, c, d, f do not, of course, apply to molecular propositions; they are of interest only after the extension of $\mathscr{M}$ to the σ-field $\mathscr{E}$.

We shall soon state two methodological rules in a general form, applicable to an unspecified language $\mathscr{L}$. First, we list here some assumptions and definitions to be used in the rules.

(20-3) **(a)** Let $\mathscr{L}$ be a language and Z a possibility space for $\mathscr{L}$.

    (b) Let $\mathscr{A}$ be a field of propositions on Z. (For our monadic predicate languages we think of $\mathscr{E}^{\text{mol}}$.)

    (c) Let AS be a system of axioms for $\mathscr{C}$-functions that have been accepted for $\mathscr{L}$. We assume that AS is consistent, and that it contains the basic axioms (A1 through A4, §1).

    (d) Assume that we have accepted a function $\mathscr{C}'$ on $\mathscr{A} \times \mathscr{A}^{\text{poss}}$, satisfying AS.

    (e) Let $\mathscr{M}'$ on $\mathscr{A}$ be related to $\mathscr{C}'$.

    (f) Let $\mathscr{D}$ the σ-field generated by $\mathscr{A}$. (For our languages, this is $\mathscr{E}$.)

Now we state a *methodological rule* for the *extension of $\mathscr{M}$-functions* in an arbitrary language $\mathscr{L}$.

MR20-1 We presuppose the assumptions and definitions in (3), and furthermore:

    (i) We consider a field $\mathscr{D}_*$ such that $\mathscr{A} \subset \mathscr{D}_* \subset \mathscr{D}$.

    (ii) We consider a function $\mathscr{M}_*$ on $\mathscr{D}_*$ such that $\mathscr{M}_*$ is an extension of $\mathscr{M}'$ and satisfies AS. If now we can show the following:

(*) $\mathscr{M}_*$ is the only extension of $\mathscr{M}'$ to $\mathscr{D}_*$ that satisfies AS,

then we shall decide to accept $\mathscr{M}_*$.

In accordance with this rule, in the case of our languages, where we have the axiom A8, we decide as follows (taking for $\mathcal{D}_*$ $\mathcal{D}$ itself, which is here $\mathscr{E}$).

(20-4) Whenever we have chosen a function $\mathcal{M}'$ on $\mathscr{E}^{\text{mol}}$, we shall accept for the σ-field $\mathscr{E}$ that function $\mathcal{M}$ which is (by T4e) the unique extension of $\mathcal{M}'$.

In view of A8, the decision just mentioned is almost trivial. We shall explain later that for certain other languages we shall not make $\mathcal{M}$ generally σ-additive. For such languages, MR1 becomes important.

So far we have discussed the extension of $\mathcal{M}$-functions to the σ-field. Now we turn to the problem of the extension of $\mathscr{C}$-functions. Here the problem situation is more complicated.

We shall now state *the second methodological rule*, which concerns *the extension of $\mathscr{C}$-functions* in an arbitrary language $\mathscr{L}$. (The rules MR1 and MR2 are similar to Reichenbach's "rule of existence" in [1949, §11].)

MR20-2. We presuppose, in addition to the assumptions and definitions in (3), the following ones:

> **(i)** Let $\mathcal{D}_*$ be a field such that $\mathcal{A} \subset \mathcal{D}_* \subset \mathcal{D}$.
>
> **(ii)** Suppose that we have accepted a function $\mathcal{M}_*$ on $\mathcal{D}_*$ such that $\mathcal{M}_*$ is an extension of $\mathcal{M}'$ and that $\mathcal{M}_*$ satisfies the system AS.
>
> **(iii)** $\mathcal{D}_*^{\text{poss}}$, $\mathcal{D}_*^{0}$, and $\mathcal{D}_*^{+}$ are defined as in D2e, f, g.
>
> **(iv)** We consider a class of pairs $\mathcal{G}_\Delta$ such that $(\mathcal{A} \times \mathcal{A}^{\text{poss}}) \subset \mathcal{G}_\Delta \subset (\mathcal{D}_* \times \mathcal{D}_*^{\text{poss}})$.
>
> **(v)** We consider a $\mathscr{C}$-function $\mathscr{C}_\Delta$ such that $\mathscr{C}_\Delta$ is an extension of $\mathscr{C}'$ to $\mathcal{G}_\Delta$, $\mathscr{C}_\Delta$ is related to the restriction of $\mathcal{M}_*$ to the propositions occurring in $\mathcal{G}_\Delta$, and $\mathscr{C}_\Delta$ satisfies AS.

If now the following can be shown:

(**) $\mathscr{C}_\Delta$ is the *only* $\mathscr{C}$-function that satisfies the conditions in (v), then the function $\mathscr{C}_\Delta$ shall be accepted.

We shall now develop a few consequences of MR2 for an arbitrary language $\mathscr{L}$. In T5 we shall deal with two general kinds of cases, and later in T6 with a more special situation.

T20-5. We presuppose the assumptions and definitions in (3) and in MR2, and further the following ones.

(i) We take as $\mathcal{D}_*$ the σ-field $\mathcal{D}$ itself.

(ii) Let $\mathcal{D}^{\text{poss}}$, $\mathcal{D}^0$, and $\mathcal{D}^+$ be defined as in D2e, f, g, with respect to $\mathcal{M}_*$.

(iii) We assume that a function $\mathcal{M}_*$ on $\mathcal{D}$ as in MR2(ii) has been accepted. (We do not presuppose here the condition (**) in MR2, nor σ-additivity.) ($\mathcal{M}_*$ may have been determined by MR2 or in any other way.)

   a. We take as $\mathcal{G}_\Delta$ the class of pairs $\mathcal{D} \times \mathcal{D}^+$. We take as $\mathcal{C}_\Delta$ the function $\mathcal{C}_*$ on $\mathcal{D} \times \mathcal{D}^+$, related to $\mathcal{M}_*$. Then, by MR2, we must accept $\mathcal{C}_*$.

Proof. For every pair H, E in $\mathcal{G}_\Delta$, $\mathcal{M}_*(E) > 0$. Therefore, $\mathcal{C}_*(H \mid E) = \mathcal{M}_*(E \cap H)/\mathcal{M}_*(E)$. Thus $\mathcal{C}_*$ is uniquely determined by $\mathcal{M}_*$. Hence, since $\mathcal{M}_*$ has been accepted, $\mathcal{C}_*$ must be accepted. ∎

   b. Let $\mathcal{G}_\Delta$ and $\mathcal{C}_*$ be as in (a). If $\mathcal{M}_*$ is σ-additive, then, for any given E in $\mathcal{D}^+$, the function $\mathcal{C}_*(\cdot \mid E)$ is a σ-additive measure function.

Proof. Let $\mathcal{B} = \{B_1, B_2, \ldots\}$ with $\mathcal{B} \subset \mathcal{D}$, be a denumerable disjoint sequence. Let $B =_{\text{Df}} \bigcup \mathcal{B}$. Then, for any E in $\mathcal{D}^+$, $\mathcal{C}_*(B \mid E).\mathcal{M}_*(E) =$

$$\mathcal{M}_*(E \cap B) = \mathcal{M}_*(E \cap \bigcup_{n=1}^{\infty} B_n) = \mathcal{M}_* \bigcup_{n=1}^{\infty} (E \cap B_n) = \sum_{n=1}^{\infty} \mathcal{M}_*(E \cap B_n).$$

Hence $\mathcal{C}_*(B \mid E) = [\sum_{n=1}^{\infty} \mathcal{M}_*(E \cap B_n)]/\mathcal{M}_*(E) = \sum_{n=1}^{\infty} \mathcal{C}_*(B_n \mid E)$. ∎

[We shall see later (remark on T6r below) that the condition in (b), which requires that $E \in \mathcal{D}^+$, i.e., that $\mathcal{M}_*(E) > 0$, is essential.]

   c. We define: $\mathcal{G}_\Delta =_{\text{Df}} (\mathcal{A} \times \mathcal{A}^{\text{poss}}) \cup \{E, E: E \in \mathcal{D}^{\text{poss}}\}$. Let $\mathcal{C}_\Delta$ coincide with $\mathcal{C}'$ on $\mathcal{A} \times \mathcal{A}^{\text{poss}}$ and have the value 1 for the identity pairs in $\mathcal{D}^{\text{poss}}$. Then MR2 prescribes the acceptance of $\mathcal{C}_\Delta$.

Proof. The value 1 for the identity pairs is required by the basic axioms (in our system, axiom A2 in §1). ∎

[Note that by MR2 the value 1 is mandatory even for the identity pair of any almost empty proposition, although in this case the value of $\mathcal{C}_\Delta$ is not determined by $\mathcal{M}_*$.]

T20-6. We presuppose the assumptions and definitions in (3) and in MR2, and the following ones. (For an example of a sequence $\mathcal{B}$

satisfying the conditions here specified, see (5) below.)

(i) $\mathscr{B} = \{H_1, H_2, \ldots\}$ is a denumerable sequence; $\mathscr{B} \subset \mathscr{D}^{\text{poss}}$, hence any $H_i \neq \varnothing$.

(ii) $\mathscr{B}$ is disjoint.

(iii) For any $m > 0$, $B_m =_{\text{Df}} \bigcup_{n=1}^{m} H_n$.

(iv) $B =_{\text{Df}} \bigcup \mathscr{B}$.

(v) We take as $\mathscr{D}_*$ the σ-field $\mathscr{D}$. Let $\mathscr{D}^{\text{poss}}$, $\mathscr{D}^0$, and $\mathscr{D}^+$ be as in T5(ii).

(vi) $\mathscr{G}_1 =_{\text{Df}} \{H_n, B_m : m > 1, 0 < n \leq m\}$.

(vii) $\mathscr{G}_2 =_{\text{Df}} \{H_n, B : n > 0\}$.

(viii) $\mathscr{G}_3 =_{\text{Df}} \{B_m, B : m > 0\}$.

(ix) As $\mathscr{G}_\Delta$ we take $\mathscr{G}_1 \cup \mathscr{G}_2 \cup \mathscr{G}_3$.

(x) We assume that AS contains the basic axioms, the axiom of symmetry with respect to individuals, and the axiom of σ-additivity for $\mathcal{M}$-functions.

(xi) We assume that a function $\mathcal{M}_*$ on $\mathscr{D}$ as in MR2(ii) has been accepted.

(xii) Let $\mathscr{C}_\Delta$ be any $\mathscr{C}$-function satisfying the conditions in MR2(v).

(xiii) We assume isomorphy (D9-2d) in the following cases:

(1) for any n, between H_n and H_1;

(2) for any $m > 1$, and any $n \leq m$, between the pair H_1, B_m and the pair H_n, B_m.

(3) for any n, between H_1, B and H_n, B.

Then the following holds.

   a. $\mathcal{M}_*$ is symmetric (by (x)), and hence has equal values for isomorphic propositions.

   b. Let $b =_{\text{Df}} \mathcal{M}_*(H_1)$. Then, for any $n > 0$, $\mathcal{M}_*(H_n) = b$. (From (a), (xiii)(1).)

   c. For any $m > 0$, $\mathcal{M}_*(B_m) = \sum_{n=1}^{m} \mathcal{M}_*(H_n) = mb$. (From (iii), (ii), (b).)

   d. $\mathcal{M}_*$ is σ-additive. (From (x).)

   e. $\mathcal{M}_*(B) = \sum_{n=1}^{\infty} \mathcal{M}_*(H_n)$, (from (d) and (ii)),

   $\qquad = \lim_{m} \mathcal{M}_*(B_m)$, (from (c)),

   $\qquad = \lim_{m} mb$ (from (c)).

   f. For any n, $\mathcal{M}_*(H_n) = b = 0$.

Proof. If b were positive, then by (e) $\mathcal{M}_*(B)$ would be infinite. Hence the assertion from (b). ■

g. For any $m > 0$, $\mathcal{M}_*(B_m) = 0$. (From (c) and (f).)

h. $\mathcal{M}_*(B) = 0$. (From (e) and (g).)

i. $\mathcal{C}_\Delta$ is symmetric (by (x)), and hence it has equal values for isomorphic pairs of propositions.

j. For any $m > 0$, and any $n \leqq m$, $\mathcal{C}_\Delta(H_1 \mid B_m) = \mathcal{C}_\Delta(H_n \mid B_m)$. (From (i) and (xiii)(2).)

k. For any $m > 0$, and any $n \leqq m$, $\mathcal{C}(H_n \mid B_m) = 1/m$.

Proof. By (i) and (iii), $B_m \neq \varnothing$. Hence by T5c, $\mathcal{C}_\Delta(B_m \mid B_m) = 1$. Thus by (iii) and (ii), $\sum_{n=1}^{m} \mathcal{C}(H_n \mid B_m) = 1$. Hence the assertion by (j). ■

l. $\mathcal{C}_\Delta(B \mid B) = 1$. (From T5c.)

m. For any $n > 1$, $\mathcal{C}_\Delta(H_1 \mid B) = \mathcal{C}_\Delta(H_n \mid B)$. (From (j) and (xiii)(3).)

n. Let $c =_{\mathrm{Df}} \mathcal{C}_\Delta(H_1 \mid B)$. Then $\mathcal{C}_\Delta(B_m \mid B) = mc$.

Proof. From (iii) and (ii), $\mathcal{C}_\Delta(B_m \mid B) = \sum_{n=1}^{m} \mathcal{C}_\Delta(H_n \mid B)$. Hence the assertion by (m). ■

o. For c as in (n), $c = 0$.

Proof. For an indirect proof, let us assume that $c > 0$. Hence $1/c$ is finite, and hence there is an integer m' such that $m' > 1/c$ and thus $m'c > 1$. Then by (n) $\mathcal{C}_\Delta(B_{m'} \mid B = m'c > 1$. But this is impossible. Therefore $c \ngtr 0$, hence $c = 0$. ■

p. For any $n > 0$, $\mathcal{C}_\Delta(H_n \mid B) = 0$. (From (m) and (o).)

q. For any $m > 0$, $\mathcal{C}_\Delta(B_m \mid B) = 0$, (From (n) and (o).)

r. For a given B, the function $\mathcal{C}_\Delta(\cdot \mid B)$ is not σ-additive.

Proof. If this function were σ-additive, we should have:

$$\mathcal{C}_\Delta\left(\bigcup_{n=1}^{\infty} H_n \mid B\right) = \lim_m \mathcal{C}_\Delta\left(\bigcup_{n=1}^{m} H_n \mid B\right) = \lim_m \mathcal{C}_\Delta(B_m \mid B) = 0$$

(by (q)). However, the first-mentioned $\mathcal{C}_\Delta$-value is $\mathcal{C}_\Delta(B \mid B) = 1$ (by (l)). ■

s. Under the conditions here assumed, MR2 prescribes the acceptance of the function $\mathcal{C}_\Delta$, with its values for $\mathcal{G}_1$ determined by (k), those for $\mathcal{G}_2$ by (p), and those for $\mathcal{G}_3$ by (q).

Proof. We have shown that any admissible extension of $\mathscr{C}'$ to $\mathscr{G}$ has the values stated for $\mathscr{C}_\Delta$ in (k), (p), and (q). Thus the function $\mathscr{C}_\Delta$ with these values is the only admissible extension of $\mathscr{C}'$ to $\mathscr{G}$. Therefore, by MR2, $\mathscr{C}_\Delta$ must be accepted. ∎

[Note that T6r shows that T5b would not be valid without the condition that E is in $\mathscr{D}^+$, i.e., $\mathscr{M}_*(E) > D$.]

The following example is intended to illustrate the situation assumed in the above theorem T6.

(20-5) Example. Let $\mathscr{L}$ be a language with one family of attributes. We define:

    (i) For any $n > 0$, $H_n =_{\mathrm{Df}} A_n^1 \cap \bigcap_{i \neq n} -A_i^1$(where i runs through all positive integers except n; A_i^1 is the atomic proposition $P_1(a_i)$; H_n says that a_n is the only individual with attribute P_1.)

    (ii) For any $m > 0$, $B_m =_{\mathrm{Df}} \bigcup_{n=1}^{m} H_n$. ($B_m$ says that one of the first m individuals is the only one with P_1.)

    (iii) $B =_{\mathrm{Df}} \bigcup_{n=1}^{\infty} H_n$. ($B$ says that there is exactly one individual with P_1.)

For most of the assumptions in T6 it is easily seen that they are satisfied in the example (5). We shall show it here only for the assumptions (xiii) about isomorphy.

(20-6) For the propositions defined in (5), the following holds.
    (a) For any n, H_1 is isomorphic to H_n.

Proof. For any n, let the permutation π_n be defined as the transposition $(1, n)$. Then, for any n, $\pi_n''(H_n) = H_1$. Hence the assertion.

    (b) For any $m > 1$, and any $n \leqq m$, the pair H_1, B_m is isomorphic to H_n, B_m.

Proof. With π_n as above, $\pi_n''(B_m) = B_m$.

    (c) For any n, the pair H_1, B is isomorphic to H_n, B.

Proof. $\pi_n''(B) = B$.

(d) The propositions defined in the example (5) satisfy the assumptions (1), (2), and (3) under (xiii) in T6. (From (a), (b), and (c), respectively.)

Those who have a strong preference for σ-additivity, would perhaps be inclined to accept the following general requirement, in contrast to the result T6r in our system:

(20-7)   For any E in $\mathscr{E}^{\text{poss}}$, the function $\mathscr{C}(\cdot \mid E)$ with fixed E is σ-additive.

This can easily be accomplished by stating as an axiom the modification (7') of (7), with '$\mathscr{E}^0$' in lieu of '$\mathscr{E}^{\text{poss}}$'. This would be sufficient because, for any E in $\mathscr{E}^+$, (7) is provable (T5b). If someone accepts an axiom system AS' which includes (7) (or (7')), he may still keep rule MR2. AS' is not incompatible with MR2, but has merely the effect of making MR2 inapplicable to certain pairs H, E with E in $\mathscr{E}^0$, because for these pairs $\mathscr{C}_\Delta$ does not satisfy AS', which is required in MR2(v). There is no $\mathscr{C}$-value for the pair H_n, B that would be compatible with AS'. To sum up, we have only the choice between the following alternatives:

(20-8)   (a) Suppose that we accept (7) (the σ-additivity of $\mathscr{C}$). Then we cannot assign any value to $\mathscr{C}(H_n \mid B)$.
   (b) Suppose we accept an axiom system containing the basic axioms and symmetry, but not implying (7). Then there are two possibilities.
     (1) If we accept MR2, we must accept $\mathscr{C}(H_n \mid B) = 0$.
     (2) If we do not accept MR2 (or an equivalent rule), we are free to assign to $\mathscr{C}(H_n \mid B)$ either no value or the value 0.

Thus the situation with respect to possible system forms is quite clear. And from a purely theoretical point of view, there is no objection against the no-value-decision (8)(a). From a practical point of view it seems an advantage to have additional $\mathscr{C}$-values, unless they appear as unnatural. Judgments on intuitive naturalness are notoriously subjective. However, if the advocates of σ-additivity for $\mathscr{C}$ regard the $\mathscr{C}$-values resulting in the case (8)(b)(1) as unnatural, then I would offer the following considerations as arguments, admittedly subjective, for their naturalness. For comparison, let us first consider the following results for $m = 5$:

(20-9)   (a) $\mathscr{C}\left(\bigcup_{n=1}^{5} H_n \mid B_5 \right) = 1$;
   (b) For every n $(0 < n \leqq 5)$, $\mathscr{C}(H_n \mid B_5) = 1/5$.

Here, (a) is unquestionable; it follows from the basic axioms (the union mentioned is B_5 itself). Then (b) seems natural in this way: the five $\mathscr{C}$-values must be equal; their sum is 1; hence each is 1/5. In order to show that the reasoning in the infinite case is analogous to the finite case with $m = 5$, let us use the extended real number system, including the improper real numbers ∞ and $-\infty$. Here, of course, we have to be careful to use the symbol '∞' only within well-formed expressions; we should avoid indefinite expressions, i.e., those which do not have a unique value. [Strictly speaking, they should be treated as not-well-formed, that is, they should be excluded by suitable rules of formation, e.g., '∞^0' and '∞/∞', and also '0/0', although it does not contain '∞'.]

In the infinite case, let us now write 'B_∞' (instead of the earlier 'B') for the denumerable union $\bigcup_{n=1}^{\infty} H_n$, because it is the counterpart of B_m for $m = \infty$. The values in question are (T61 and p):

(20-10)   **(a)** $\mathscr{C}\left(\bigcup_{n=1}^{\infty} H_n \mid B_\infty\right) = 1.$

   (b) For every n $(n = 1, 2, \ldots)$, $\mathscr{C}(H_n \mid B_\infty) = 1/\infty = 0.$

This case is perfectly analogous to that in (9). But here the number of the propositions H_n is not $m = 5$, but $m = \infty$. The result (a) is again unquestionable, since the denumerable union is the same as B_∞. The $\mathscr{C}$-values for the propositions H_n in (b) must again be equal, because of symmetry; and their sum is 1. Therefore, assuming the expression '$1/\infty$' to be well-formed, each of these $\mathscr{C}$-values must be $1/\infty$. It seems to me entirely natural to evaluate this expression as $\lim_m 1/m$, hence as 0. I do not see any reason at all for regarding the expression '$1/\infty$' as ambiguous or as having no meaning and hence no value. [To be sure, we have then also $2/\infty = 0$, $3/\infty = 0$, etc., and likewise $0/\infty = 0$. But this shows merely that the inverse operation has no unique result, and therefore the expression '$\infty \cdot 0$' must indeed be regarded as indefinite. But these results do not argue against the acceptance of '$1/\infty$' as definite.] And some well-known books give indeed among the formulas for the extended real number system this:

For any (finite) real number x, $x/\infty = 0$. (Halmos [1950, p. 1], Munroe [1953, p. 8].)

For our predicate-languages (with finite families) we accepted σ-activity for $\mathcal{M}$. But then we found that, for certain almost empty propositions E, the measure function $\mathscr{C}(\cdot \mid E)$ (with E fixed) is inevitably non-σ-additive, unless we abstain from assigning $\mathscr{C}$-values to pairs of propositions of this kind.

For other languages we shall likewise usually accept σ-additivity for $\mathscr{M}$, unless there are strong reasons against it. For the formal procedure, σ-additivity has certainly great advantages, especially the uniqueness of the extension of $\mathscr{M}$ to the σ-field.

However, in the case of certain languages it seems necessary to give up σ-additivity for $\mathscr{M}$, if we wish $\mathscr{M}$ to have values on the whole σ-field. A general kind of situation in which this would hold is as follows.

T20-7. We presuppose the assumptions and definitions in (3), and (i) through (v) as in T6 (but with $\mathscr{M}$ instead of $\mathscr{M}'$ and $\mathscr{M}_*$); and further:

(vi $\mathscr{M}(B) > 0$.

(vii) It is assumed that, on the basis of AS, for any $n > 0$,

$$\mathscr{M}(H_n) = \mathscr{M}(H_1) = b.$$

Then the following holds.
a. For any $m > 0$, $\mathscr{M}(B_m) = mb$. (As in T6c.)
b. For any $n > 0$, $\mathscr{M}(H_n) = b = 0$.

Proof. Suppose that $b > 0$. Then $1/b$ is finite. Hence there is an m' such that $m' > 1/b$, and thus, by (a), $\mathscr{M}(B_{m'}) = m'b > 1$, which is impossible (for normalized $\mathscr{M}$). ∎

c. For any $m > 0$, $\mathscr{M}(B_m) = 0$. (From (a) and (b).)
d. $\mathscr{M}$ is not σ-additive.

Proof. Suppose that $\mathscr{M}$ were σ-additive. Then we should have: $\mathscr{M}(B) = \lim_m \mathscr{M}(B_m) = 0$, in contradiction to (vi). ∎

Thus we see that, in a language $\mathscr{L}$, $\mathscr{M}$ cannot be σ-additive, if there is a proposition B with an $\mathscr{M}$-value $d > 0$, and a denumerable partition of B whose parts have all the same $\mathscr{M}$-value b. Here we have $b = d/\infty = 0$. We shall now give *two examples* of this kind. The first one is somewhat similar to (5), but the roles of the individuals and the attributes in (5) are here interchanged.

(20-11) Example. Let $\mathscr{L}$ contain one family F, with a denumerable number of attributes of equal widths. For a fixed individual a_1, let H_n be the atomic proposition A_1^n saying that a_1 has attribute P_n $(n = 1, 2, \ldots)$. Since every individual has exactly one attribute, the propositions $H_1, H_2, \ldots$ are disjoint, and their union B is necessary. Hence $\mathcal{M}(B) = 1$. Because of the equality of the widths, the values $\mathcal{M}(H_n)$ $(n = 1, 2, \ldots)$ are equal; thus each of them is $1/\infty = 0$.

We shall not easily find a situation of the kind described in (11) in the field of *qualitative* attributes like colors or pitches of sounds. In cases of this kind we usually assume that the attribute space is finite and the attribute regions have positive width. Under this assumption, in the case of a denumerable family, the widths must be unequal. But a numerical value space, in contrast to a qualitative attribute space, may have infinite volume; and here a denumerable partition with equal widths may occur.

Our further discussion will concern a language $\mathcal{L}$ with a real-valued basic function ψ_1 (§3). We assume that its value-space is R^1 (the set of all real numbers). Let $\mathcal{B}$ be the class of the Borel sets ($\mathcal{B}$ can be defined as the σ-field generated by the class of all rational intervals in $\mathbf{R}$). We define (for the present discussion only):

(20-12)   For any $A \in \mathcal{B}$,

$$*A =_{\mathrm{Df}} \{Z : Z(1) \in A\}.$$

Thus $*A$ is the proposition that $\psi_1(a_1) \in A$. Therefore $*\mathbf{R} = \mathbf{Z}$; and hence $\mathcal{M}(*\mathbf{R}) = 1$.

(20-13) Example   of a non-σ-additive $\mathcal{M}$-function.
    (i) For any integer $n(\leqq 0)$, let $D_n =_{\mathrm{Df}} [n, n+1)$, and $H_n =_{\mathrm{Df}} *D_n$.

Thus H_n is the proposition that $n \leq \psi(a_1) < n+1$. Since the class of all D_n is a denumerable partition of $\mathbf{R}$ with parts of equal width, it seems natural to assume:

    (ii) For any n, $\mathcal{M}(H_n) = \mathcal{M}(H_0)$.

Then we have:

    (iii) For any n, $\mathcal{M}(H_n) = 0$. (As in T7b.)

Hence:

    (iv) $\mathcal{M}$ is *not σ-additive*.

Several authors have expressed doubts about a *general* requirement of σ-additivity for probability functions. B. O. Koopman thinks that "complete additivity is not a general property but holds only in some important special cases, due to physical circumstances rather than to the logical aspect of probability" [1940b, p. 770]. Savage [1954, pp. 40–43] admits the great convenience of the assumption of σ-additivity in certain situations, but points out that it must be rejected in other situations, e.g., when a uniform probability density is assumed for a denumerable or continuous space. He refers to De Finetti who has shown in a detailed discussion of various situations [1949] that σ-additivity can be assumed only in particular situations (classes of events), while in others it is impossible. I. G. Good lists an axiom of σ-additivity as "optional" [1962, p. 324].

For our present language with ψ_1 (and likewise for a language with a denumerable family as in (11)), there is an alternative solution using a non-normalized $\mathcal{M}$-function, i.e., a function $\mathcal{M}'$ such that $\mathcal{M}'(\mathbf{Z})$ is not 1 (but still positive, and sometimes even infinite). From the point of view of our system, there is no objection in principle against such a function, since the $\mathcal{M}$-functions are here regarded merely as auxiliary concepts, while the $\mathcal{C}$-functions are basic. In view of the interpretations of the $\mathcal{C}$-functions, e.g., as yielding fair betting quotients or estimates of relative frequency, it seems usually preferable to require normalization for them; i.e., for any nonempty $A \in \mathcal{D}$, $\mathcal{C}(A \mid A) = 1$. So far, at least, I have not found any occasion where a nonnormalized $\mathcal{C}$-function seemed useful. If now $\mathcal{C}$ is normalized, and $\mathcal{M}$ is defined in the usual way, then obviously $\mathcal{M}$ is normalized too. Therefore a nonnormalized $\mathcal{M}$-function cannot be defined in this way; it must be introduced independently of $\mathcal{C}$. Nevertheless, even if $\mathcal{M}$ is nonnormalized, it may be related to $\mathcal{C}$, i.e., we may have:

(20-14)   For any pair H, E in $\mathcal{D} \times \mathcal{D}^{\text{poss}}$,

$$\mathcal{M}(E \cap H) = \mathcal{M}(E)\mathcal{C}(H \mid E).$$

In this case the following holds:

(20-15)   For any H, E in $\mathcal{D} \times \mathcal{D}^{\text{poss}}$, if $\mathcal{M}(E) > 0$ and $\mathcal{M}(E \cap H) < \infty$, then $\mathcal{C}(H \mid E) = \mathcal{M}(E \cap H)/\mathcal{M}(E)$.

For any propositions H, E that fulfill the conditions stated, (15) determines a $\mathcal{C}$-value in the interval $[0, 1]$. This holds even if $\mathcal{M}(E) = \infty$ or $\mathcal{M}(E \cap H) = 0$ or both; in these cases $\mathcal{C} = 0$.

If a proposition A and a function $\mathcal{M}$ are such that $\mathcal{M}(A)$ is positive and finite, we shall say that $\mathcal{M}$ and A are *appropriate* for each other. If $\mathcal{M}(A) = 0$ and $\mathcal{M}(B) = \infty$ (with a nonnormalized $\mathcal{M}$), we shall say that A is *too small* and B is *too large* for $\mathcal{M}$.

In this discussion we use the symbol 'μ' (also with a subscript and a prime) to denote a *measure function on Borel sets* in $\mathbf{R}$ which fulfills the customary axioms (except that neither σ-additivity nor normalization is required), and is furthermore invariant under any translation in $\mathbf{R}$ and under any reflection at a fixed point. We define:

(20-16) The function $\mathcal{M}$ is *based upon* the measure function $\mu =_{\text{Df}}$ for any Borel set $A \subset \mathbf{R}$, $\mathcal{M}(*A) = \mu(A)$. (For '$*A$' see (12).)

Thus we may, in the case of starred propositions, represent the $\mathcal{C}$-value directly in terms of μ (from (15)):

(20-17) For any Borel sets A and B, if $\mu(A) > 0$ and $\mu(A \cap B) < \infty$, then $\mathcal{C}(*B \mid *A) = \mu(A \cap B)/\mu(A)$.

If, for a Borel set A, $\mu(A)$ is positive and finite, we shall say that μ and A are *appropriate* for each other. (Then $\mathcal{M}$ and $*A$ are appropriate for each other.) If $\mu(A) = 0$ and $\mu(B) = \infty$, we shall say that A is *too small* and B is *too large* for μ. (Then $*A$ is too small and $*B$ is too large for $\mathcal{M}$.)

Consider a Borel set $A_0 \subset [0, b)$ $(b > 0)$. We assume that $\mu(A_0) = a$ and $0 < a < \infty$. Thus μ is appropriate for the bounded set A_0. We may say that the mean μ-density of A_0 within the interval $[0, b)$ is a/b. For any integer $i(\lesseqgtr 0)$, let A_i be the image of A_0 through a translation by ib; then $A_i \subset [ib, (i+1)b)$. Let A be the union of all these sets A_i. Then A has the mean μ-density a/b in any interval of length b, and hence in the whole of $\mathbf{R}$. A is too large for μ. We can define a measure function μ' appropriate for A in the following way:

(20-18) For any function μ, let μ' be defined as follows: For any Borel set B,

$$\mu'(B) =_{\text{Df}} \lim_n \left[\frac{1}{2n} \mu(B^{(n)}) \right],$$

where $B^{(n)} = B \cap [-n, n]$. Then we call the function μ' *the overall mean μ-density*.

In the above example $\mu'(A) = a/b$. This set A was a special case, with the same mean μ-density in any interval of length b. But in general, for an arbitrary Borel set B, $\frac{1}{2n} \mu(B^{(n)})$ is the mean μ-density in the interval $[-n, n]$; therefore we may regard the limit as the μ-density of B in the whole of $\mathbf{R}$.

We shall now consider a few examples of μ-functions; we shall see that each of the $\mathcal{M}$-functions based upon them yields a partial definition of $\mathscr{C}$. For each of our first three μ-functions we state one example:

(20-19)   **(a)** $\mu_1([0, 1)) = 1$.
       (b) $\mu_2([0, 1) \cap \text{Rat}) = 1$.
       (c) $\mu_3(\{0\}) = 1$.

According to our characterization of μ-functions (preceding (16)), each of these three μ-functions is hereby uniquely determined. μ_1 is the Lebesgue measure function; for any interval of any length l, it has the value l. μ_2 is analogous to Lebesgue measure. It has the value l for the set of all rational numbers of $[0, l)$ or of any other interval of length l, but also for the set obtained from any of these sets through a translation by an irrational number. μ_3 has the value n for any finite set of n numbers.

Now we introduce three more functions: μ_1', μ_2', and μ_3':

(20-20)   For $i = 1, 2, 3$, μ_1' is defined as the overall mean μ_i-density (18). Then $\mu_1'(\mathbf{R}) = 1$; for any real number x, $\mu_1'((-\infty, x]) = \mu_1'([x, \infty)) = 1/2$. Similarly, $\mu_2'(\text{Rat}) = 1$. Let $A_{a,b} = \{a + bn : n = 0, 1, 2, \ldots ; -1, -2, \ldots\}$. Then $\mu_3'(A_{a,b}) = 1/b$; hence for the set of all integers I, $\mu_3'(I) = 1$.

Let us order the six functions in this way:

$$\mu_1', \mu_1, \mu_2', \mu_2, \mu_3', \mu_3.$$

Then, if a given Borel set A is appropriate for one of these functions, say μ, then A is too small for each function preceding μ in the given sequence, and too large for each function following μ.

(20-21)   **(a)** The Lebesgue measure μ_1, is known to be σ-additive; μ_2 and μ_3 are likewise.
       (b) μ_1' is not σ-additive, since its value is 0 for each unit interval $[i, i+1)$, but 1 for $\mathbf{R}$. Similarly, μ_2' and μ_3' are not σ-additive.

Now we define the corresponding $\mathcal{M}$-functions:

(20-22)   For $i = 1, 2, 3$, let $\mathcal{M}_i$ be based upon μ_i (16), and $\mathcal{M}_i'$ upon μ_i'.

Then we have from (21):

(20-23)   **(a)** $\mathscr{M}_1$, $\mathscr{M}_2$, and $\mathscr{M}_3$ are σ-additive.
    (b) $\mathscr{M}_1'$, $\mathscr{M}_2'$, and $\mathscr{M}_3'$ are not σ-additive.

Now let us consider the determination of $\mathscr{C}$-values. If μ is one of our six functions, and A and B are such that $\mu(A) > 0$ and $\mu(A \cap B) < \infty$, then $\mathscr{C}(*B \mid *A)$ is determined by (17). (This holds even if $\mu(A) = \infty$ or $\mu(A \cap B) = 0$ or both; in these cases $\mathscr{C} = 0$.) And we see easily that $0 \leqq \mathscr{C}(*B \mid *A) \leqq 1$. Thus $\mathscr{C}$, as far as its values are determined by (17), is normalized, although our μ-functions (with the sole exception of μ_1', because $\mu_1'(\mathbf{R}) = 1$) are not normalized, since they are infinite for $\mathbf{R}$.

No Borel set is appropriate for more than one of our six μ-functions. But those appropriate for one of them constitute merely an arbitrary selection from $\mathscr{B}$. Obviously, no Borel set is too large for μ_1', and no nonempty one is too small for μ_3. But between any two consecutive functions of the series other μ-functions are needed, and indeed an infinite number of them. This holds even in the three gaps between μ_1' and μ_i ($i = 1$, 2, 3), although the appropriate sets of μ_1' seem rather close in measure to those of μ_i. For example, even the largest set appropriate for μ_1', viz. $\mathbf{R}$, although certainly too large for μ_1, is still merely a denumerable union of sets appropriate for μ_1 (in the usual terminology: μ_1 is at $\mathbf{R}$ infinite, but σ-finite, see Halmos [1950, p. 31]).

(20-24)   Let μ be any μ-function. Let A and B be such that, for any n, $\mu(A \cap B)^{(n)} < \infty$ and for any sufficiently large n, $\mu(A^{(n)}) > 0$. Then we may apply the following partial definition of $\mathscr{C}$:

$$\mathscr{C}(*B \mid *A) =_{\mathrm{Df}} \lim_n \frac{\mu(A \cap B)^{(n)}}{\mu(A^{(n)})}.$$

Let us consider now the results that can be obtained by this definition.

(20-25)   If μ, A and B satisfy the conditions stated, the definition in (24) yields $\mathscr{C}$-values for the following three kinds of pairs B, A:
      (i) The first kind contains the pairs B, A such that $\mu[A \cap B] < \infty$ and $\mu(A) > 0$. For these pairs, (24) provides the same $\mathscr{C}$-values as (17).
      (ii) The second kind contains the pairs B, A such that, for the function μ' defined on the basis of μ by (18),

$\mu'(A \cap B) < \infty$ and $\mu'(A) > 0$. In these cases (24) yields the same $\mathscr{C}$-values as the application of (17) to μ'.

(iii) The third kind contains those pairs B, A, for which, in contrast to (i), $\mu(A \cap B) = \infty$ (and hence $\mu(A) = \infty$), and further, in contrast to (ii), $\mu'(A) = 0$; but $\mu(A^{(n)})$ is finite for every n, and is positive for at least some n.

We shall now consider a case of the third kind.

(20-26) Example. Let μ be a σ-additive μ-function appropriate for certain bounded infinite sets (e.g., μ_1, or μ_2). We assume that both A and $A \cap B$ are unbounded Borel sets and that, for any sufficiently large n (say $n > a + 3$), μ has the following values, with constants a $(0 < a < \infty)$ and b $(0 < b \leq 1)$:

(i) $$\mu(A^{(n)}) = \sqrt{n} + a,$$

(ii) $$\mu(A \cap B)^{(n)} = b\sqrt{n} + a.$$

We wish to determine $\mathscr{C}(*A \mid *B)$. Since μ is σ-additive, we have:

(iii) $$\mu(A) = \lim_n \mu(A^{(n)}) = \infty,$$

(iv) $$\mu(A \cap B) = \lim_n \mu(A \cap B)^{(n)} = \infty.$$

Thus $\mathscr{C}$ cannot be determined by (17). If μ' is defined in terms of μ as in (18), we have from (i):

(v) $$\mu'(A) = \lim_n \left[\frac{1}{2n} (\sqrt{n} + a) \right] = 0.$$

Hence also:

(vi) $$\mu'(A \cap B) = 0.$$

Thus the $\mathscr{C}$-value cannot be determined by applying (17) to μ'. The direct application of (17) either to μ or to μ' fails because A (and likewise $A \cap B$) is too large for μ and too small for μ'. But (24) is applicable:

(vii) $\mathscr{C}(*B \mid *A) = \lim_n \dfrac{\mu(A \cap B)^{(n)}}{\mu[A^{(n)})},$

$$= \lim_n \frac{b\sqrt{n}+a}{\sqrt{n}+a} = b.$$

The use of (24) has the advantage that we need not use those μ-functions which are defined by (18). Thus, of our six example functions, we need only use μ_1, μ_2, and μ_3. In general terms, we may restrict our attention to those μ-functions that are appropriate to (among others) bounded Borel sets (for any μ of this kind, $\mu(\mathbf{R}) = \infty$, and thus μ is nonnormalized); and of these functions, we need only their restrictions to bounded sets.

If a pair A, B is given and we wish to determine $\mathscr{C}[*B \mid *A)$, then we have to search for a function μ which fulfills one of the following two conditions:

either (1) μ is appropriate for A, or (2) $\mu(A) = \infty$ while $\mu(A^{(n)})$ is finite for every n and positive for some n.

In case (1), the $\mathscr{C}$-value is determined by (17), in case (2) by (24).

We return now to monadic predicate languages. Our problem is the extension of $\mathscr{C}$. As we have seen, the extension of $\mathscr{M}$ to the σ-field $\mathscr{E}$ determines a unique extension of $\mathscr{C}$ to $\mathscr{E} \times \mathscr{E}^+$. There remains the problem of an extension of $\mathscr{C}$ to $\mathscr{E} \times \mathscr{E}^0$, i.e., to pairs H, E where E is almost empty. I shall briefly indicate two ways for finding partial definitions of $\mathscr{C}$ for such pairs. *The finite way* consists in trying to find a new function $\mathscr{M}'$ which, in contrast to $\mathscr{M}$, is positive for some propositions in $\mathscr{E}^0$. Suppose that $\mathscr{M}'(A) > 0$, for some $A \in \mathscr{E}^0$. Now our original function $\mathscr{M}$ was normalized, that is, $\mathscr{M}(Z) = 1$, and we have $\mathscr{M}(A) = 0$. Thus A is, in some sense, infinitely small in comparison to Z. Hence, since $\mathscr{M}'(A) > 0$, we may expect to find $\mathscr{M}'(Z) = \infty$; hence $\mathscr{M}'$ will be nonnormalized. Thus this way is analogous to the use of nonnormalized functions μ and $\mathscr{M}$ in our earlier discussion of a language with Ψ_1. Then, for any pair H, E such that $\mathscr{M}'(E) > 0$ and $\mathscr{M}'(E \cap H) < \infty$, we can define $\mathscr{C}(H \mid E)$ on the basis of $\mathscr{M}'$ by (15).

The second way does not make use of an $\mathscr{M}$-function but defines $\mathscr{C}(H \mid E)$, where $E \in \mathscr{E}^0$, in terms of other $\mathscr{C}$-values $\mathscr{C}(H \mid E')$ where $E' \in \mathscr{E}^+$. Here we try to find a rule which assigns to each proposition A of a kind of almost empty propositions in which we are interested, a denumerable sequence $\{A_{(p)}\}(p = 1, 2, \dots)$ such that the following three conditions are fulfilled:

(20-27)   **(a)** $\lim_p A_{(p)} = A$; i.e., the sequence converges toward A.
   (b) If $A = \varnothing$, every $A_p = \varnothing$.
   (c) If $A \neq \varnothing$, then the members of the sequence—or at least an infinite number of them—belong to $\mathscr{E}^+$.

Then, if the rule is applicable to E, we define:

(20-28) $\mathscr{C}(H \mid E) =_{\mathrm{Df}} \lim_p \mathscr{C}(H \mid E_{(p)})$. (Here p runs only through those positive integers for which $E_{(p)} \in \mathscr{E}^+$.) (We could also take $H_{(p)}$ instead of H; in some cases this will be simpler.)

Here is an example of a rule of this kind:

(20-29)   For any proposition A,

$$A_{(p)} =_{\mathrm{Df}} \{z: \text{ for some } z' \in A, \text{ for every } i \in \mathbf{N}_p, z(i) = z'(i)\}.$$

Thus $A_{(p)}$ contains just those models which agree on $\mathbf{N}_p$ with some model in A; in other words, $A_{(p)}$ is the union of the cylinder sets based upon the submodels (§6) for $\mathbf{N}_p$ of all models in A. Therefore, for any p, $A_{(p)} \in \mathscr{E}^{\mathrm{mol}}$; and if A is non-empty, $A_{(p)}$ is non-empty and belongs, in virtue of regularity, to $\mathscr{E}^+$.

Another rule is the following:

(20-30)   If A is a denumerable intersection:

$$A = \bigcap_{n=1}^{\infty} A_n,$$

then we define:

$$A_{(p)} =_{\mathrm{Df}} \bigcap_{n=1}^{p} A_n.$$

This rule is applicable only in simple cases. If A is defined by an expression with several nested set-operators for denumerable intersection or union, then an analogous but more complex rule is to be used. For example, for three nested operators, the rule would be as follows:

(20-31)   Suppose that the definition of A contains three nested infinite set-operators, e.g.,

$$A =_{Df} \bigcap_{n_1=1}^{\infty} \left[\dots \bigcup_{n_2=1}^{\infty} \left(\dots \bigcap_{n_3=1}^{\infty} [\dots n_1 \dots n_2 \dots n_3 \dots] \right) \right].$$

Then we define:

$$A_{(p_1,p_2,p_3)} =_{Df} \bigcap_{n_1=1}^{p_1} \left[\dots \bigcup_{n_2=1}^{p_2} \left(\dots \bigcap_{n_3=1}^{p_3} [\dots n_1 \dots n_2 \dots n_3 \dots] \right) \right].$$

If this definition is applicable to a given E, we define, in analogy to (28):

(20-32) $\mathscr{C}(H \mid E) =_{Df} \lim_{p_3} \lim_{p_2} \lim_{p_1} \mathscr{C}(H \mid E_{(p_1,p_2,p_3)})$.

[This procedure is analogous to the one proposed in [1950., D56-2], but much more general. The old method applied only to individual variables because only variables of this kind occur with quantifiers in the languages there considered. Here we make no such restriction; the values of 'n_1', for example, may be individual indices or attribute indices (in a denumerable family of attributes) or family indices (with respect to a language containing a denumerable sequence of families) or natural numbers with none of these interpretations.]

It would be useful to investigate the question under which conditions the rules proposed in (29), (30), and (31) or other rules of this kind yield new $\mathscr{C}$-values. If $\mathscr{C}$-values of a certain kind are found, it may or may not be that uniqueness can be shown. If we can prove that the value found for $\mathscr{C}(H \mid E)$ is the only $\mathscr{C}$-value for this pair of propositions that is compatible with our axioms, then we must, according to MR2, accept this value. Otherwise we try to judge the plausibility of the value found; if we do not see any disadvantages, we may accept the value tentatively, with the intention of abandoning it if and when a more satisfactory value is found.

It would further be of great value to find a way of making the extension of $\mathscr{C}$ unique, in analogy to the assumption of σ-additivity for $\mathcal{M}$, which made the extension of $\mathcal{M}$ unique. As we have seen, we cannot accept a *general* assumption of σ-additivity for $\mathscr{C}$ without excluding from the domain of $\mathscr{C}$ some pairs which we definitely wish to include. It might perhaps be possible to accept an assumption of σ-additivity restricted to a comprehensive part of the domain (including, of course, $\mathscr{E} \times \mathscr{E}^+$) and then find another assumption suitable for the rest of the domain.

21

The Problem of a More General Concept of Regularity

(*Editor's Note*. These speculations about non Archimedean $\mathscr{C}$-functions formed §8 of *An axiom system of inductive logic*, dated August 1960 and unrevised since. Carnap meant to publish some version of this material later in the series.)

This section discusses mostly some unsolved problems. ... I hope that some mathematicians who are interested in a classification of sets of real numbers, in particular sets with Lebesgue measure zero, will read it and try to find solutions for the problems here outlined.

In the definitions and axioms of regularity of $\mathscr{M}$ and $\mathscr{C}$, the requirement that certain values of $\mathscr{M}$ and $\mathscr{C}$ be positive was restricted to molecular propositions. The question whether analogous requirements for other propositions could or should be made, involves difficult problems not yet sufficiently investigated. I shall only outline some of the problems involved without offering solutions.

First let us consider nonmolecular propositions of a monadic predicate language with denumerably many individuals. A simple example of this kind is the proposition H designated by '$(x)P_1^1x$'. The $\mathscr{M}$-functions of the λ-system with $\lambda > 0$ are very simple; they are those which I have mostly studied and which appear to me under ordinary circumstances the most plausible ones. For any $\mathscr{M}$ of this kind, we have $\mathscr{M}(H) = 0$. On the other hand, there are also $\mathscr{M}$-functions which have positive values for propositions like H. (I shall give definitions of such $\mathscr{M}$-functions in a later article.)[1] These $\mathscr{M}$-functions are considerably more complicated than those in the λ-system.

However, there is no $\mathscr{M}$-function with positive values for *all* nonempty propositions involving one finite family. For example, for every model Z, $\{Z\} \in \mathscr{C}$ (T3-1h). But the class of all models Z, and hence likewise the class of all model propositions $\{Z\}$, is nondenumerable. These propositions are disjoint, their union is $\mathbf{Z}$ and hence the sum of their $\mathscr{M}$-values is 1. Therefore these $\mathscr{M}$-values cannot all be positive.

More serious problems arise with respect to a language $\mathscr{L}$ with real-valued functions. Let us consider two propositions E and H,

---

[1] Editor's note: As far as I know, this article was never written, but the following two articles are relevant here.

which involve only the function Φ_1 and the individual a_1, and two sets A_1 and A_2 such that the following holds:

(1)   **(a)** The set of all possible values of Φ_1 is **R**, i.e., the set of real numbers.
  (b) $A_2 \subset A_1 \subset \mathbf{R}, \qquad A_2 \neq A_1.$
  (c) $E = \{Z: Z(1, 1) \in A_1\}$, where $Z(1, 1)$ is the value assumed by '$\Phi_1(a_1)$' in the model Z.
  (d) $H =_{\mathrm{Df}} \{Z: Z(1, 1) \in A_2\}.$

Then we have:

  (e) $H \subset E, \qquad H \neq E.$

Let $\mathscr{R}$ be the class of all subsets of **R**. Suppose we could give an explication of the *relation IS*, where '$IS(A, B)$' means roughly this: "$A, B \in \mathscr{R}$ and A is *infinitely small* in comparison to B". Then it would seem plausible to lay down the following requirements (2)a and b for propositions E and H defined as in (1)c and d:

(2)   **(a)** If $IS(A_2, A_1)$, then $\mathscr{C}(H \mid E) = 0$.
  (b) If not $IS(A_2, A_1)$, then $\mathscr{C}(H \mid E) \neq 0$.

We might then state as axioms the requirement (2)b and analogous requirements for other propositions on $\mathscr{L}$. Then we could regard these axioms as axioms of regularity for $\mathscr{L}$; and we would call $\mathscr{C}$ regular iff it fulfilled all these axioms. However, to carry out this program would be a task beset with great difficulties. I shall here no more than sketch some of the problems involved, mostly unsolved.

   For the sake of convenience, I shall use in what follows some customary notations of the logic of relations. A relation R is regarded as a set of ordered pairs; I write usually '$R(A, B)$' for '$\langle A, B \rangle \in R$'. '$R^{-1}$' denotes the converse (or inverse) of R (i.e., $R^{-1}(A, B)$ iff $R(B, A)$). '$\mid$' is the symbol for the relative product; i.e., $(R \mid T)(A, B)$ iff, for some C, $R(A, C)$ and $T(C, B)$. (I shall use the customary terminology of the theory of relations; for explanations, see Carnap, *Introduction to Symbolic Logic*, §31.)

   The first problem is that of laying down axioms for the relations *SEq* and *IS* as primitives. '$SEq(A, B)$' means roughly: "$A, B \in \mathscr{R}$ and A is smaller or equal in size to B". We shall propose now some axioms for *SEq* and *IS*. (This set of axioms is a preliminary one. Further axioms should be added, and redundant axioms should be eliminated. The same holds for the later sets of axioms in this section.)

(3)   *Axioms for SEq:*

    (a) *SEq* is transitive.

    (b) If $A \subset B$, $SEq(A, B)$.

    (c) If A and B are congruent (i.e., one results from the other by translation), then $SEq(A, B)$.

    (d) Let B be symmetric to A (or the reflection of A) with respect to some $x \in \mathbf{R}$ (i.e., $B = \{y$: for some $u \in A$, $y = 2x - u\}$). Then $SEq(A, B)$.

    (e) If $(A \cap B) = (A' \cap B') = \varnothing$ and $SEq(A, A')$ and $SEq(B, B')$, then $SEq(A \cup B, A' \cup B')$.

    (f) Let $\mathscr{A} = \{A_1, A_2, \ldots\}$ be a denumerable disjoint class, and $\mathscr{B} = \{B_1, B_2, \ldots\}$ likewise. If for every i $(i = 1, 2, \ldots)$ $SEq(A_i, B_i)$, then $SEq(\bigcup \mathscr{A}, \bigcup \mathscr{B})$.

Another axiom (9) will be stated later.

On the basis of *SEq*, we define the relations *Eq* ("equal in size") and *S* ("smaller in size") as follows (all these notations and subsequent ones are for this section only):

(4) $Eq =_{Df} SEq \cap SEq^{-1}$.

(5) $S =_{Df} SEq - SEq^{-1}$.

On the basis of the axioms and the definitions, the following theorems hold:

(6)   *Theorems.*

    (a) *SEq* is reflexive. (From (3c).)

    (b) *S* is transitive and asymmetric (but not connected, hence not a series).

    (c) *Eq* is transitive and symmetric, hence reflexive and an equivalence relation.

    (d) $S \subset -Eq$.

    (e) $S \mid Eq \subset S$.

    (f) $Eq \mid S \subset S$.

    (g) If A and B are congruent, then $Eq(A, B)$. (From (3c).)

    (h) If B is symmetric to A with respect to some $x \in R^1$, then $Eq(A, B)$. (From (3d).)

Note that *SEq* is not antisymmetric, since this relation together with its converse implies only *Eq*, not identity. Hence *SEq* is not a partial order.

(7)   *Axioms for IS.*

    (a) $IS \subset SEq$.

    (b) $IS \subset -SEq^{-1}$.

    (c) $IS \mid SEq \subset IS$.

    (d) $SEq \mid IS \subset IS$.

    (e) If $IS(A, C)$ and $IS(B, C)$, then $IS(A \cup B, C)$.

    (f) If $IS(A, B \cup C)$, then $IS(A, B)$ or $IS(A, C)$ or both.

    (g) If $SEq(A, B)$ and $SEq(B, C)$ and $IS(A, C)$, then $IS(A, B)$ or $IS(B, C)$ or both.

    (h) Let $\mathcal{B} = \{B_1, B_2, \ldots\}$ be a denumerable, disjoint class. If for every i $(i = 1, 2, \ldots)$ $SEq(A, B_i)$, then $IS(A, \bigcup \mathcal{B})$.

    (i) Let $\mathcal{B} = \{B_1, B_2, \ldots, B_n\}$ be a finite class. If for every i $(i = 1, 2, \ldots, n)$ $SEq(B_i, A)$, then not $IS(A, \bigcup \mathcal{B})$.

    (j) If A is empty and B is not empty, then $IS(A, B)$.

    (k) If A is finite and B is infinite, then $IS(A, B)$.

    (l) If A and B are infinite and the cardinal number of A is smaller than that of B, then $IS(A, B)$.

    (m) Let μ be the Lebesgue measure function. If $\mu(A) = 0$ and $\mu(B) > 0$, then $IS(A, B)$.

    (n) If $\mu(A) < \infty$ and $\mu(B) = \infty$, then $IS(A, B)$.

    (p) Let A^{ac} be the set of accumulation points of A and B^{ac} that of B. If $SEq(A, B)$ and $IS(A^{ac}, B^{ac})$, then $IS(A, B)$.

(8)   *Theorems on IS.*

    (a) IS is transitive.

    (b) IS is irreflexive and hence asymmetric.

    (c) $IS \subset S$.

    (d) $IS \subset -Eq$.

    (e) If $\mathcal{A} = \{A_1, \ldots, A_n\}$ and for every i $(i = 1, \ldots, n)$ $IS(A_i, B)$, then $IS(\bigcup \mathcal{A}, B)$.

    (f) If $\mathcal{B} = \{B_1, \ldots, B_n\}$ and $IS(A, \bigcup \mathcal{B})$, then for at least one B_i $(i = 1, \ldots, n)$, $IS(A, B_i)$.

    (g) If the relation $SEq - IS$ holds both for A, B and for B, C, then not $IS(A, C)$. (From (7g).)

    (h) If $A, B \in \mathcal{R}$ and both A and B are nonempty finite sets, then not $IS(A, B)$.

    (i) If both A and B are intervals (of finite length) of real numbers, then not $IS(A, B)$. (From (6g), (7i).)

    (j) If both A and B are intervals (of finite length) of rational numbers, then not $IS(A, B)$. (From (6g), (7i).)

In preparation for the second problem we shall accept a *further axiom for SEq:*

(9)   The relation *SEq* is connected (i.e., $\mathcal{R} \times \mathcal{R} \subset SEq \cup SEq^{-1}$).

This axiom is perhaps somewhat problematic; it is at present not quite clear whether there might be incomparable sets.

Axiom (9) yields the following theorem:

(10)   For any pair of $\mathcal{R} \times \mathcal{R}$, exactly one of the following five relations holds: *IS*, $S - IS$, *Eq*, $S^{-1} - IS^{-1}$, IS^{-1}.

We shall define two further relations. Roughly speaking, '*FinS(A, B)*' means that *A* is finitely smaller than *B*, i.e., smaller but not infinitely smaller. '*Fin(A, B)*' means that *A* is finitely related to *B*, i.e., either *A* and *B* are equal or one of them is finitely smaller than the other:

(11)   **(a)** $FinS =_{Df} S - IS$.
      (b) $Fin =_{Df} FinS \cup Eq \cup FinS^{-1}$.

(12)   *Theorems on FinS and Fin.*
      (a) For any pair of $\mathcal{R} \times \mathcal{R}$, exactly one of the following three relations holds: *IS*, *Fin*, IS^{-1}. (From (10).)

The following items (b) to (m) serve mainly as lemmas for (n).

      (b) $FinS \mid Eq \subset FinS$.
      (c) $Eq \mid FinS \subset FinS$.
      (d) $FinS \subset S$.
      (e) $IS \mid FinS \subset IS$.   (From (7c).)
      (f) $FinS \mid IS \subset IS$.   (From (7c).)
      (g) *FinS* is transitive.   (From (8g).)
      (h) $FinS \mid FinS^{-1} \subset -IS$.   (From (7c).)
      (i) $FinS^{-1} \mid FinS \subset -IS^{-1}$.   (From (7d).)
      (j) $FinS \mid FinS^{-1} \subset -IS^{-1}$.   (From (e).)
      (k) $FinS^{-1} \mid FinS \subset -IS$.   (From (f).)
      (l) $FinS \mid FinS^{-1} \subset Fin$.   (From (h), (j), (a).)
      (m) $FinS^{-1} \mid FinS \subset Fin$.   (From (i), (k), (a).)
      (n) *Fin* is transitive.   (From (b), (c), (g), (l), (m).)
      (o) *Fin* is symmetric and reflective.
      (p) *Fin is an equivalence relation.*   (From (n) and (o).)

The second problem concerns the construction of explicit definitions for *SEq* and *IS* such that the axioms are satisfied (both those stated above and others that appear plausible). While an incomplete axiom system provides merely a partial explication, a full explication is given only by an explicit definition. There may, of course, be several alternative explications, each satisfying the main requirements.

Let us suppose that the second problem were solved. We should then have also explicit definitions for the relations *FinS* and *Fin*. We found that *Fin* is an equivalence relation (12p). We define:

(13) $\mathfrak{Q} =_{\text{Df}} \{\mathscr{A}: \mathscr{A}$ is an equivalence class with respect to *Fin*$\}$.

Now the *third problem* is that of investigating the classes in $\mathfrak{Q}$ and, in particular, the following relation *IS** among these classes, which corresponds to the relation *IS* among the sets belonging to these classes:

(14) $IS^*(\mathscr{A}, \mathscr{B}) =_{\text{Df}} \mathscr{A}, \mathscr{B} \in \mathfrak{Q};$ for some $A \in \mathscr{A}$ and some $B \in \mathscr{B}$, $IS(A, B)$.

(15)   *Theorems.*
    (a) Let $\mathscr{A} \subset \mathscr{R}$ and $A \in \mathscr{A}$. Then $\mathscr{A} \in \mathfrak{Q}$ iff $\mathscr{A} = \{B: Fin(B, A)\}$.
    (b) If $IS^*(\mathscr{A}, \mathscr{B})$, then $\mathscr{A} \times \mathscr{B} \subset IS$.
    (c) IS^* is transitive.   (From (8a).)
    (d) IS^* is irreflexive and hence asymmetric.   (From (8b).)
    (e) IS^* is connected, i.e., if $\mathscr{A}, \mathscr{B} \in \mathfrak{Q}$, $\mathscr{A} \neq \mathscr{B}$, then either $IS^*(\mathscr{A}, \mathscr{B})$ or $IS^*(\mathscr{B}, \mathscr{A})$.

Proof.   Suppose that $\mathscr{A}, \mathscr{B} \in \mathfrak{Q}$, $\mathscr{A} \neq \mathscr{B}$, $A \in \mathscr{A}$, $B \in \mathscr{B}$. Then not $Fin(A, B)$ (from (13)). Thus, by (12a), either $IS(A, B)$ or $IS(B, A)$.
    (f) IS^* *is a series.*   (From (c), (d), (e).)
    (g) If $A \in \mathscr{R}$ is empty, and $\mathscr{A}_0 = \{A\}$, then $\mathscr{A}_0 \in \mathfrak{Q}$.   (From (7j).)
    (h) If $\mathscr{A}_1 = \{A: A \in \mathscr{R}, A$ is nonempty and finite$\}$, then $\mathscr{A}_1 \in \mathfrak{Q}$.   (From (7k), (8h).)
    (i) If $\mathscr{A}_0$ is as in (g) and $\mathscr{A}_1$ as in (h), then $IS^*(\mathscr{A}_0, \mathscr{A}_1)$; and, for any $\mathscr{B}$, if $\mathscr{B} \in \mathfrak{Q}$, $\mathscr{B} \neq \mathscr{A}_0$, and $\mathscr{B} \neq \mathscr{A}_1$, then $IS^*(\mathscr{A}_1, \mathscr{B})$. (From (7k).) In other words, $\mathscr{A}_0$ is the initial member and $\mathscr{A}_1$ the second member of the series IS^*.

It would be useful to construct a mapping of $\mathfrak{Q}$ into a set of numbers as an index set D, such that the following holds:

(16)   If $\mathscr{A}_u$ and $\mathscr{A}_v$ are classes in $\mathfrak{Q}$ with the numbers $u, v \in D$ as indices, then $IS^*(\mathscr{A}_u, \mathscr{A}_v)$ iff $u < v$.

What kind of numbers are suitable as indices, depends on the basic structural properties, as yet unknown, of the series IS^*. It is not even clear at present, whether $\mathfrak{Q}$ is denumerable or not. If $\mathfrak{Q}$ turns out to be denumerable, a suitable set of rational numbers or a set of ordered n-tuples of integers, might serve as D; if $\mathfrak{Q}$ is nondenumerable, maybe a set of real numbers or a set of ordered n-tuples of real numbers might be suitable. For the time being we have to leave open the question of the kind of numbers in D.

For any $u \in D$, let $\mathcal{A}_u$ be the class in $\mathfrak{Q}$ with the index u. If $A \in \mathcal{A}_u$, we shall say that A is a set of *rank u*. It follows from (15i) that there is a least number in D; let this be 0; and there is a second number in D (i.e., a least number in $D - \{0\}$); let this be 1. Then the $\mathfrak{Q}$-classes with the indices 0 and 1 are those classes which are denoted in (15g) and (15h) by '$\mathcal{A}_0$' and '$\mathcal{A}_1$' respectively. Thus we have:

(17)   **(a)** $0 \in D$; for any $u \in D$, if $u \neq 0$ then $0 < u$.
  (b) $1 \in D$; $0 < 1$; for any $u \in D$, if $u \neq 0$ and $u \neq 1$ then $1 < u$.
  (c) The $\mathfrak{Q}$-class with the index 0 is $\mathcal{A}_0 = \{\varnothing\}$.
  (d) The $\mathfrak{Q}$-class with the index 1 is $\mathcal{A}_1 = \{A : A \in \mathcal{R}$ and A is nonempty and finite$\}$.
  (e) Let the rank of the interval $(0, 1)$ be u_{re}. Then every interval (of finite length) has the rank u_{re}. (From (8i).)
  (f) Let the rank of the set of all rational numbers of the interval $(0, 1)$ be u_{rat}. Then the set of the rational numbers of any interval (of finite length) has the rank u_{rat}. (From (8j).) We have $u_{rat} < u_{re}$. (From (7l).)

Suppose that the third problem were solved, i.e., the class $\mathfrak{Q}$, the relation IS^*, the index set D, and the assignment of index numbers to the classes in $\mathfrak{Q}$ were defined. Then *the fourth problem* would aim at the construction of a *measure function* π for all sets in $\mathcal{R}$. The values of π are not real numbers but numbers of a *non-Archimedean number system* Ω to be constructed. A number system (in which a number 0, a relation $<$ and a function $+$ are defined) is said to be Archimedean if the following principle (18) holds; otherwise non-Archimedean (see Hilbert [1899] §§8, 33, and Appendix VI: the Archimedean axiom IV1; Hausdorff [1914], Chap. VI, §11):

(18)   *Archimedes' principle.* For any numbers α, β such that $0 < \alpha$ and $0 < \beta$, there is a sum of a finite number of terms, each term being α, such that the sum exceeds β: $\beta < \alpha + \alpha + \ldots + \alpha$.

I shall first describe the system Ω; later I shall come back to the measure π. The main features of Ω are as follows.

(19)   (a) For every number $\alpha \in \Omega$ there is a unique ϵ_u called the *unit* of α, and a unique real number r, called the *coefficient* of α, such that $\alpha = r\epsilon_u$.

   (b) The index set D discussed earlier (but not specified), is also the index set for the units in Ω; for any $u \in D$, there is a unit ϵ_u with the index u.

   (c) Since 0 is the first number in D, and 1 is the second, ϵ_0 is the first (smallest) unit, and ϵ_1 is the second.

   (d) The coefficient of ϵ_0 is always 0.

   (e) For any $u > 0$, any coefficient of ϵ_u is a (finite) positive real number.

(20)   Definition of *equality* for Ω-numbers:

$$r_1\epsilon_u =_\Omega r_2\epsilon_v =_{Df} u = v \text{ and } r_1 = r_2.$$

(21)   Definition of $<_\Omega$ for Ω-numbers: $r_1\epsilon_u <_\Omega \overline{r_2\epsilon_v} =_{Df}$ either $u < v$, or $u = v$ and $r_1 < r_2$.

The relation $<_\Omega$ is transitive irreflexive, asymmetric, and connected; hence it is a series. Henceforth I shall write simply '=' instead of '$=_\Omega$', and '<' instead of '$<_\Omega$'. On the basis of '=' and '<', the symbols '>', '$\leq$' and '$\geq$' are assumed to be defined in the customary way.

Definition of *addition* for Ω-numbers:

(22)   (a) $r_1\epsilon_u +_\Omega r_2\epsilon_u = (r_1 + r_2)\epsilon_u$.

   (b) If $u < v$ (and hence, by (19e), $r_2 > 0$), then $r_1\epsilon_u +_\Omega r_2\epsilon_v = r_2\epsilon_v +_\Omega r_1\epsilon_u = r_2\epsilon_v$.

(22b) expresses the fact that ϵ_u is infinitely small in relation to ϵ_v. ((22b) is analogous to '$\aleph_0 + 3 = \aleph_0$'; however, in some other respects, addition of Ω-numbers is quite different from that of cardinal numbers.) It follows from (22) that $+_\Omega$ is commutative and associative. From now on I shall write '+' instead of '$+_\Omega$'.

Conditions of convergence for the sum of a sequence of Ω-numbers:

(23)   Let Γ be a sequence of Ω-numbers with the same unit ϵ_u: $\alpha_1, \alpha_2, \ldots$, where α_i $(i = 1, 2, \ldots)$ is $r_i\epsilon_u$. The sum of Γ converges iff $\sum_{i=1}^{\infty} r_i$ converges. If the latter sum equals r, then: $\sum_{i=1}^{\infty} \alpha_i = r\epsilon_u$.

(24) Let Γ be the sequence $\alpha_1, \alpha_2, \ldots$ For each i ($i = 1, 2, \ldots$), let α_i be $r_i\epsilon_{u_i}$. (For $i \neq j$, u_i and u_j are not necessarily distinct.) Let $D' \subset D$ be the set of index numbers u_i occurring in Γ. For every $v \in D'$, let Γ_v be the subsequence of Γ containing those terms α_i for which $u_i = v$. The total sum $\sum\limits_{i=1}^{\infty} \alpha_i$ for Γ converges iff the following conditions (i) and (ii) are fulfilled:

    (i) For every $v \in D'$, the sum of Γ_v converges (depending on the condition stated in (23)).

    (ii) Among the index numbers in D' there is a maximum, say w.

If both conditions (i) and (ii) are fulfilled, the sum of Γ is equal to the sum of Γ_w:

    (iii) $\sum\limits_{i=1}^{\infty} \alpha_1 = r_w\epsilon_w$, where $r_w = \sum\limits_{\substack{i \\ (u_i = w)}} r_i$.

    Multiplication of an Ω-number by a positive real number is defined as follows:

(25) If $r_2 > 0$, $r_2 \times (r_1\epsilon_u) =_{\mathrm{Df}} (r_2 \times r_1)\epsilon_u$.

Now we shall define the *quotient* of two Ω-numbers (excluding the case that both index numbers u_1 and u_2 are 0). The value of a quotient is a real number (in the extended real number system).

(26) $\dfrac{r_2\epsilon_{u_2}}{r_1\epsilon_{u_1}} =_{\mathrm{Df}} r$, where r is determined as follows:

    (a) If $u_2 < u_1$, $r = 0$.

    (b) If $u_2 = u_1 \neq 0$, $r = r_2/r_1$. (Since, by (19e), $r_1 > 0$ and $r_2 > 0$, $0 < r < \infty$.)

    (c) If $u_2 > u_1$, $r = \infty$.

These are the arithmetical rules for the numbers of the non-Archimedean system Ω. Now we shall use the Ω-numbers as values of the *measure function* π. To give a definition of such a function π is a very difficult and complicated task. All we intend to do here, is to give a few general rules for π.

(27) If $SEq(A, B)$, then $\pi(A) \leqq \pi(B)$. It follows that, if $Eq(A, B)$, then $\pi(A) = \pi(B)$.

(27) If $SEq(A, B)$, then $\Pi(A) \leqq \Pi(B)$. It follows that, if $Eq(A, B)$, then $\Pi(A) = \Pi(B)$.

(28) If $A \in \mathcal{R}$ is a rank, then $\pi(A)$ is an Ω-number with the unit ϵ_u.

(29) **(a)** Since $\varnothing \in \mathcal{R}$ is the only set of rank 0, $\pi(A) = 0\epsilon_0$ iff $A = \varnothing$.
   (b) Any nonempty $B \in \mathcal{R}$ has a positive rank u: $\pi(B) = r\epsilon_u$, where $u > 0$ and $r > 0$.

Finite additivity. Let $A, B \in \mathcal{R}$ and $A \cap B = \varnothing$. Then:

(30) $\pi(A \cup B) = \pi(A) + \pi(B)$.

Denumerable additivity. Let $A \in \mathcal{R}$ be the union of a denumerable, disjoint class of sets A_i $(i = 1, 2, \ldots)$. For every i let $\Pi(A_i)$ be α_i. Then:

(31) $\pi(A) = \sum\limits_{i=1}^{\infty} \alpha_i$, provided this sum converges (see (23), (24)).

If the sum does not converge, $\pi(A)$ has still an Ω-number as its value. However, this value is not uniquely determined by the measures of the sets A_i but depends also on the locations of these sets. In this case the rank of A is higher than the rank of any of the sets A_i.

We have stated only some general rules for the measure function π. We do not intend to investigate here the complicated task of giving specific rules determining for every rank u the values of $\pi(B)$ for all sets B of rank u. These rules must be in accord with the general rules stated and, moreover, be intuitively plausible so that they lead, with the help of the rule (33) below, to plausible values of $\mathscr{C}$.

For some kinds of sets, the rules for π can be very simple. We have given the trivial rule for rank 0 (rule (28a)). We shall state simple rules for three other classes.

(32) **(a)** Let A be $\{0\}$. Then $A \in \mathcal{A}_1$ (see (17d) and (19c)).
   (b) Let A be the interval $(0, r)$ $(r > 0)$. Then A has the rank u_{re} (17e). We take $\pi(A) = r\epsilon_{u_{re}}$.
   (c) Let B be the set of all rational numbers of the interval $(0, r)$ $(r > 0)$. Then B has the rank u_{rat} (17f). We take $\pi(B) = r\epsilon_{u_{rat}}$.

(32a) yields that for a nonempty, finite set A of n real numbers $\pi(A) = n\epsilon_1$. The rule (32b) can be applied first to any other interval (by (27)), and then to all finite unions of disjoint intervals (by (30)), and to certain denumerable unions (by (31)). The rule (32c) can be used analogously.

For the definition of a generalized concept of regularity for language $\mathscr{L}$ it would not be necessary to construct a measure function π of the kind here indicated. However, it seems to me that such a construction would still be desirable for several reasons. First, without regard to applications, it would be of interest in itself as a complete measure function, one that has a value for *all* subsets of **R**, and a positive value for all nonempty subsets (which is, of course, not possible for a real-valued measure function). Second, it could serve as a basis for a definition of $\mathscr{C}$, as we shall see.

Suppose that a definition of a measure function π of the kind described were given. Then we can easily give a rule for the values of $\mathscr{C}$ for propositions H and E (on language $\mathscr{L}$) of the forms specified in (1). Since $\mathscr{C}$ is intended to be a $\mathscr{C}$-function, it must satisfy the basic axioms; in particular, its values must be, not Ω-numbers, but real numbers of the interval $[0, 1]$. This requirement is fulfilled if the following rule is accepted:

(33) Let the propositions E and H be defined on the basis of the sets A_1 and A_2, respectively, as stated in (1). Then we define:

$$\mathscr{C}(H \mid E) =_{\mathrm{Df}} \frac{\pi(A_2)}{\pi(A_1)}.$$

Let the ranks of A_1 and A_2 be u_1 and u_2, respectively. Since $A_1 \neq \varnothing$, $u_1 > 0$. Therefore the definition (26) of the quotient is applicable. Since $A_2 \subset A_1$, we have $\pi(A_2) \leqq \pi(A_1)$ and $u_2 \leqq u_1$. Hence only (26a) and (26b) come into consideration, not (26c). Therefore:

(34) $$0 \leqq \mathscr{C}(H \mid E) \leqq 1.$$

In certain cases, when $\pi(A_1) = \infty$ or, more generally, A_1 is not bounded, it may be useful to apply the following definition (35) instead of (33); here the values of 'x' are the positive real numbers (or the positive integers) and B_x is the closed interval $[-x, +x] \subset R^1$:

(35) $$\mathscr{C}(H \mid E) =_{\mathrm{Df}} \lim_{x \to \infty} \frac{\pi(A_2 \cap B_x)}{\pi(A_1 \cap B_x)}.$$

Here (34) still holds, of course.

7

An Axiomatic Foundation for the Logic of Inductive Generalization*

BY JAAKKO HINTIKKA AND ILKKA NIINILUOTO

I. THE REPRESENTATIVE FUNCTION OF AN INDUCTIVE METHOD

One of the most interesting viewpoints from which inductive logic can be looked at is to ask what the different factors are that must be taken into account in singular inductive inference, i.e., in the usual technical jargon, what the arguments of the representative functions of one's system of inductive methods are. It is well known that Carnap's λ-continuum of inductive methods can be derived from essentially one single assumption concerning these arguments of the representative function.[1] It is shown in this paper that a logic of inductive generalization is obtained if this assumption is weakened in a natural way.

---

* Reprinted by permission from *Formal Methods in the Methodology of Empirical Sciences*, ed. Marian Przełęcki, Klemens Szaniawski and Ryszard Wójcicki (Wrocław, Warsaw, Krakow, Gdansk: Ossolineum and Dordrecht: D. Reidel, 1976).

[1] This assumption is Carnap's "Axiom of Predictive Irrelevance". For the derivation of Carnap's λ-continuum, see J. G. Kemeny, "Carnap's theory of probability and induction", in P. A. Schilpp, ed., *The Philosophy of Rudolf Carnap* (LaSalle, Ill.: Open Court, 1963), pp. 711–738; R. Carnap and W. Stegmüller, *Induktive Logik und Wahrscheinlichkeit* (Vienna: Springer-Verlag, 1958), pp. 242–249; and R. Carnap, "Notes on probability and induction", *Synthese* 25 (1973), 286–292. This assumption is termed "W. E. Johnson's sufficiency postulate" in I. J. Good, *The Estimation of Probabilities*, Research Monograph No. 30 (Cambridge, Mass.: MIT Press, 1965), p. 17.

A *representative function* is a numerical function which "represents" an inductive probability measure defined for the statements of the underlying language. Suppose that the individuals of a universe U are classified in K exclusive classes into one of which each individual of U must fall, i.e., that universe U is partitioned into K 'cells'. Given a sample of n individuals of which n_i belong to the ith cell ($i = 1, \ldots K$), the representative function f specifies the probability that an unknown further individual ("next individual to be observed") falls into a given cell. (We may think of this probability as a betting ratio for the bet that the next individual belongs to the ith cell.) The *symmetry assumption*, de Finetti's "exchangeability",[2] says that f depends on the sample only through the numbers $n_1, n_2, \ldots, n_K$, not on the order in which the several individuals in the sample were observed, and that the probability of the transition from any sequence of n_i's to another one is independent of the path. (It also implies that the probability does not depend on the new "unknown" individual.) Thus it is already one of the kinds of assumptions that limits the choice of the arguments of the representative function.

II. CARNAP'S λ-CONTINUUM

The assumption that Carnap employs for the derivation of his λ-continuum goes a long way further than the symmetry assumption and says that f depends on the sample only through its size n (i.e., the sum $n_1 + \ldots + n_K$) and the number n_i of sample individuals in the cell in question. Thus the probability that the next individual belongs to a cell with n' individuals so far observed in it will be of the form $f(n', n)$. (The function f depends also on the classification system through the fixed number K of cells.) It is course required also that this representative function must give rise to a symmetric probability distribution, that is, to a probability measure satisfying probability calculus. From this assumption and the assumption concerning the arguments of f it follows that f must be of the form

(1) $$f(n', n) = \frac{n' + \dfrac{\lambda}{K}}{n + \lambda}$$

where λ is a positive, real-valued constant. The parameter λ is

---

[2] See B. de Finetti, "Foresight: Its logical laws, its subjective sources," in H. E. Kyburg and H. E. Smokler, eds., *Studies in Subjective Probability* (New York: John Wiley, 1964), pp. 93–158.

determined by the equation

$$f(0, 1) = \frac{\frac{\lambda}{K}}{1 + \lambda},$$

which yields as a solution

(2) $$\lambda = \frac{K \cdot f(0, 1)}{1 - K \cdot f(0, 1)}$$

Strictly speaking, (1) follows only if $K > 2$. In the case $K = 2$ it follows only in conjunction with the additional assumption that f be a linear function of n'.

The parameter λ can be interpreted as an index of caution with respect to singular inductive inference, or alternatively as a measure of the disorder (randomness) in the universe U.[3] It can also be interpreted as the size of an imaginary homogeneous sample of λ individuals which is combined with the real sample of n individuals in estimating the frequency of different kinds of individuals in the whole universe U.

III. THE PROBLEM OF INDUCTIVE GENERALIZATION

The main disadvantage with Carnap's λ-continuum is that it assigns zero prior probabilities to all nontrivial generalizations in an infinite universe, and hence likewise assigns zero probabilities to them a posteriori on any finite evidence. Moreover, in a finite universe appreciable posterior probabilities are associated with nontrivial generalizations only when our sample is of the same order of magnitude as the whole universe. This makes Carnap's λ-continuum useless as a logic of inductive generalization.

Inductive logics which are free of this defect have been proposed in the literature. A case in point is Hintikka's α-λ-*system*.[4] However, these systems have so far not been motivated on the basis of simple assumptions concerning the representative function.

IV. A NEW ARGUMENT FOR THE REPRESENTATIVE FUNCTION

In this paper, a new type of system of inductive logic is examined. It is based on an assumption which is the most natural

---

[3] For a brief discussion on the development of Carnap's own views about the intuitive interpretation of λ, see R. Hilpinen, "Carnap's new system of inductive logic," *Synthese* 25 (1973) 311–313.

[4] See J. Hintikka, "A two-dimensional continuum of inductive methods", in J. Hintikka and P. Suppes, eds., *Aspects of Inductive Logic* (Amsterdam: North-Holland, 1966), pp. 113–132.

way of loosening the axioms of the λ-system. Instead of assuming that the representative function depends only on n' and n, we assume that it may also depend on the number c of cells instantiated in the sample (i.e., on the number of i's such that $n_i > 0$). The importance of this parameter for inductive generalization is shown already by the fact that it determines the number of nonequivalent generalizations compatible with the sample. Thus our working hypothesis in this paper is that the representative function is of the form $f(n', n, c)$ and that it gives rise to a symmetric probability distribution. These two assumptions are the 'axioms' of the new system studied in this paper.

Certain members of the α-λ-continuum fall within the scope of the new assumption, but others do not. An instance of the former is the generalized 'combined system' of Hintikka.[5] Its representative function is, for $n' > 0$,

$$(3) \qquad (n'+1) \frac{\displaystyle\sum_{i=0}^{K-c} \binom{K-c}{i} \frac{(\alpha+c+i-1)!}{(n+c+i)!}}{\displaystyle\sum_{i=0}^{K-c} \binom{K-c}{i} \frac{(\alpha+c+i-1)!}{(n+c+i-1)!}}$$

which is seen to depend only on n', n, c, and K. Conversely, the new assumption allows for inductive strategies not covered by the α-λ-continuum.

The consequences of the new assumption will not receive an exhaustive analysis in this paper. What is attempted here is an exploration of some of the most important qualitative (asymptotic) consequences of this assumption, which will in the sequel be referred to as our *Basic Assumption*. In particular we shall show that it behaves vis-à-vis inductive generalization in the way we are entitled to expect, i.e., that it assigns nonzero prior probabilities to generalizations even in an infinite universe and that the posterior probabilities of generalizations (including constituents, that is, statements which specify the empty and the nonempty cells of the universe) behave in the right way in most cases. This means that the simplest constituent compatible with evidence will be highly confirmed in the long run when the evidence grows without limit. (The evidence is assumed to consist of a number, say n, individuals located in specified cells of the universe).

----

[5] The "combined system" was originally introduced in J. Hintikka, "On a combined system of inductive logic," in *Studia Logico-Mathematica et Philosophica in Honorem Rolf Nevanlinna, Acta Philosophica Fennica* 18 (1965) 21–30. For its generalization (to positive values of α), see the work referred to in n. 4.

We shall begin by establishing a number of separate results on the representative function $f(n', n, c)$. Later, some of the more general consequences of our observations, and their relations to Carnap's λ-continuum, will be discussed.

V. BASIC THEOREMS

It is useful to introduce a few defined symbols.

Definition 1. $h(n, c) = (K - c)f(0, n, c)$.

Definition 2. $g(n, c) = 1 - h(n, c)$.

The intuitive meaning of the functions h and g is clear: while g gives the probability that an unknown new individual belongs to a cell already instantiated in the sample (i.e., is of the same kind as the individuals already observed), h gives the probability that it does not (i.e., that it belongs to a new cell.)

Theorem 1.   If $n'_1, n'_2, \ldots, n'_c$ are positive integers ≥ 1 whose sum is n, and if $0 \leq c \leq K$, then

$$\sum_{i=1}^{c} f(n'_i, n, c) + (K - c)f(0, n, c) = 1.$$

Proof.   Follows immediately from the assumption that f defines a probability distribution.   ∎

Corollary 1.1. $f(0, 0, 0) = \dfrac{1}{K}$.

Corollary 1.2. $f(1, K, K) = \dfrac{1}{K}$.

Corollary 1.3. $f(n, n, 1) + (K - 1)f(0, n, 1) = 1$.

Corollary 1.4. $f(n', n, 2) + f(n - n', n, 2) + (K - 2)f(0, n, 2) = 1$, provided that $n > n' > 0$.

Corollary 1.5. $f(n', cn', c) = \dfrac{1}{c} g(cn', c)$, provided that $c > 0$.

Corollary 1.6. $\sum_{i=1}^{c} f(n'_i, n, c) = g(n, c)$,   on   the   assumptions   of Theorem 1.

The next theorem is based on the assumption that f defines a symmetric probability distribution.

Theorem 2. $f(n', n, c) \cdot f(n'', n+1, c) = f(n'', n, c) \cdot f(n', n+1, c)$, provided that $n - n' - n'' \geqq c - 2$, $n' \geqq 1$, $n'' \geqq 1$, $K \geqq c \geqq 2$, and that $n = n' + n''$ if $c = 2$.

Proof. This theorem is proved by considering the two orders in which two new individuals can be found, one falling into a cell with n' individuals $(n' > 0)$ and the other into a cell with n'' individuals $(n'' > 0)$, and by identifying the two transition probabilities. ∎

Theorem 2 says essentially that $f(n', n, c)$ is a linear function of $n' > 0$. Later, a more explicit form of this fact will be found.

Corollary 2.1. $f(n', n+1, c) = f(n'', n+1, c) \cdot \dfrac{f(n', n, c)}{f(n'', n, c)}$ on the assumptions of Theorem 2.

Corollary 2.2. $f(n', n, 2) = f(n - n' - 1, n, 2) \cdot \dfrac{f(n', n-1, 2)}{f(n - n' - 1, n-1, 2)}$ provided that $n - 1 > n' > 1$.

Because of our Basic Assumption, Theorem 2 will generally be false in the case $n'' = 0$ (and $c < K$). Instead of Theorem 2, the following result is obtained for this case.

Theorem 3. $f(n', n, c) \cdot f(0, n+1, c) = f(0, n, c) \cdot f(n', n+1, c+1)$, provided that $n - n' \geqq c - 1$, $n' \geqq 1$, $K > c \geqq 1$, and that $n' = n$ if $c = 1$.

Proof. This theorem may be proved by considering the two orders in which two new individuals can make their appearance, one belonging to an already instantiated cell with n' individuals and the other to a given empty cell, and by identifying the two transition probabilities. ∎

Corollary 3.1. $f(n', n, c) = \dfrac{f(0, n, c-1)}{f(0, n-1, c-1)} f(n', n-1, c-1)$,

provided that $n - n' \geqq c - 1$, $n' \geqq 1$, $K \geqq c \geqq 2$, and that $n - 1 = n'$ if $c = 2$.

Corollary 3.2. $f(n', n, c) = \dfrac{f(0, n, c-1)}{f(0, n-1, c-1)} \cdot \dfrac{f(0, n-1, c-2)}{f(0, n-2, c-2)} \cdot$

$$\cdots \dfrac{f(0, n-c+3, 2)}{f(0, n-c+2, 2)} f(n', n-c+2, 2),$$

with the assumptions of Corollary 3.1.

Corollary 3.3. $f(n', n, c) = \dfrac{f(0, n, c)}{f(0, n+1, c)} f(n', n+1, c+1)$ provided that $n - n' \geqq c - 1$, $n' \geqq 1$, $K > c \geqq 1$, and that $n = n'$ if $c = 1$.

Corollary 3.4. $f(n', n, c) = \dfrac{f(0, n, c)}{f(0, n+1, c)} \cdot \dfrac{f(0, n+1, c+1)}{f(0, n+2, c+1)} \cdot$

$$\cdots \dfrac{f(0, n+K-c-1, K-1)}{f(0, n+K-c, K-1)} f(n', n+K-c, K),$$

provided that $n - n' \geqq c - 1$, $n' \geqq 1$, and that $n' = n$ if $c = 1$.

Corollary 3.4 shows that $f(n', n, c)$ can be computed by multiplying $f(n', n+K-c, K)$ with a factor which does not depend on n', On the other hand, when each of the K cells has been exemplified, the representative function behaves essentially in the same way as in Carnap's λ-continuum.

Theorem 4. $f(n', n, K) = \dfrac{n' + \dfrac{\lambda_K}{K}}{n + \lambda_K}$,

where λ_K is a constant, $\lambda_K > -K$,

$$\lambda_K = \dfrac{Kf(1, K+1, K)}{1 - Kf(1, K+1, K)} - K,$$

provided that $n - n' \geqq K - 1$, and $n' \geqq 1$.

Proof. This theorem can be proved essentially in the same way as the main result for Carnap's λ-continuum. The argument is given in Appendix 1. ∎

If $K = 2$, Theorem 4 depends on the auxiliary assumption as Carnap's λ-continuum in the analogous case.

By combining Corollary 3.4 and Theorem 4, the following theorem is immediately obtained.

Theorem 5. $f(n', n, c)$ is of the form

$$\mu(n, c) \dfrac{n' + \dfrac{\lambda_K}{K}}{n + K - c + \lambda_K},$$

provided that $n - n' \geqq c - 1$, and $n' \geqq 1$.

Corollary 5.1. $f(n', n, c)$ is a linear function of $n' > 0$, provided that $n - n' \geqq c - 1$,

If we introduce the notation

$$\alpha(n, c) = \frac{\mu(n, c)}{n + K - c + \lambda_K},$$

then the following result is obtained by Theorem 5, Corollary 1.6, and Definitions 1 and 2.

Theorem 6. (a) $f(n', n, c) = \alpha(n, c) \left(n' + \dfrac{\lambda_K}{K} \right)$, provided that $n - n' \geqq c - 1$, and $n' \geqq 1$,

(b) $g(n, c) = \alpha(n, c) \left(n + \dfrac{c\lambda_K}{K} \right)$, if $n \geqq c$,

(c) $f(0, n, c) = \dfrac{1 - \alpha(n, c) \left(n + \dfrac{c\lambda_K}{K} \right)}{K - c}$, if $n \geqq c$.

In this theorem, we have separated the role of n' in f from those of n and c.

In the sequel, we shall write simply λ for the parameter λ_K given in Theorem 4.

Theorem 7. When $n \geqq c$ and $K > c \geqq 1$.

$$\alpha(n + 1, c + 1) \left[n + \frac{c\lambda}{K} - \frac{1}{\alpha(n, c)} \right] - \alpha(n + 1, c) \left[n + \frac{c\lambda}{K} + 1 \right] + 1 = 0.$$

Proof. Substitute values given by Theorem 6(a) and (c) into Theorem 3. ■

Corollary 7.1. When $n \geqq c$ and $K > c \geqq 1$.

$$\alpha(n + 1, c + 1) \left[n + \frac{c\lambda}{K} - \frac{1}{\alpha(n, c)} \right]$$

$$= \alpha(n + 1, c) \left[n + 1 + \frac{c\lambda}{K} - \frac{1}{\alpha(n + 1, c)} \right].$$

Corollary 7.2. When $n \geqq K - 1$,

$$\alpha(n + 1, K - 1) = \frac{2(n + \lambda) + 1 - \dfrac{\lambda}{K} - \dfrac{1}{\alpha(n, K - 1)}}{(n + \lambda + 1) \left(n + \lambda + 1 - \dfrac{\lambda}{K} \right)}.$$

Proof. Substitute $K-1$ for c in Theorem 7, and recall that $\alpha(n, K) = \dfrac{1}{n+\lambda}$. ∎

Corollary 7.2 expresses a nonlinear difference equation for $\alpha(n, K-1)$. Its solution, which can be written as a continued fraction, gives the value of $\alpha(n, K-1)$ as a function of n, λ, K, and $\alpha(K-1, K-1)$. When the values $\alpha(n, K-1)$, $n \geq K-1$, are known, a difference equation for $\alpha(n, K-2)$ is obtained from Theorem 7, and similarly for $\alpha(n, c)$ for all $c = 1, \ldots, K-1$.

VI. THE PARAMETERS OF THE NEW SYSTEM

Theorem 8. $f(0, c, c)$, $c = 1, 2, \ldots, K-1$, and $f(1, K+1, K)$ can be chosen as the independent free parameters of the new system.

Proof. Note first that we can determine $f(n', n, c)$ and $g(n, c)$, by Theorems 4 and 6, if we know $\alpha(n, c)$ and $f(1, K+1, K)$. What we are claiming is that $f(n', n, c)$ is determined for arbitrary values of $n', n, c (K \geq c \geq 1, n - n' \geq c - 1)$ if $f(0, c, c)$ $(c = 1, 2, \ldots, K-1)$ and $f(1, K+1, K)$ are fixed.

This claim holds for $c = K$ by Theorem 4. Assume now that it holds when $c > c_0$ and $n < n_0$. Then Theorem 7 shows that it holds when $c = c_0$ and $n = n_0$. This amounts to an inductive proof of Theorem 8, for the smallest value that can be used in Theorem 7 is just $n = c$, which corresponds to $\alpha(c, c)$ or $f(0, c, c)$. ∎

Corollary 8.1. There are K free parameters in the new system.

The values of the parameters $f(0, c, c)$ $(c = 1, 2, \ldots, K-1)$ are not determined by our Basic Assumption, but we shall see later that there is a constraint imposed upon them in that they cannot be chosen so that they yield more "pessimistic" probabilities than the corresponding Carnapian ones. The values of $f(0, c, c)$ thus belong to certain subintervals of $[0, 1]$ with 0 as the left end point. The point 0 is excluded if f is to define a regular probability measure. The same holds for the parameter $f(1, K+1, K)$. If a principle of "instantial relevance" to the effect that

$$f(2, K+1, K) > f(1, K, K)$$

is assumed, then it follows that

$$f(1, K+1, K) < \frac{1}{K}.$$

Note also that if $f(1, K+1, K)$ is determined in Carnap's λ-continuum with *his* $\lambda = \lambda_0$, i.e., if

$$f(1, K+1, K) = \frac{1 + \dfrac{\lambda_0}{K}}{K + 1 + \lambda_0},$$

then by Theorem 4

$$\lambda_K = \frac{K + \lambda_0}{K + 1 + \lambda_0}(K + 1 + \lambda_0) - K = \lambda_0.$$

In other words, if parameter $f(1, K+1, K)$ is given its Carnapian value, then *our* λ (i.e., λ_K) equals the λ of Carnap's λ-continuum.

As soon as the value of $f(1, K+1, K)$ is fixed, $f(0, c, c)$, $\alpha(c, c)$, and $f(1, c, c)$ determine each other through the equations

$$f(0, c, c) = \frac{1 - c\left(1 + \dfrac{\lambda}{K}\right)\alpha(c, c)}{K - c}$$

and

$$f(1, c, c) = \left(1 + \frac{\lambda}{K}\right)\alpha(c, c).$$

Thus, instead of $f(0, c, c)(c = 1, 2, \ldots, K-1)$ and $f(1, K+1, K)$ we could choose as the free parameters of the new system $f(1, c, c)$ $(c = 1, 2, \ldots, K-1)$ and $f(1, K+1, K)$.

For example, in the case $K = 2$, the free parameters can be taken to be $f(1, 3, 2)$ and either $f(0, 1, 1)$ or $f(1, 1, 1)$.

The intuitive interpretation of the parameters of the new system will be discussed later when we have seen what their role in inductive generalization is.

VII. POSTERIOR PROBABILITIES FOR CONSTITUENTS: CASE $c = K - 1$

After these preliminary results, we shall address ourselves to the most central task of this paper. One of the most important things we can hope to find out about the new system of inductive logic is how the posterior probabilities of generalizations behave when evidence for them accumulates. In certain cases, the calculation of these probabilities can be carried out explicitly.

Let us consider the case in which the evidence exemplifies $K - 1$ cells, leaving just one of the cells empty. Let us assume that the evidence e consists of a complete classification of n individuals. Then the posterior probability of the constituent $C^{(K-1)}$ which says that all the $K-1$ cells exemplified in the evidence are instantiated, but leaves the one cell empty that was not exemplified in the sample, either, is

(4) $$P(C^{(K-1)}/e) = \prod_{i=0}^{\infty} g(n+i, K-1).$$

This formula holds whenever e is a sample from an infinite (denumerable or nondenumerable) universe. Assuming e, constituent $C^{(K-1)}$ is equivalent to a universal statement claiming that all individuals of the universe belong to the $K-1$ cells already exemplified in e. According to the results of Gaifman, Scott and Krauss,[6] the probability $P(C^{(K-1)}/e)$ equals the infimum of the probabilities of this universal statement on finite subsets of the universe (containing the sample e). This is precisely what we get from formula (4).

The value of (4) can be calculated by considering the transition given in figure 1 as being accomplished in two different ways and equating the resulting probabilities.

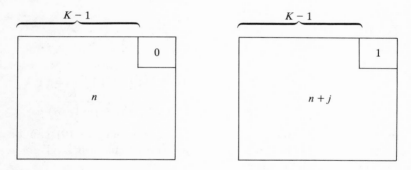

Fig. 1.

This yields

(5) $g(n, K-1)g(n+1, K-1) \ldots g(n+j-1, K-1)(1-g(n+j, K-1))$

$\qquad = (1-g(n, K-1))(1-f(1, n+1, K)) \ldots (1-f(1, n+j, K)).$

Here

(6) $$1 - f(1, n+i, K) = 1 - \frac{1 + \dfrac{\lambda}{K}}{n+i+\lambda} = \frac{n+i-1+\dfrac{K-1}{K}\lambda}{n+i+\lambda}.$$

---

[6] See H. Gaifman, "Concerning measures on first-order calculi", *Israel Journal of Mathematics* 2 (1964), 1–18; and D. Scott and P. Krauss, "Assigning probabilities to logical formulas", in J. Hintikka and P. Suppes, eds., *Aspects of Inductive Logic* (Amsterdam; North-Holland, 1966), p. 224.

From (5) and (6) we get

(7) $\displaystyle\prod_{i=0}^{j-1} g(n+i, K-1) - \prod_{i=0}^{j} g(n+i, K-1)$

$$= (1-g(n, K-1)) \prod_{i=1}^{j} \frac{n+i-1+\dfrac{K-1}{K}\lambda}{n+i+\lambda}$$

Taking the sum over values $j = 1, 2, \ldots, m$ on both sides of (7) we obtain the partial product

(8) $\displaystyle\prod_{i=0}^{m} g(n+i, K-1) = g(n, K-1) - (1-g(n, K-1))$

$$\times \sum_{j=1}^{m} \prod_{i=1}^{j} \frac{n+i-1+\dfrac{K-1}{K}\lambda}{n+i+\lambda}$$

Hence, the desired probability equals

(9) $g(n, K-1) - (1-g(n, K-1)) \dfrac{\Gamma(n+1+\lambda)}{\Gamma\left(n+\dfrac{K-1}{K}\lambda\right)}$

$$\times \sum_{j=1}^{\infty} \frac{\Gamma\left(n+j+\dfrac{K-1}{K}\lambda\right)}{\Gamma(n+j+1+\lambda)}.$$

Here Γ is the Gamma function. The infinite sum in (9) can be evaluated when λ is a multiple of K. The calculation is given in Appendix 2. It yields the following result.

Theorem 9. If λ is a multiple of K, then the posterior probability (4) of constituent $C^{(K-1)}$ is

(10) $\displaystyle\prod_{i=0}^{\infty} g(n+i, K-1) = 1 - \frac{n+\lambda}{\dfrac{\lambda}{K}} f(0, n, K-1).$

The posterior probability (10) is greater than zero if and only if

$$f(0, n, K-1) < \frac{\dfrac{\lambda}{K}}{n+\lambda},$$

i.e., if and only if the inductive method determined by f is more optimistic than the methods in Carnap's λ-continuum. When

$f(0, n, K-1)$ equals the Carnapian value, the conditional (a posteriori) probability of $C^{(K-1)}$ equals zero. In other words, in the special case at hand, Carnap's λ-continuum represents the most pessimistic possible strategy of inductive generalization.

Notice, incidentally, that for λ which is a multiple of K we obtain as the probability of $C^{(K-1)}$ on evidence which consists of $K-1$ individuals in $K-1$ cells

$$1 - \frac{(K-1+\lambda)K}{\lambda} f(0, K-1, K-1)$$

which is greater than zero if and only if $f(0, K-1, K-1)$ is chosen more optimistically than by Carnap. It equals zero for the Carnapian value of $f(0, K-1, K-1)$, and is smaller than zero for a more pessimistic value of $f(0, K-1, K-1)$. This shows that the parameter $f(0, K-1, K-1)$ cannot be chosen more pessimistically than by Carnap.

It remains to estimate the asymptotic behavior of $f(0, n, K-1)$ when n grows without limit. For the purpose, note first that if we are more optimistic than Carnap with respect to the probability $f(1, K-1, K-1)$, we must ever since be more optimistic than Carnap:

Theorem 10.
$$f(n', n, K-1) > \frac{n' + \dfrac{\lambda}{K}}{n + \lambda},$$

if

$$f(1, K-1, K-1) > \frac{1 + \dfrac{\lambda}{K}}{K-1+\lambda}.$$

Proof. By induction on n by means of Corollary 7.2. ∎

The condition for $f(1, K-1, K-1)$ in Theorem 10 is equivalent to

(11)
$$f(0, K-1, K-1) < \frac{\dfrac{\lambda}{K}}{K-1+\lambda}.$$

Note further that

$$f(0, n+1, K-1) = f(0, n, K-1) \frac{f(n', n+1, K)}{f(n', n, K-1)}$$

by Theorem 3, where

$$f(n', n+1, K) = \frac{n' + \dfrac{\lambda}{K}}{n + \lambda}$$

by Theorem 4. A simple inductive argument shows then that

$$f(0, n+1, K-1) < \frac{\dfrac{\lambda}{K}}{n+1+\lambda}$$

for a suitable value of $f(0, K-1, K-1)$, that is, for a value satisfying (11). Hence the posterior probability (10) will be greater than zero for a suitable initial value of $f(0, K-1, K-1)$, viz. for those values of this parameter which are more optimistic than Carnap's value. A closer analysis shows that when $n \to \infty$, in this case, the posterior probability (10) will approach one as the limit.

A sketch of such an argument can be given as follows. Suppose that $f(0, K-1, K-1)$ satisfies the condition (11). By Theorem 10, for any $m \geq K-1$ there is a $\mu > 1$ such that $\alpha(m, K-1)$ is μ times better than Carnap's value, i.e.,

$$\alpha(m, K-1) = \frac{\mu}{m+\lambda}.$$

Then by Corollary 7.2

$$(12) \qquad \alpha(m+1, K-1)(m+\lambda+1) = 1 + \frac{m+\lambda - \dfrac{m+\lambda}{\mu}}{m+\lambda+1-\dfrac{\lambda}{K}}$$

$$= \frac{\mu-1}{\mu} \cdot \frac{m+\lambda}{m+\lambda+1-\dfrac{\lambda}{K}} + 1.$$

By Theorems 3, 4, and 6, we obtain $(m+\lambda)f(0, m, K-1)$

$$= (m+\lambda)f(0, m+1, K-1)\frac{f(n', m, K-1)}{f(n', m+1, K)}$$

$$= (m+\lambda)f(0, m+1, K-1)\alpha(m, K-1)(m+1+\lambda)$$

$$= (m+j+\lambda)f(0, m+j, K-1)\prod_{i=0}^{j-1} \alpha(m+i, K-1)(m+i+\lambda).$$

It thus follows that

$$(13) \qquad \lim_{j \to \infty} \frac{f(0, m+j, K-1)}{\dfrac{\dfrac{\lambda}{K}}{m+j+\lambda}} = \frac{\dfrac{K}{\lambda}(m+\lambda)f(0, m, K-1)}{\lim\limits_{j \to \infty} \prod\limits_{i=0}^{j-1} \alpha(m+i, K-1)(m+i+\lambda)}$$

For sufficiently large values of m, the infinite product in the denominator of (13) is, by formula (12), approximately

$$\mu\left(1+\frac{\mu-1}{\mu}\right)\left(1+\frac{1+\frac{\mu-1}{\mu}+1}{1+\frac{\mu-1}{\mu}}\right)\cdots$$

$$=\mu\left(1+\frac{\mu-1}{\mu}\right)\left(1+\frac{\mu-1}{2\mu-1}\right)\cdots\left(1+\frac{\mu-1}{i\mu-i+1}\right)\cdots$$

The general term here is

$$1+\frac{\mu-1}{i\mu-i+1}=\frac{i(\mu-1)+\mu}{i(\mu-1)+1}.$$

Hence the product up to $j-1$ grows without limit when $j\to\infty$. It follows that formula (13) receives the value zero.

This argument shows that the posterior probability (10) approaches one when $n\to\infty$ and condition (11) holds. We have thus established the following theorem.

Theorem 11. Whenever the parameter $f(0, K-1, K-1)$ is more optimistic than Carnap's value (i.e., satisfies condition (11)), the posterior probability (10) of constituent $C^{(K-1)}$ receives asymptotically the value one.

VIII. POSTERIOR PROBABILITIES FOR CONSTITUENTS: GENERAL CASE

Although the results of Section 7 concern directly only the special case in which $c = K-1$ and λ is a multiple of K, they can be generalized. It can be seen that the product

(14) $$\prod_{i=0}^{j} g(n+i, K-1)$$

is a monotonic function of λ, when $\lambda \geq K$. Hence we can see qualitatively the behavior of the product (14) at large $(\lambda \geq K)$ by interpolating from our special result (Theorem 11). For all values of $\lambda \geq K$ the product (14), and hence the posterior probability of constituent $C^{(K-1)}$, approaches one when $j\to\infty$, provided that $f(0, K-1, K-1)$ is smaller (i.e., more optimistic) than its Carnapian value.

This result can be extended to other values of c, $c < K-1$, by considering the transition given in figure 2 and by identifying the probabilities of two special ways in which it can be accomplished.

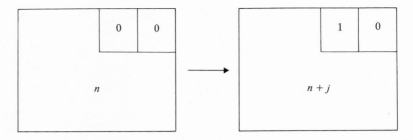

Fig. 2.

This yields

$$f(0, n, K-2) \prod_{i=0}^{j-1} [g(n+1+i, K-1) - f(1, n+1+i, K-1)]$$

$$= \prod_{i=0}^{j-1} g(n+i, K-2) f(0, n+j, K-2).$$

Since $f(0, n, K-2) > f(0, n+j, K-2)$ for sufficiently large values of j, we have, by Theorem 6(a) and (b), for non-Carnapian values

$$\textbf{(15)} \qquad \prod_{i=0}^{j-1} g(n+i, K-2) > \prod_{i=0}^{j-1} \left(1 - \frac{1+\dfrac{\lambda}{K}}{n+1+i+\dfrac{(K-1)\lambda}{K}} \right) \times$$

$$\times g(n+1+i, K-1).$$

Since the right-hand expression in (15) approaches one when $j \to \infty$ (for non-Carnapian parameter values), the left-hand expression must do likewise.

By putting these results together, the following theorem is obtained.

Theorem 12. Whenever $\lambda \geq K$, $1 \leq c < K$, and the parameters $f(0, c, c)$ are chosen more optimistically than their Carnapian values, the posterior probability on increasing evidence is asymptotically one for the simplest constituent $C^{(c)}$ compatible with evidence and asymptotically zero for other constituents compatible with evidence.

This theorem shows that we in fact obtain, from our Basic Assumption, a qualitatively (asymptotically) satisfactory treatment of inductive generalization.

IX. INTERRELATIONS OF THE NEW SYSTEM AND CARNAP'S λ-CONTINUUM

In earlier sections, we have established a number of results which illustrate the relation of our Basic Assumption to Carnap's λ-continuum. Theorem 10 which concerns the case $c = K - 1$ can be generalized other values of c by a simple inductive argument.

Theorem 13. Assuming

$$f(0, c+i, c+i) < \frac{\dfrac{\lambda}{K}}{c+i+\lambda}$$

for $i = 0, 1, \ldots, K - c - 1$, we have

$$f(n', n, c) > \frac{n' + \dfrac{\lambda}{K}}{n + \lambda}.$$

Proof. Assume that the claim of this theorem holds when $c > c_0$ and when $n < n_0$. Then from Theorem 7 it follows that it holds for c_0 and n_0, i.e., that it holds for c_0 if it holds for $c > c_0$. The rest follows now from Theorem 10. ∎

We have also seen that the only exception to Theorem 12 concerning inductive generalization is the case when the free parameters of our system have their Carnapian values. In brief, it can be said that Carnap's λ-continuum represents the worst possible case in our wider continuum.

The parameters $f(0, c, c)$ $(c = 1, 2, \ldots, K - 1)$ of the new system can be chosen, in several ways, more optimistically than their corresponding Carnapian values. One such possibility which seems interesting is to choose them in Carnapian way, but with a value λ_0 of λ which yields more optimistic values than the λ corresponding to the case $c = K$, i.e.,

(16) $$f(0, c, c) = \frac{\dfrac{\lambda_0}{K}}{c + \lambda_0} < \frac{\dfrac{\lambda}{K}}{c + \lambda}.$$

Here $0 < \lambda_0 < \lambda$. The difference $\lambda - \lambda_0$ in a sense measures the 'distance' of the choice (16) of the parameters from Carnap's λ-continuum, and λ_0 serves as a kind of an index of caution with respect to inductive generalization.

X. THE INTERPRETATION OF THE PARAMETERS

A feeling for the intuitive interpretation of the parameters of our system is obtained from the simplest case $K = 2$. In this case, there are two free parameters for which we can choose $f(0, 1, 1)$ and $f(1, 3, 2)$. They behave somewhat like parameters α and λ, respectively, within Hintikka α-λ-continuum. In fact, by Theorem 4

$$f(n', n, 2) = \frac{n' + \dfrac{\lambda_2}{2}}{n + \lambda_2},$$

where λ_2 is uniquely determined by $f(1, 3, 2)$. When λ_2 is an even positive integer, Theorem 9 yields as the a priori probability of constituent $C^{(1)}$

(17) $\dfrac{1}{2}\left(1 - \dfrac{2(\lambda_2 + 1)}{\lambda_2} f(0, 1, 1)\right) = \dfrac{1}{2} - \dfrac{\lambda_2 + 1}{\lambda_2} f(0, 1, 1).$

Since $f(1, 1, 1) = 1 - f(0, 1, 1)$, in this case, (17) is equal to

(18) $\dfrac{1}{2}\left[f(1, 1, 1) - (1 - f(1, 1, 1))\dfrac{\lambda_2 + 2}{\lambda_2}\right].$

Here $C^{(1)}$ is a constituent which claims that precisely one particular cell of the partition is instantiated. The a priori probability of the constituent $C^{(2)}$ which claims that both cells are instantiated can be evaluated as follows:

(19) $2g(0, 0)(1 - g(1, 1)) + \displaystyle\sum_{m=1}^{\infty} 2g(0, 0)g(1, 1) \ldots g(m, 1)$

$$\times (1 - g(m+1, 1) = 1 - g(1, 1) + g(1, 1) - \prod_{i=1}^{\infty} g(i, 1)$$

$$= 1 - \prod_{i=1}^{\infty} g(i, 1) = \frac{2(\lambda + 1)}{\lambda} f(0, 1, 1).$$

It follows that the a priori probability of the constituent $C^{(0)}$ which claims that both cells are empty is zero. (This fact is already implicit in Corollary 1.1.)

The a priori probability of $C^{(2)}$ is thus proportional to $f(0, 1, 1)$, while the probability of $C^{(1)}$ is inversely related to $f(0, 1, 1)$. When $f(0, 1, 1)$ grows towards the Carnapian value

$$\frac{\dfrac{\lambda_2}{2}}{1 + \lambda_2},$$

the probability of $C^{(1)}$ approaches zero and the probability of $C^{(2)}$ approaches one. This corresponds to the case $\alpha \to \infty$ within Hintikka's α-λ-continuum. When $f(0, 1, 1) = 0$, the probabilities (17) and (19) reduce to 1/2 and 0, respectively. This case falls outside the scope of Hintikka's α-λ-continuum: here the a priori probability is one for the hypothesis that there exists individuals in one and only one cell of the universe, so that already one observation is enough to raise the posterior probability of the corresponding constituent $C^{(1)}$ to one.

When $\lambda_2 \to \infty$, the probabilities (17) and (19) approach the values $1/2 - f(0, 1, 1)$ and $2f(0, 1, 1)$ respectively. These probabilities are equal, in this case, if $f(0, 1, 1) = 1/6$.

In the general case ($K \geqq 2$), parameter $f(1, K+1, K)$ helps to govern the behavior of our system with respect to singular inductive inference, while parameters $f(0, c, c)$, $c = 1, 2, \ldots, K-1$, help to govern its behavior both with respect to singular inductive inference and with respect to inductive generalization. The two kinds of inference are thus less sharply distinguished from one another than in Hintikka's α-λ-system, and their intuitive content accordingly is less clear.

The interpretation of our parameters along these lines can be further illustrated by pointing out that when $\lambda = K$ and when the parameters $f(0, c, c)$, $c = 1, 2, \ldots, K-1$, are chosen in a suitable way we obtain Hintikka's generalized combined system, which likewise results from setting the λ of Hintikka's α-λ-continuum equal to K. This possibility of deriving the generalized combined system in two essentially different ways seems to be a strong argument for its naturalness.

The representative function of Hintikka's generalized combined system was given above in formula (3). It follows from (3) that

$$f(n', n, K) = \frac{n'+1}{n+K},$$

which corresponds to Theorem 4 with $\lambda_K = K$. By (3) we obtain further

$$f(n', n, K-1) = \frac{(n'+1)(n+2K+\alpha-1)}{(n+K)(n+2K+\alpha-2)}.$$

Hence

$$f(0, n, K-1) = \frac{K+\alpha-1}{(n+K)(n+2K+\alpha-2)}.$$

and, in particular,

(20) $$f(0, K-1, K-1) = \frac{1}{(2K-1)\left(1+\dfrac{2K-2}{K+\alpha-1}\right)}$$

From formula (20) and Theorem 9 we see that the posterior probability of constituent $C^{(K-1)}$ on evidence exemplifying $K-1$ cells is

$$1 - \frac{K+\alpha-1}{n+2K+\alpha-2}.$$

Formula (20) defines a one-to-one correspondence between certain values of the parameter $f(0, K-1, K-1)$ of the new system and the parameter α of Hintikka's generalized combined system. When α grows from 0 to ∞, $f(0, K-1, K-1)$ grows from $\dfrac{1}{3(2K-1)}$ to $\dfrac{1}{2K-1}$. The latter equals the corresponding Carnapian value, in this case. On the other hand, the values

$$f(0, K-1, K-1) < \frac{1}{3(2K-1)}$$

fall outside the scope of the combined system, i.e., they are more optimistic than the inductive strategies within Hintikka's α-λ-continuum with $\lambda(w) = w$.

XI. CONCLUSIONS

What are the philosophical implications of our results? The following are among the general points that can be made on the basis of our observations.

(1) It is possible to build on a simple axiomatic basis a logic of inductive generalization which is at least qualitatively adequate and which allows for a considerable flexibility in the choice of its characteristic parameters. This can be done in such a way that we obtain Carnap's λ-continuum as a limiting case and Hintikka's generalized combined system as another special case.

Thus our results serve to emphasize the naturalness of a logic of inductive *generalization*. It is only when the representative function is allowed to disregard completely the generalization aspect (i.e., disregard c) that one does not assign nonzero probabilities to generalizations also in an infinite universe.

(2) On earlier occasions, Hintikka has emphasized that if the symmetry (exchangeability) assumption is adhered to, to "bet" on (associate behavioristically detectable probabilities with) *strict generalizations* (in an infinite universe) amounts to betting in a certain manner on singular events (on the basis of finite evidence).[7] How one is willing to bet on generalizations nevertheless is usually shown by no particular finite bets one makes but rather one's whole strategy of betting on singular events (on finite evidence).

However, if the Basic Assumption is made, we can go further. Given the Basic Assumption, how I am going to bet on generalizations is shown by the finite set of values I give to $f(1, c, c)$ $(c = 1, 2, \ldots, K-1)$ and $f(1, K+1, K)$, i.e., is shown by a finite number of odds for betting on singular event on finite (and in fact quite small) evidence. This demonstrates strikingly the possibility of connecting closely bets on generalizations and bets on finite events.

APPENDIX 1

A proof for Theorem 4 is given in this appendix. The following lemmas are immediate corollaries of Theorem 1.

Lemma 1. $f(n-K+1, n, K) = 1 - (K-1)f(1, n, K)$, if $n \geq K$.

Lemma 2. $f(n-K+1, n+1, K) + f(2, n+1, K) + (K-2)f(1, n+1, K) = 1$, if $n \geq K$.

As a special case of Corollary 2.1 we obtain

Lemma 3. $f(n', n+1, K) = f(1, n+1, K)\dfrac{f(n', n, K)}{f(1, n, K)}$, provided that $0 < n' \leq n - K + 1$.

By combining Lemma 2 and Lemma 3, we obtain

Lemma 4.

$$f(1, n+1, K)\left[\frac{f(n-K+1, n, K)}{f(1, n, K)} + \frac{f(2, n, K)}{f(1, n, K)} + (K-2)\right] = 1.$$

---

[7] Cf. J. Hintikka, "Unknown probabilities, Bayesianism, and de Finetti's Representation Theorem", in R. C. Buck and R. S. Cohen, eds., *Boston Studies in the Philosophy of Science* VIII (Dordrecht: D. Reidel, 1971), 325–341.

Lemma 1 and Lemma 4 together yield

Lemma 5. $\dfrac{f(1, n+1, K)}{f(1, n, K)} = \dfrac{1}{1 - f(1, n, K) + f(2, n, K)}.$

We are now ready to prove the following result.

Claim. $f(n', n, K) = \dfrac{(n'-1) - (K(n'-1)-1)\beta}{(n-K) - (n-K-1)K\beta}$

where $\beta = f(1, K+1, K)$, $0 \leq \beta \leq 1$, $n' > 0$, and $n \geq K > 2$.

Proof. By induction on $n \geq K$. Note first that when $n = K$, then $n' = 1$ and $f(1, K, K) = \dfrac{1}{K}$. When $n = K+1$ and $n' = 1$,

$$f(1, K+1, K) = \frac{0 - (K \cdot 0 - 1)\beta}{1 - 0 \cdot K\beta} = \beta.$$

Inductive step:

$$f(n', n+1, K) = f(n', n, K)\frac{f(1, n+1, K)}{f(1, n, K)} \quad \text{(by Lemma 3)}$$

$$= \frac{f(n', n, K)}{1 - f(1, n, K) + f(2, n, K)} \quad \text{(by Lemma 5)}$$

$$= \frac{[(n'-1) - (K(n'-1)\beta][(n-K) - (n-K-1)K\beta]}{[(n-K) - (n-K-1)K\beta][(n-K) - (n-K-1)K\beta - \beta + 1 - (K-1)\beta]}$$

$$= \frac{(n'-1) - (K(n'-1)-1)\beta}{(n-K+1) - (n-K)K\beta}. \quad \begin{array}{l}\text{(by inductive}\\ \text{hypothesis)}\end{array}$$

Theorem 4 follows from the above Claim by putting

$$\lambda_K = \frac{K\beta}{1 - K\beta} - K.$$

APPENDIX 2

A proof of Theorem 9 is given in this appendix. We shall first prove the following result.

Lemma 6. If a and b are positive integers, then

$$\sum_{j=1}^{\infty} \frac{\Gamma(j+a)}{\Gamma(j+a+b+1)} = \frac{\Gamma(a+1)}{b\Gamma(a+b+1)}.$$

Proof.   Let

$$r(j, b) = \frac{\Gamma(j+a)}{\Gamma(j+a+b+1)} = \frac{1}{(j+a)(j+a+1)\ldots(j+a+b)}.$$

Then $r(j, b)$ can be expressed as a sum

$$r(j, b) = \sum_{k=0}^{b} \frac{c_k}{j+a+k}$$

where the coefficients c_k, $k = 0, 1, \ldots, b$, are determined by

$$c_k = \lim_{j \to -(a+k)} \frac{1}{(j+a)\ldots(j+a+k-1)(j+a+ \quad +k+1)\ldots(j+a+b)}$$

$$= \frac{(-1)^k}{k!(b-k)!} = \frac{(-1)^k \binom{b}{k}}{b!}.$$

A simple inductive argument shows that

$$d_k = \sum_{i=0}^{k} c_i = \frac{(-1)^k}{k!(b-k-1)!b} = \frac{(-1)^k \binom{b-1}{k}}{b!}$$

for $k = 0, 1, \ldots, b-1$, and

$$d_b = \sum_{i=0}^{b} c_i = 0.$$

Hence the infinite sum of $r(j, b)$, $j = 1, 2, \ldots$, reduces to a finite sum, and can be evaluated as follows:

$$\sum_{j=1}^{\infty} r(j, b) = \sum_{k=0}^{b-1} \frac{d_k}{a+k+1} = \sum_{k=0}^{b-1} \frac{(-1)^k \binom{b-1}{k}}{b!(1+a+k)}$$

$$= \frac{(b-1)!}{b!} r(1, b-1) = \frac{r(1, b-1)}{b} = \frac{\Gamma(a+1)}{b\Gamma(a+b+1)}.$$

This completes the proof of Lemma 6.   ■

Suppose now that $\lambda(=\lambda_K)$ is a multiple of K, i.e., $\dfrac{\lambda}{K} = b$ is a positive integer. Let $a = n + (K-1)b$. Then, by Lemma 6,

$$\frac{\Gamma(n+1+\lambda)}{\Gamma\left(n+\frac{K+1}{K}\lambda\right)} \sum_{j=1}^{\infty} \frac{\Gamma\left(n+j+\frac{K-1}{K}\lambda\right)}{\Gamma(n+j+1+\lambda)}$$

$$= \frac{\Gamma(a+b+1)}{\Gamma(a)} \sum_{j=1}^{\infty} \frac{\Gamma(j+a)}{\Gamma(j+a+b+1)}$$

$$= \frac{\Gamma(a+b+1)\Gamma(a+1)}{b\Gamma(a)\Gamma(a+b+1)} = \frac{a}{b} = \frac{K}{\lambda}\left(n+\frac{K-1}{K}\lambda\right).$$

By formula (9), we obtain as the a posteriori probability of constituent $C^{(K-1)}$

$$g(n, K-1) - (1 - g(n, K-1))\frac{K}{\lambda}\left(n+\frac{K-1}{K}\lambda\right)$$

which equals

$$1 - f(0, n, K-1)\frac{K}{\lambda}(n+\lambda),$$

since $g(n, K-1) = 1 - f(0, n, K-1)$ by Theorem 6.

POSTSCRIPT 1976

This paper is printed here essentially in the form in which it was presented at the Conference on Formal Methods in the Methodology of Empirical Sciences in Warsaw, June 17–27, 1974, and in which it appears in the *Proceedings* of that conference, edited by M. Przełęcki, K. Szaniawski, and R. Wójcicki, and published in 1976 by Ossolineum (Poland) and Reidel (Holland).

Additional results about the new system have been obtained by I. Niiniluoto; they are contained in the paper "On a K-dimensional system of inductive logic", presented at the meeting of the Philosophy of Science Association in Chicago, October 29–31, 1976. Among these results, the following may be mentioned:

(1) Reichenbach's axiom and the principle of positive instantial relevance are valid in the new system.

(2) If one denotes $\gamma_c = f(0, c, c)$, for $c = 1, \ldots, K-1$, and if the Carnapian values of these parameters are denoted by

$$\delta_c^K = \frac{\lambda/K}{c+\lambda},$$

then

$$P(C^{(K)}) = \frac{\gamma_1 \cdots \gamma_{K-1}}{\delta_1^K \cdots \delta_{K-1}^K}.$$

This formula gives directly the result that, for any choice of $\lambda > 0$, $\gamma_c \leqq \delta_c^K$ for all $c = 1, \ldots, K-1$.

(3) The representative function relativized to a constituent $C^{(w)}$ is given by the equation

$$P(Q_i(a_{n+1})/e_n \& C^{(w)}) = \frac{\lambda/K}{c + \dfrac{w\lambda}{K}}.$$

(4) The intersection of the new system with Hintikka's λ-α-continuum contains precisely those members of the latter which satisfy the condition that $\lambda(w) = aw$ for some constant a. The generalized combined system is obtained by putting $a = 1$. (The observation that all members of the λ-α-system of this kind are also members of the new system is due to T. A. Kuipers.)

(5) $f(0, n, c)$, $n \geqq c$, is proportional to γ_c but inversely proportional to other relevant γ-parameters. Hence, $f(n', n, c)$, $n > 0$, and $g(n, c)$ are inversely proportional to γ_c but proportional to other relevant γ-parameters. Similarly, $P(C^{(w)})$ is inversely proportional to γ_w. If $n = c = w$, then $P(C^{(w)}/e_n) \to 1$ when e_n is compatible with $C^{(w)}$ and $\gamma_w \to 0$. The parameter γ_w can thus be regarded as an index of caution about the truth of constituents of width w.

I. N.

8

A Survey of
Inductive Systems

BY THEO A. F. KUIPERS

1. INTRODUCTION

In *Studies in Inductive Probability*...[1] we reformulated Carnap's program of inductive logic (or probability) in terms of "rational expectation with respect to theories and (outcomes of) experiments". It turned out to be convenient to formulate the "pure systems" behind Carnap's λ-continuum[2] and Hintikka's α-λ-continuum[3] in set theoretical terms. In other words, the "logico-linguistic" approaches of Carnap are set aside, and the assignment of probabilities to the sentences of a language is reconstructed as a particular type of application of pure systems.

Besides two chapters on pure systems, the main chapters in the book are concerned with a general characterization of rational expectation patterns and with a precise characterization of the contexts in which two main types of pure systems (C-systems, corresponding to the λ-continuum, and (open) NH-systems, described by Hintikka and Niiniluoto in article 7 above) give rise to such rational patterns of expectation.

---

[1] Theo A. F. Kuipers, *Studies in Inductive Probability and Rational Expectation*, Synthese Library 123 (Dordrecht: D. Reidel, 1978).

[2] Rudolf Carnap, *The Continuum of Inductive Methods* (Chicago: University of Chicago Press, 1952).

[3] Jaakka Hintikka, "A two-dimensional continuum of inductive methods", in *Aspects of Inductive Logic*, ed. J. Hintikka and P. Suppes (Amsterdam: North-Holland, 1966), pp. 113–132.

In this article we shall formulate, without proofs, only the main results of the chapters on pure systems as far as the axiomatic relations and the "inductive" properties are concerned. Because of the reconstructive character, a number of results are reformulations of known results. Definitions and terminology differ slightly from that in the book, in order to avoid complications in this article.

The proof of a main theorem (T9 below) is also given in "On the generalization of the continuum of inductive methods".[4] That theorem states that the NH-systems are in fact systems belonging to the class of background systems (H-systems) of the α-λ-continuum.

2. CONSISTENT PROBABILITY PATTERNS

Let K be a nonempty finite set $\{Q_1, Q_2, \ldots, Q_k\}$. Let e_n indicate an arbitrary element and E_n an arbitrary subset of K^n, i.e., the nth Cartesian product of K. By $n_i(e_n)$ we indicate the number of occurrences of Q_i in e_n. As variables for *nonempty* subsets of K we use W and V. The size of a subset of K is indicated by the corresponding small letter, e.g., $|W| = w$.

In addition, we use the following abbreviations: $M(e_n) = \{Q_i : n_i(e_n) > 0\}$; $H_W(n) = \{e_n : M(e_n) = W\}$ with $n \geqq w$; finally, $H_W = \bigcup_{n=w}^{\infty} H_W(n)WWW\ldots$. Note that H_W contains those infinite sequences in which all members of W occur at least once and members outside W never occur. Because there is a 1–1-correspondence between these subsets of K^∞ and the so-called constituents in the application-context of "A two dimensional continuum",[5] and "An axiomatic foundation",[6] we call the former *constituents* also. The constituents H_W constitute a (finite) partition of K^∞, i.e., they are mutually nonoverlapping and together exhaustive.

If misunderstandings are excluded, we write simply n_i and M, instead of $n_i(e_n)$ and $M(e_n)$.

Def. 1. A *consistent probability pattern* (CPP) w.r.t. $K, K^2, K^3, \ldots$ is a real-valued function for which:

(1.1) $$p(e_n) \geqq 0$$

---

[4] Theo A. F. Kuipers, "On the generalization of the continuum of inductive methods to universal hypotheses", in *Synthese* 37.3 (1978), pp. 255–284.

[5] Jaakko Hintikka, "A two-dimensional continuum".

[6] Jaakko Hintikka and Ilkka Niiniluoto, "An axiomatic foundation".

(1.2)
$$\sum_{e_n \in K^n} p(e_n) = 1$$

(2)
$$\sum_{Q_i \in K} p(e_n Q_i) = p(e_n)$$

(3)
$$p(E_n) = \sum_{e_n \in E_n} p(e_n)$$

The pattern is *regular* (RCPP) if (1.1) may be replaced by (1.1R) $p(e_n) > 0$.

A *special value* of a CPP is defined by

(4)
$$p(Q_i/e_n) = p(e_n Q_i)/p(e_n) \qquad (p(e_n) \neq 0)$$

Similarly we use e.g., the abbreviations: $p(Q_i Q_j/e_n) = p(e_n Q_i Q_j)/p(e_n)$ and $p(MM/e_n) = p(e_n MM)/p(e_n)$. However, $p(Q_i/e_n M)$, $Q_i \in M$, is short for $p(e_n Q_i)/p(e_n M)$. All probability expressions with '$./e_n$' are supposed to include e_0 in a straight-forward way, e.g., $p(Q_i/e_0) = p(Q_i)$.

It is easy to see that a CPP is completely determined by its special values (if $p(e_n) = 0$ then also $p(e_n Q_i) = 0$) and they satisfy

(5.1)
$$p(Q_i/e_n) \geqq 0$$

(5.2)
$$\sum_{Q_i \in K} p(Q_i/e_n) = 1$$

for all e_n for which $p(e_n) \neq 0$. In a RCCP (5) holds unconditionally and the equality-sign in (5.1) may be omitted.

The well-known extension theorem of Kolmogorov guarantees that the definition, on the basis of a CPP,

(6)
$$p(E_n KKK\ldots) = p(E_n)$$

leads to a unique probability measure on the set of (measurable) subsets of K^∞, e.g., $p(H_W)$ is uniquely determined by (6). Because the constituents constitute a partition we have

(7.1)
$$p(H_W) \geqq 0$$

(7.2)
$$\sum_{W \subset K} p(H_W) = 1$$

The function $p(H_W)$ is called *the prior constitutional distribution* of the CPP. If $p(H_K) = 1$ (and hence $p(H_W) = 0$ for all $W \neq K$) the CPP is said to be *closed*, otherwise it is called *open*.

If $p(H_W) \neq 0$, we define for $e_n \in W^n$ and $Q_i \in W$

(8) $p_W(e_n) = p(H_W \cap e_n WWW \ldots)/p(H_W)$

(9) $p_W(Q_i/e_n) = p_W(e_n Q_i)/p_W(e_n)$

It is easy to check that p_W is a CPP w.r.t. W, W^2, $W^3, \ldots$ and that it is closed: $p_W(H_W) = 1$. Moreover we have

(10) $p(e_n) = \sum_{W \supset M} p(H_W) p_W(e_n)$

From (10) it follows that in case of an RCCP we may add to (7):

(7.3) $p(H_K) > 0$

We may conclude from this analysis that a CCP can also be determined by the prior constitutional distribution and (the special values of) the relativized patterns.

On the bases of the *relativized patterns* p_W we define *the posterior constitutional distribution*, of course, as

(11) $p(H_W/e_n) = p(H_W) p_W(e_n)/p(e_n)$ $W \supset M$

which is easily seen to be a probability distribution on the H_W with $W \supset M$.

3. *C*-SYSTEMS

Let $0(e_n, e'_n)$ indicate that e'_n is a permutation of (the order of) e_n. Hence, 0 is an equivalence-relation in K^n, for all n. Consider the principles

SPOI *Strong principle of order indifference*

$$p(e'_n) = p(e_n) \quad \text{if} \quad 0(e_n, e'_n)$$

POI $p(Q_i Q_j/e_n) = p(Q_j Q_i/e_n)$

POI' $p(Q_i/e'_n) = p(Q_i/e_n) \quad \text{if} \quad 0(e_n, e'_n)$

These principles are related by the following theorem:

T1. A CPP satisfies SPOI iff it satisfies POI and POI′ (the proof of the if-clause is not trivial).

All systems to be presented satisfy SPOI. Consider now the principle

PERR *Principle of equal restricted relevance*

$$p(Q_i/e_n) = f(n, n_i)$$

(i.e., $p(Q_i/e_n)$ depends only on n and n_i.) Note that PERR implies POI′. The axiomatic introduction of the λ-continuum is based on

T2. If $k > 2$, a CPP satisfying POI and PERR has special values according to

(12) $$p(Q_i/e_n) = (n_i + \lambda/k)/(n + \lambda)$$

in which λ is a real number with $0 \leqq \lambda \leqq \infty$.

Def. 2. A *Carnapian system* (*C*-system) is a RCPP for which there is a real number λ, $0 < \lambda < \infty$, such that (12) holds. Note that the exclusion of $\lambda = 0$ guarantees that *C*-systems are regular. The next theorem is of fundamental importance:

T3. A *C*-system is closed, i.e., $p(H_K) = 1$ (and $p(H_W) = 0$, $W \neq K$). It has frequently been said that *C*-systems assign zero probability to all nontrivial generalizations. In our approach it becomes clear that this statement is highly problematic, for $p(H_K) = 1$ implies the expectation that *all* members of K will occur sooner or later. Note that a *C*-system "remains closed": $p(H_K/e_n) = 1$ for all e_n.

The main confirmation properties of *C*-systems are

  instantial confirmation

(13) $p(Q_i/e_n Q_i) > p(Q_i/e_n)$

  strong universal-instance confirmation

(14) $p(M/e_n Q_i) > p(M/e_n)$ $Q_i \in M$

The last property implies

  universal-instance confirmation

(15) $p(M/e_nM) > p(M/e_n)$

The following convergence properties can be formulated in a precise way

  instantial convergence

(16) $p(Q_i/e_n) \to n_i/n$ if $n \to \infty$

  universal-instance convergence

(17) $p(M/e_n) \to 1$ if $n \to \infty$ and M remains constant

In this article we call confirmation and convergence properties together: *inductive properties*.

4. *NH*-SYSTEMS

Consider now the following weak variant of PERR (again implying POI'):

WPERR $p(Q_i/e_n) = f_m(n, n_i)$

This principle is equivalent to the conjunction of

NH1. $p(M/e_n) = g(n, m) = 1 - h(n, m) = 1 - p(\bar{M}/e_n)$

NH2.1. $p(Q_i/e_n\bar{M}) = 1/(k - m)$ $Q_i \notin M$

NH2.2. $p(Q_i/e_nM) = k_m(n, n_i)$ $Q_i \in M$

The proof of the following theorem is analogous to that of T2

T4. In a RCCP, satisfying POI and WPERR, there is a real number ρ, $-1 < \rho \leqq \infty$, such that

(18) $p(Q_i/e_nM) = (n_i + \rho)/(n + m\rho)$ $Q_i \in M$

Def. 3. A *Niiniluoto–Hintikka-system* (*NH*-system) is a RCCP, satisfying NH1, NH2.1 and POI, for which there is a real number ρ, $0 < \rho < \infty$, such that (18) holds.

T5. A NH-system is completely determined by the k parameters ρ, $h(m, m)$, $m = 1, 2, \ldots, k-1$.

T6. A NH-system with $h(m, m) = (m + \rho)/(m + k\rho)$, $1 \leq m \leq k - 1$, is a C-system with $\lambda = k\rho$, and therefore it is also closed.

5. H-SYSTEMS, H_s-SYSTEMS, UNIVERSAL SYSTEMS

In Section 2 we saw that a CCP can be obtained by a prior constitutional distribution and closed relativized patterns.

Def. 4.1. A *Hintakka-system* (H-system) is a RCPP with C-systems as relativized patterns (with λ_W as parameter) such that we can write: $\lambda_W = \lambda_w$ (and $\rho_W =_{Df} \lambda_W/w = \rho_w$) and with prior constitutional distribution satisfying $p(H_K) > 0$ and

H3.
$$p(H_W) = q(w)$$

The principles leading to the relativized patterns are:

H1. $\qquad p_W(Q_i/e_n) = f^w(n, n_i) \qquad e_n Q_i \in W^{n+1}$

H2. $\qquad p_W(Q_i Q_j/e_n) = p_W(Q_j Q_i/e_n) \qquad e_n Q_i Q_j \in W^{n+2}$

which correspond to PERR and POI resp.

T7. A H-system satisfies SPOI.

Def. 4.2. A *special H-system* (H_s-system) is a H-system with constant $\rho_W (= \rho)$.

A H_s-system can be based on H1, H2, H3 and

H4. $\quad p_W(Q_i/e_n M) = p_V(Q_i/e_n M) \qquad Q_i \in M, W \supset M, V \supset M$

T8. A H-system is determined by $2k - 2$ parameters: $q(w)$, λ_w (or ρ_w), $1 \leq w \leq k - 1$; a H_s-system by k-parameters: $q(w)$, $1 \leq w \leq k - 1$ and ρ.

The next theorem, of which the proof is rather complicated, simplifies the study of NH-systems very much

T9. NH-systems are H_s-systems, and vice versa.

In relation with C-systems we have

T10. **1.** A closed H-system is, of course, a C-system
2. An open H_s-system satisfies

(19) $p(M/e_n) > (m + \rho)/(m + k\rho)$ $M \neq K$

The values at the right side are called the corresponding C-values. It is important to remark that the $h(m, m)$-parameters of T5 have to be in accordance with (19) to guarantee an open NH-system, but that this condition is not sufficient. The necessary and sufficient condition is rather complex and follows from the proof of T9, which will not be given here.

We call a H-system satisfying **UR** $p(H_W) > 0$ for all (nonempty) W a Universal (Regular) system (U-system). We call a H_s-system with this property a special U-system (U_s-system). Note that U-systems are *open* (H-)systems.

U-systems share with C-systems the properties of instantial and universal-instance confirmation and convergence. U_s-systems share in addition the property of *strong* universal-instance confirmation.

Unlike C-systems, U-systems have the following properties:

universal confirmation

(20) $p(H_M/e_n M) > p(H_M/e_n)$ $M \neq K$

universal convergence

(21) $p(H_M/e_n) \rightarrow 1$ if $n \rightarrow \infty$ and $M(\neq K)$ remains constant.

U_s-systems satisfy, in addition,

strong universal confirmation

(22) $p(H_M/e_n Q_i) > p(H_M/e_n)$ $M \neq K, Q_i \in M$

Hintikka's α-λ-continuum is a class of H-systems with a particular prior constitutional distribution which satisfies UR; hence it are U-systems with all listed inductive properties. However, in this article we shall not pay attention to prior distributions, except to one in the next section.

6. STRUCTURAL-INDIFFERENT SYSTEMS

Let $\ddot{e}_n$ indicate the *order-equivalence-class* (with respect to 0) of order-permutations of e_n. Consider the principle

PSI *principle of structural indifference*

$$p(\ddot{e}_n) = p(\ddot{e}'_n)$$

T11. A CPP satisfying SPOI and PSI is a C-system with $\lambda = k$, indicated as C^*-system.

Consider next the weak variant of PSI:

WPSI $p(\ddot{e}_n) = p(\ddot{e}'_n)$ if $m(e'_n) = m(e_n)$

T12. A CPP satisfying SPOI and WPSI is a H_s-system with $\rho = 1$, indicated as a H^*-system (or as U^*-system if UR holds).

If $m(e'_n) = m(e_n)$ we say that $\ddot{e}'_n$ and $\ddot{e}_n$ *have the same size.*
    In a discussion of Hintikka's α-λ-continuum, Carnap suggested a very interesting prior constitutional distribution. Let Z_w indicate the union of the sets H_W with $|W|$ equal to a fixed w. Z_w is called a *structure.* In a H-system we have, because of H3,

$$(23) \qquad p(Z_w) = \binom{k}{w} q(w)$$

Carnap suggested choosing $q(w)$ so that $p(Z_w) = 1/k$. Let a $^*U^*$-system be a U_s-system with $\rho = 1$ and this particular prior distribution. These systems do only depend on k, i.e., the size of K. In our opinion we may say that, for given K, the (unique) $^*U^*$-system is the most sophisticated application of the so-called (classical) principle of indifferences: equal probabilities for order-permutations, for order-equivalence-classes of the same size and for the structures.

7. GENERALIZED SYSTEMS

Def. 5. A Generalized C-system (GC-system) is a RCCP for which there are real numbers $\gamma_i > 0$, $\sum \gamma_i = 1$, and λ, $0 < \lambda < \infty$, such that

$$(24) \qquad p(Q_i/e_n) = (n_i + \gamma_i \lambda)/(n + \lambda)$$

T13. A GC-system satisfies POI and

PRR $p(Q_i/e_n) = f_i(n, n_i)$ (with $f_i(0, 0) = \gamma_i$)

and, consequently, POI' and SPOI. *Moreover, it is closed.*

Def. 6. **1.** A *Generalized H-system* (*GH-system*) is a RCCP with GC-systems as relativized patterns (with parameters γ_i^w and $\lambda_w(\rho_w = \lambda_w/w)$) and with an arbitrary prior constitutional distribution with $p(H_K) > 0$.

        2. A *special GH-system* (*GH_s-system*) is a GH-system satisfying, with $\gamma^w =_{\text{Df}} \sum\limits_{Q_i \in W} \gamma_i^K$, $\lambda_w = \lambda_K \cdot \gamma^w$ $\left(\text{or } \rho_w = \dfrac{k}{w} \rho_K \gamma^w\right)$ and $\gamma_i^w = \gamma_i^K/\gamma^w$.

T14. A GH-system satisfies SPOI.

T15. A closed GH-system is, of course, a GC-system.

    The GH_s-systems can directly be seen as generalization of the NH-systems: they arise from POI and

WPRR $p(Q_i/e_n) = f_{i,M}(n, n_i)$

Of course, we speak of GU- resp. GU_s-systems if UR is satisfied.

    All treated inductive properties of C-, U-, and U_s-systems hold also for GC-, GU-, and GU_s-systems, respectively.

    We conclude with a diagram of all treated systems, in which an arrow indicates inclusion.

9

On the Condition of
Partial Exchangeability

BY BRUNO DE FINETTI

Translation, by Paul Benacerraf and Richard Jeffrey, of "Sur la condition d'équivalence partielle", Actualités scientifiques et industrielles, No. 739 (Colloque Genève d'Octobre 1937 sur la Théorie des Probabilités, 6^{ieme} partie), Paris: Hermann & Cie., 1938.

From a philosophical point of view, the essential problem about the theory of probability is that of interpreting its connections with inductive reasoning: the answer to that question determines the role to be attributed to probability in science and, still more generally, in the theory of knowledge. Is it still possible to believe in the principle of causality and to use it as a justification of inductive reasoning? I would think not. The inductive method would then be applicable only in cases where the laws we are led to formulate have an apodictic character conforming to the conception of a rigid causality which we have assumed as a hypothesis; if instead we are led to formulate a "statistical" law, one having only a "probable" value, we cannot derive its justification from a principle which is, if not incompatible with it, at least totally alien to it.

Perhaps we could avoid the difficulty by modifying the principle of causality, but I do not think that principle was ever more than an illusory escape from David Hume's careful analysis and from the conception of causality which he urged; any modification in the direction indicated would only make this illusory character more obvious.

That is why I think we must return to Hume's position, which lends itself quite naturally to development and completion with the degree of precision which science requires, and in such a way that the two cases of "statistical" laws and "rigid" laws become completely unified (the latter appearing as a limiting case of the former).

To adopt this point of view and make it precise one must invert the roles of inductive reasoning and probability theory: it is the latter that has autonomous validity, whereas induction is the derived notion. One is thus led to conclude with Poincaré that "whenever we reason by induction we make more or less conscious use of the calculus of probabilities".

I think that the way in which I have sought to resolve the problem of inductive reasoning is nothing but a translation into logico-mathematical terms of Hume's ideas—a translation that follows the foregoing idea which Poincaré had advanced and clarified with penetrating considerations, but without drawing from it and accepting the radical consequences which strike me as unavoidable and on which my point of view is systematically based.

On this view, every evaluation of probability has only a subjective value, being subject only to the condition which I have called "coherence", and which simply reduces to the requirement that the probabilities attributed to different events not contradict the theorems of total and composite probabilities. To give this a precise interpretation one must note that—in the terminology which I prefer and which deviates in this respect from the usual terminology—an "event" is always a well-determined particular fact. What are sometimes called *repetitions* or *trials* of the same event are for us so many distinct events. In general, they will have common or symmetric characteristics which make it natural to attribute equal probabilities to them, but there is no a priori reason which prevents us in principle from attributing to the events $E_1, \ldots, E_n$ distinct and absolutely arbitrary probabilities $p_1, \ldots, p_n$. In principle, there is no difference for us between this case and that of n events which exhibit no similarities; the similarity which suggests the name "trials of the same event" (we would say: "of the same phenomenon") is not intrinsic: at the very most, its importance lies in the influence it may have on our psychological judgment, inclining us to attribute equal or nearly equal probabilities to the different events. In the same way what underlies probability evaluations based on observations of frequencies is only the inclination to psychological judgments derived from such an impression of similarity: inductive reasoning is completely reduced in this way to Hume's justification, which itself can yield explanations which penetrate and analyze more thoroughly the mechanism of that influence. It is a very simple mechanism, which basically reduces to the application of the principle of composite probabilities: if we expect with probability $p = P(E)$ that a given event E will happen, our attitude about E could be modified in the course of learning that certain other events $A_1, A_2, A_3, \ldots, A_m$ have happened, for our judgment will then be expressed by the respective subordinate (or conditional) probabilities

$$p_1 = P(E/A_1) = P(EA_1)/P(A_1)$$

and then

$$p_2 = P(E/A_1A_2) = P(EA_1A_2)/P(A_1A_2), \quad \text{etc.,}$$

and finally

$$p_m = P(E/A_1A_2 \ldots A_m) = P(EA_1A_2 \ldots A_m)/P(A_1A_2 \ldots A_m).$$

The simplest case, one already developed in earlier works,[1] is that of "exchangeable" events. The events $E_1, E_2, \ldots, E_h, \ldots$ (one might think of them, e.g., as a series of trials of the same phenomenon) are said to be exchangeable if they play a symmetrical role with respect to every problem of probability, which simply means that the probability that, among these events, n given events $E_{i_1} E_{i_2} \ldots E_{i_n}$ will happen depends only on n, and not on the particular n-tuple chosen. If we denote this probability by ω_n, the sequence $\omega_0(=1), \omega_1, \omega_2, \ldots, \omega_n, \ldots$ completely characterizes the family of exchangeable events E_h; in particular, the probability that, among n given events of that family, r take place and s ($=n-r$) do not, is

$$\omega_r^{(n)} = \binom{n}{r}\left\{\omega_r - \binom{s}{1}\omega_{r+1} + \binom{s}{2}\omega_{r+2} - \ldots + (-1)^s \omega_{r+s}\right\}$$

$$= \binom{n}{r}(-1)^s \Delta^s \omega_r.$$

---

[1] See *La prévision: ses lois logiques, ses sources subjectives*, Annales de l'institut Henri Poincaré, t. VII, fasc. I (1937), and the earlier works cited there. (Added in translation) English translation: *Foresight, Its Logical Laws, Its Subjective Sources*, in *Studies in Subjective Probability*, eds. Henry E. Kyburg, Jr., and Howard E. Smokler (New York: Wiley, 1964). For further material, including translations of some of the earlier works, see my *Probability, Induction, and Statistics* (New York: Wiley, 1972) and *Theory of Probability* (New York: Wiley, vol. 1, 1974; vol. 2, 1975).

For a given n, $\omega_0^{(n)}, \omega_1^{(n)}, \ldots, \omega_n^{(n)}$ $\Big($where, evidently, $\sum_0^n \omega_r^{(n)} =$
$1\Big)$ are the probabilities of the $n+1$ values $0, 1/n, 2/n, \ldots, n/n$
which can be assumed by the frequency of favorable results in n
fixed events (trials). It is easily shown that when n is very large this
distribution Φ_n merges with a limit distribution $\Phi = \lim \Phi_n$, and that
the moments of Φ are $\omega_0, \omega_1, \ldots, \omega_n, \ldots$. To be precise, we have
$\omega_n = \int_0^1 \xi^n \, d\Phi(\xi)$; analogously, $\omega_r^{(n)} = \binom{n}{r} \int_0^1 \xi^r (1-\xi)^s \, d\Phi(\xi)$, and, in
general, the probability of an arbitrary event E constructed from the
E_h is

$$P(E) = \int_0^1 P_\xi(E) \, d\Phi(\xi),$$

where $P_\xi(E)$ is the probability that E would have if the E_h were all
independent events of probability ξ. With these results in mind, let
us see what follows from them when the problem of induction is
posed for exchangeable events. Suppose that we know the results of
the first m trials $E_1, \ldots, E_m$ of which h and k $(=m-h)$ have been
favorable and unfavorable respectively; the combination which has
been realized can then be written $A = E_{i_1}E_{i_2} \ldots E_{i_h}\bar{E}_{j_1}\bar{E}_{j_2} \ldots \bar{E}_{j_k}$
(where $\bar{E}$ signifies "not E"). The probability of a further trial E_l
$(l > m)$ will then be

$$P(E_l/A) = P(AE_l)/P(A) = \frac{\omega_{h+1}^{(m+1)}}{\binom{m+1}{h+1}} : \frac{\omega_h^{(m)}}{\binom{m}{h}}$$

$$= \frac{\int_0^1 \xi \cdot \xi^h (1-\xi)^k \, d\Phi(\xi)}{\int_0^1 \xi^h (1-\xi)^k \, d\Phi(\xi)} = \int_0^1 \xi \, d\bar{\Phi}(\xi)$$

with

$$\bar{\Phi}(\xi) = \alpha \int_0^\xi \xi^h (1-\xi)^k \, d\Phi(\xi), \qquad \alpha = 1 : \int_0^1 \xi^h (1-\xi)^k \, d\Phi(\xi);$$

similarly, the probability that of n further trials, a determinate r and
s give favorable and unfavorable results respectively will be (desig-
nating that event by E)

$$P(E/A) = P(AE)/P(A) = \frac{\omega_{h+r}^{(m+n)}}{\binom{m+n}{h+r}} : \frac{\omega_h^{(m)}}{\binom{m}{h}}$$

$$= \frac{\int_0^1 \xi^n (1-\xi)^s \xi^h (1-\xi)^k \, d\Phi(\xi)}{\int_0^1 \xi^h (1-\xi)^k \, d\Phi(\xi)} = \int_0^1 \xi^r (1-\xi)^s \, d\bar{\Phi}(\xi)$$

and in general, the probability of an event E constructed from some of the E_h (after E_m) will be

$$P(E/A) = P(AE)/P(A) = \int_0^1 P_\xi(E) \, d\bar{\Phi}(\xi)$$

(P_ξ still having the same meaning). We now see that, given knowledge of the result of the first m trials, the subsequent trials will again be judged exchangeable, but the limit distribution Φ will be replaced by $\bar{\Phi}$; that is to say, the probability that the frequency in a very great number n of trials will lie between ξ and $\xi + d\xi$, a probability which was initially $d\Phi$, will be altered proportionally to $\xi^h(1-\xi)^k$. The probabilities around the maximum point $\bar{\xi} = h/m = $ the "observed frequency" will be reinforced (provided that $d\Phi \neq 0$ for $\xi = \bar{\xi}$), the more so, the larger m is; it follows that one will be led closer and closer to the judgment that the trials are independent and equally probable, with probability equal to the observed frequency. The mathematical aspect of these developments was of course well known; I only wanted to point out that they can be related to the notion of exchangeability, thus eliminating consideration of "unknown probabilities" and reinterpreting cases of reasoning along lines which accord with the subjective point of view. In other words, it explains the psychological reasons which quite often force us to attach to the probability of certain events a value near the frequency observed in analogous events.

But the case of exchangeability can only be considered as a limiting case: the case in which this "analogy" is in a certain sense *absolute* for all the events under consideration. Nor is the way of posing the problem limited to this simple case; in itself, it has a completely general validity, in that it reduces to the principle of composite probabilities: $P(E/A) = P(AE)/P(A)$. But in the absence of particular hypotheses concerning the influence of A on E, no determinate conclusion can be deduced. By this principle one can only indicate the direction of the conclusions, which is always the same: observation cannot confirm or disconfirm an opinion, which is and can be nothing but an opinion, and so neither true nor false; observation can only give us information which is capable of *influencing* our opinion. To get from the case of exchangeability to other cases which are more general but still tractable, we must take up the case where we still encounter "analogies" among the events under consideration, but without their attaining the limiting case of exchangeability.

Let us consider some examples, starting with the simplest possible one. Imagine a game of heads and tails, played with two irregular-looking coins. If the two coins look exactly alike, one may be led to judge all tosses as exchangeable, no matter which coin is used. If, on the contrary, the coins are completely different, we may be led, at the opposite extreme, to consider as separately exchangeable the tosses made with the one and with the other of the two coins, these two types being completely independent of each other. But there is also an intermediate case, and it is precisely that case which leads us to the generalization which we envisage. Suppose that the coins look only *almost* alike, even that they seem alike, but without this leading us to regard all trials as exchangeable—perhaps because we suspect hidden differences, or perhaps for some other reason; then observations of the tosses of one coin will still be capable of influencing—but in a *less direct* manner—our probability judgment regarding tosses of the other coin.

The same considerations can be applied to the case where there is only one coin but the tosses are made by two different people, or at two different degrees of temperature, of atmospheric pressure, etc. More generally, one can have any number of types of trials corresponding to different coins, people, temperatures, pressures, etc. (or combinations of these characteristics); temperature and pressure also give us an example of the limiting case where these "types" vary continuously, as functions of one parameter or of two (considering temperature and pressure together), and clearly one can imagine three or more parameters.

All the conclusions and formulas which hold for the case of exchangeability are easily extended to the present case of *partially exchangeable* events which we could define by the same symmetry condition, specifying that the events divide into a certain number of types $1, 2, \ldots, g$, and that it is only events of the same type which are to be treated as "interchangeable" for all probabilistic purposes. Here again, for this definition to be satisfied quite generally, it need only be satisfied in a seemingly much more special case: it suffices that there be a unique probability $\omega_{n_1, n_2, \ldots, n_g}$ that n given events all happen, where $n_1, n_2, \ldots, n_g$ belong respectively to the first, second, ..., gth types and $n_1 + n_2 + \ldots + n_g = n$— and where this unique probability is independent of the choice of particular events from each type. The g-fold infinite sequence of numbers $\omega_{n_1, n_2, \ldots, n_g}$ completely characterizes the events for all probabilistic purposes. Then the probability that, in $n_1 + n_2 + \ldots + n_g$ given events (n_1 of the first type, n_2 of the second, etc.; hereafter that will always be understood), there will be $r_1, r_2, \ldots, r_g$ favorable cases, is always (independently of the particular events)

$$\omega_{r_1, r_2, \ldots, r_g}^{(n_1, n_2, \ldots, n_g)} = (-1)^{s_1 + s_2 + \ldots + s_g} \binom{n_1}{r_1} \binom{n_2}{r_2} \ldots \binom{n_g}{r_g} \Delta_1^{s_1} \Delta_2^{s_2} \ldots \Delta_g^{s_g} \omega_{r_1, r_2, \ldots, r_g}$$

where $s_i = n_i - r_i$ and Δ_i is the difference with respect to the ith variable:

$$\Delta_1 \omega_{r_1, r_2, \ldots, r_g} = \omega_{r_1 + 1, r_2, \ldots, r_g} - \omega_{r_1, r_2, \ldots, r_g},$$

$$\Delta_2 \omega_{r_1, r_2, \ldots, r_g} = \omega_{r_1, r_2 + 1, \ldots, r_g} - \omega_{r_1, r_2, \ldots, r_g}, \ldots$$

The explicit formula is obtained by development (e.g., by setting $\Delta_i = \theta_i - 1$):

$$\Delta_1^{s_1} \Delta_2^{s_2} \ldots \Delta_g^{s_g} \omega_{r_1, r_2, \ldots, r_g}$$

$$= \sum_{0}^{s_1} \sum_{h_1}^{s_2} \sum_{0}^{s_g} \ldots \sum_{0}^{s_g} \binom{s_1}{h_1} \binom{s_2}{h_2} \ldots \binom{s_g}{h_g} \omega_{r_1 + h_1, r_2 + h_2, \ldots, r_g + h_g}.$$

For given $n_1, n_2, \ldots, n_g$, the $(n_1 + 1)(n_2 + 1) \ldots (n_g + 1)$ values $\omega_{r_1, r_2, \ldots, r_g}^{(n_1, n_2, \ldots, n_g)}$ with $0 \leq r_i \leq n_i$ give the probabilities of the $(n_1 + 1)$ $(n_2 + 1) \ldots (n_g + 1)$ possible combinations of the g frequencies: to fix our ideas, if $g = 2$, we have the $(n_1 + 1)(n_2 + 1)$ pairs of possible frequencies corresponding to the values $0, 1/n_1, 2/n_1, \ldots, 1$ for the first type and $0, 1/n_2, 2/n_2, \ldots, 1$ for the second, and the respective probabilities are

$$
\text{II} \left\{
\begin{array}{c|ccccccc}
1 & \omega_{0,n_2}^{(n_1, n_2)} & \omega_{1,n_2}^{(n_1, n_2)} & \omega_{2,n_2}^{(n_1, n_2)} & \ldots & \omega_{r_1,n_2}^{(n_1, n_2)} & \ldots & \omega_{n_1,n_2}^{(n_1, n_2)} \\
\vdots & \cdots & \cdots & \cdots & \cdots & \cdots & \cdots & \cdots \\
r_2/n_2 & \omega_{0,r_2}^{(n_1, n_2)} & \omega_{1,r_2}^{(n_1, n_2)} & \omega_{2,r_2}^{(n_1, n_2)} & \ldots & \omega_{r_1,r_2}^{(n_1, n_2)} & \ldots & \omega_{n_1,r_2}^{(n_1, n_2)} \\
\vdots & \cdots & \cdots & \cdots & \cdots & \cdots & \cdots & \cdots \\
2/n_2 & \omega_{0,2}^{(n_1, n_2)} & \omega_{1,2}^{(n_1, n_2)} & \omega_{2,2}^{(n_1, n_2)} & \ldots & \omega_{r_1,2}^{(n_1, n_2)} & \ldots & \omega_{n_1,2}^{(n_1, n_2)} \\
1/n_2 & \omega_{0,1}^{(n_1, n_2)} & \omega_{1,1}^{(n_1, n_2)} & \omega_{2,1}^{(n_1, n_2)} & \ldots & \omega_{r_1,1}^{(n_1, n_2)} & \ldots & \omega_{n_1,1}^{(n_1, n_2)} \\
0 & \omega_{0,0}^{(n_1, n_2)} & \omega_{1,0}^{(n_1, n_2)} & \omega_{2,0}^{(n_1, n_2)} & \ldots & \omega_{r_1,0}^{(n_1, n_2)} & \ldots & \omega_{n_1,0}^{(n_1, n_2)} \\
\hline
 & 0 & 1/n_1 & 2/n_1 & \ldots & r_1/n_1 & \ldots & 1 \\
\end{array}
\right.
$$

$$\underbrace{}_{\text{I}}$$

Let us designate this distribution by $\Phi_{n_1, n_2, \ldots, n_g}$; more exactly, with $\xi_1, \xi_2, \ldots, \xi_g$ being variables over the interval $(0, 1)$, let $\Phi_{n_1, n_2, \ldots, n_g}(\xi_1, \xi_2, \ldots, \xi_g)$ be the distribution function of g variables which represents the probability that $r_i/n_i \leq \xi_i$ $(i = 1, 2, \ldots, g)$; it is obtained by adding the $\omega_{r_1, r_2, \ldots, r_g}^{(n_1, n_2, \ldots, n_g)}$ with $r_i \leq n_i \xi_i$ $(i = 1, 2, \ldots, g)$. Here again, as the numbers $n_1, n_2, \ldots, n_g$ tend toward ∞, $\Phi_{n_1, n_2, \ldots, n_g}$ tends toward a limiting distribution Φ, as a function of which one can express

$$\omega_{n_1, n_2, \ldots, n_g} = \int \xi_1^{n_1} \xi_2^{n_2} \ldots \xi_g^{n_g} \, d\Phi.$$

and, more generally,

$$\omega_{r_1,r_2,\ldots,r_g}^{(n_1,n_2,\ldots,n_g)} = \binom{n_1}{r_1}\binom{n_2}{r_2}\ldots\binom{n_g}{r_g}$$

$$\times \int \xi_1^{r_1}(1-\xi_1)^{s_1}\xi_2^{r_2}(1-\xi_2)^{s_2}\ldots\xi_g^{r_g}(1-\xi_g)^{s_g}\,d\Phi$$

where the Stieltjes integral extends over the g-dimensional field

$$0 \leqq \xi_i \leqq 1 \qquad (i = 1, 2, \ldots, g).$$

Again, in general we have

$$P(E) = \int P_{\xi_1,\xi_2,\ldots,\xi_g}(E)\,d\Phi,$$

where E is an arbitrary event constructed from our partially ex-changeable events, and where $P_{\xi_1,\xi_2,\ldots,\xi_g}(E)$ is the probability that E would have if the events of each of the types $1, 2, \ldots, g$ were equiprobable within type, with probabilities $\xi_1, \xi_2, \ldots, \xi_g$, and if all the events (without distinction of type) were mutually independent. In case the distribution Φ admits a probability *density* $\varphi(\xi_1, \xi_2, \ldots, \xi_g)$ we have

$$\varphi = \frac{\partial^g \Phi}{\partial\xi_1\,\partial\xi_2\ldots\partial\xi_g}$$

and the formula can be written

$$P(E) = \int_0^1\int_0^1\ldots\int_0^1 P_{\xi_1,\xi_2,\ldots,\xi_g}(E)\varphi(\xi_1,\xi_2,\ldots,\xi_g)\,d\xi_1\,d\xi_2\ldots d\xi_g$$

It may be useful to see how we fall back to the case of exchangeability for the two limiting cases mentioned in connection with the examples. When the events are exchangeable, i.e., if the types we have discerned among them are not effectively distinguish-able from the problabistic point of view, the numbers $\omega_{n_1,n_2,\ldots,n_g}$ depend only on $n = n_1 + n_2 + \ldots + n_g$, and the operators $\Delta_1, \Delta_2, \ldots, \Delta_g$ are now all equal to a single Δ, and similarly

$$\frac{\omega_{r_1,r_2,\ldots,r_g}^{(n_1,n_2,\ldots,n_g)}}{\binom{n_1}{r_1}\binom{n_2}{r_2}\ldots\binom{n_g}{r_g}}$$

depends only on $n = n_1 + n_2 + \ldots + n_g$ and $r = r_1 + r_2 + \ldots + r_g$. As to the distribution Φ, it is concentrated on the line $\xi_1 = \xi_2 = \ldots = \xi_g$ (the principal diagonal of the hypercube). When on the contrary the events are divided into types which have no interdependence, we have

$$\omega_{n_1, n_2, \ldots, n_g} = \underset{1}{\omega_{n_1}} \cdot \underset{2}{\omega_{n_2}} \cdot \ldots \cdot \underset{g}{\omega_{n_g}}$$

$(\underset{1}{\omega}, \underset{2}{\omega}, \ldots, \underset{g}{\omega}$ being relative to the types $1, 2, \ldots, g)$, the $\Delta_1, \Delta_2, \ldots, \Delta_g$ operate separately on $\underset{1}{\omega}, \underset{2}{\omega}, \ldots, \underset{g}{\omega}$, and we have

$$\omega^{(n_1, n_2, \ldots, n_g)}_{r_1, r_2, \ldots, r_g} = \underset{1}{\omega^{(n_1)}_{r_1}} \cdot \underset{2}{\omega^{(n_2)}_{r_2}} \cdot \ldots \cdot \underset{g}{\omega^{(n_g)}_{r_g}}.$$

In other words, we have $\Phi_{n_1, n_2, \ldots, n_g} = \underset{1}{\Phi_{n_1}} \cdot \underset{2}{\Phi_{n_2}} \cdot \ldots \cdot \underset{g}{\Phi_{n_g}}$ and, in the limit, $\Phi(\xi_1, \xi_2, \ldots, \xi_g) = \underset{1}{\Phi(\xi_1)} \cdot \underset{2}{\Phi(\xi_2)} \cdot \ldots \cdot \underset{g}{\Phi(\xi_g)}$ decomposes into a product of functions of one variable (and the same holds for the density φ, if it exists).

The problem of induction—outside of these limiting cases, which bring us back to the case of exchangeability—leads us again to a perfectly analogous conclusion; one can say, *to the same conclusion*, except for the aforementioned indirect influence of observations made of events of other types. Let us suppose that we know the result of $m = m_1 + m_2 + \ldots + m_g$ trials of g types: the combination A which is realized will consist in the favorable results of $h = h_1 + h_2 + \ldots + h_g$ trials, and the unfavorable results of the other $k = k_1 + k_2 + \ldots + k_g$. One can write $A = A_1 \cdot A_2 \cdot \ldots \cdot A_g$, where $A_1 = E_{i_1} \ldots E_{i_{h_1}} E_{j_1} \ldots E_{j_{k_1}}$ and analogously for $A_2 \ldots A_g$.

The probability of a further trial $E_l = E$ (which we suppose to be of type $i = 1$, with $l > m_1$) will be, after observation of A,

$$P(E/A) = \frac{P(AE)}{P(A)} = \frac{\omega^{(m_1+1, m_2, \ldots, m_g)}_{h_1+1, h_2, \ldots, h_g}}{\binom{m_1+1}{h_1+1}\binom{m_2}{h_2} \ldots \binom{m_g}{h_g}} : \frac{\omega^{(m_1, m_2, \ldots, m_g)}_{h_1, h_2, \ldots, h_g}}{\binom{m_1}{h_1}\binom{m_2}{h_2} \ldots \binom{m_g}{h_g}}$$

$$= \frac{\int \xi_1 \xi_1^{h_1}(1-\xi_1)^{k_1} \ldots \xi_g^{h_g}(1-\xi_g)^{k_g} \, d\Phi}{\int \xi_1^{h_1}(1-\xi_1)^{k_1} \ldots \xi_g^{k_g}(1-\xi_g)^{k_g} \, d\Phi} = \int \xi_1 \, d\bar{\Phi}$$

with

$$\bar{\Phi}(\xi_1, \xi_2, \ldots, \xi_g) = \alpha \int_0^{\xi_1} \int_0^{\xi_2} \ldots \int_0^{\xi_g} \xi_1^{h_1}(1-\xi_1)^{k_1} \ldots \xi_g^{h_g}(1-\xi_g)^{k_g} \, d\Phi,$$

$$\alpha = 1 : \int_0^1 \int_0^1 \ldots \int_0^1 \xi_1^{h_1}(1-\xi_1)^{k_1} \ldots \xi_g^{h_g}(1-\xi_g)^{k_g} \, d\Phi;$$

if Φ admits a density φ, $\bar{\Phi}$ also admits a density $\bar{\varphi}$:

$$\bar{\varphi}(\xi_1, \xi_2, \ldots, \xi_g) = \alpha \xi_1^{h_1}(1-\xi_1)^{k_1} \ldots \xi_g^{h_g}(1-\xi_g)^{k_g}\varphi(\xi_1, \xi_2, \ldots, \xi_g)$$

and

$$P(E/A) = \int_0^1 \xi_1 \, d\xi_2 \int_0^1 d\xi_2 \ldots \int_0^1 d\xi_g \bar{\varphi}(\xi_1, \xi_2, \ldots, \xi_g).$$

The corresponding formula continues to hold when we seek to evaluate the probability $P(E/A)$ where E means that in $n_1 + n_2 + \ldots + n_g$ further trials, a definite $r_1 + r_2 + \ldots + r_g$ and $s_1 + s_2 + \ldots + s_g$ ($r_i + s_i = n_i$) give favorable and unfavorable results respectively:

$$P(E/A) = \frac{P(AE)}{P(A)} = \int \xi_1^{r_1}(1-\xi_1)^{s_1} \ldots \xi_g^{r_g}(1-\xi_g)^{s_g} \, d\bar{\Phi}$$

$$= \int_0^1 \xi_1^{r_1}(1-\xi_1)^{s_1} \, d\xi_1 \int_0^1 \xi_2^{r_2}(1-\xi_2)^{s_2} \, d\xi_2 \ldots \int_0^1 \xi_g^{r_g}(1-\xi_g)^{s_g}$$

$$\times d\xi_g \bar{\varphi}(\xi_1, \xi_2, \ldots, \xi_g)$$

(if φ, and thus $\bar{\varphi}$, exist), and also in general, where E is a generic event constructed out of successive trials, we have again that

$$P(E/A) = \frac{P(AE)}{P(A)} = \int P_{\xi_1, \xi_2, \ldots, \xi_g}(E) \, d\bar{\Phi}$$

$$= \int_0^1 d\xi_1 \int_0^1 d\xi_2 \ldots \int_0^1 d\xi_g P_{\xi_1, \xi_2, \ldots, \xi_g}(E)\bar{\varphi}(\xi_1, \xi_2, \ldots, \xi_g).$$

The conclusion is therefore the same as in the case of exchangeability: given knowledge of the results of m observed trials, the others will remain partially exchangeable, but the limit distribution Φ will be replaced by $\bar{\Phi}$, and $d\bar{\Phi}$ is obtained from $d\Phi$ by altering it in proportion to $\gamma(\xi_1, \xi_2, \ldots, \xi_g) = \xi_1^{h_1}(1-\xi_1)^{k_1} \ldots \xi_g^{h_g}(1-\xi_g)^{k_g}$. The probabilities around the values observed for the frequencies $\left(\bar{\xi}_1 = \dfrac{h_1}{m_1}, \ \bar{\xi}_2 = \dfrac{h_2}{m_2}, \ldots, \bar{\xi}_g = \dfrac{h_g}{m_g}\right)$ will be reinforced (provided $d\Phi \neq 0$ for $\bar{\xi}_i = \xi_i$, $i = 1, 2, \ldots, g$), the more so, the greater $m_1, m_2, \ldots, m_g$ become, so that one comes closer and closer to the judgment which reduces to considering the trials as independent and of probabilities equal to the frequencies observed within each of the types $1, 2, \ldots, g$.

Thus we see that at the limit all indirect influences disappear, which underscores the distinctive behavior of indirect influences, but without diminishing their importance, contrary to what one might think at first. If we do not neglect such specific characteristics as those mentioned in the example, the normal case will be that where we cannot observe a great number of perfectly exchangeable events, and where, consequently, the indirect influences play an essential role. Furthermore, in considering types which vary in a continuous fashion, it will be normal to suppose that the m trials already observed plus the one envisaged belong to $m + 1$ different types, and the influence will be *exclusively* indirect.

Let us now see what applications we can make of these considerations concerning "partial exchangeability", and what conclusions we can draw from them. It must be pointed out that precise applications, in which Φ would have a determinate analytic expression, do not appear to be of much interest: as in the case of exchangeability, the principal interest of the present methods resides in the fact that the conclusions depend only on a gross, qualitative knowledge of Φ, the only sort we can reasonably suppose to be given (except in artificial examples).

In any case, we shall limit ourselves to some extremely schematized examples with the sole purpose of giving an insight into some interesting cases. In effect, we shall always suppose that the probability is concentrated *on* a line or a surface or, in general, on a variety τ of fewer than g dimensions: this is generally to be viewed as a schematization of the fact that the distribution Φ which characterizes the initial opinion is concentrated *around* τ. In general terms, the conclusion will then be the following: in changing the masses of the distribution proportionally to the function $\gamma(\xi_1, \xi_2, \ldots, \xi_g)$, the distribution will tend to concentrate around the point M_τ at which γ achieves its maximum on the variety τ. Only if experience becomes so rich that multiplication by γ no longer permits us to neglect masses not on τ will the definitive tendency of masses to concentrate (as we have already seen) around M begin to reveal itself—M being the point of absolute maximum ($\xi_i = h_i/m_i$). Naturally, if the masses are not sufficiently condensed around τ, the tendency toward M can take hold before that toward M_τ has been able to emerge clearly; the schematization in question is only the simplest, even from this point of view.

The most natural example is the one where the events of all the types being considered are judged *approximately* exchangeable as in the game of heads or tails in circumstances like those already mentioned; then τ is the principal diagonal $\xi_1 = \xi_2 = \ldots = \xi_g$; M_τ is the point $\xi_1 = \xi_2 = \ldots = \xi_g = h/m$. This shows clearly that experience is first used as a whole, for all of the g types together, and only when it is very rich does it permit us to discern differences among those types.

A more complex functional relationship can arise, e.g., if the events of types 2, 3, etc., depend on the simultaneous verification of 2, 3, etc., of the events of type 1 (e.g., a statistic which for insurance on two people tells us only whether or not the insured were both alive after the period in question). Then τ is the curve $\xi_2 = \xi_1^2$, $\xi_3 = \xi_1^3, \ldots$; M_τ is a point on that line corresponding to a value $\xi_1 = \bar{\xi}_1$. Only a very rich experience can lead us to admit an interdependence whose existence was almost completely excluded at the outset, and thus to draw us away from τ.

The following sort of reasoning illustrates a very common case: we observe a decline in the mortality rate, caused by a certain medical treatment for animals, and we expect an analogous result for humans. One can imagine that τ is the surface $\xi_1 : \xi_2 = \xi_3 : \xi_4$ (proportional decline). But this can be used to explain more than the mechanism of this particular reasoning: on looking deeper, the very fact of this belief in a near-proportionality should be interpreted in the framework of these same considerations, since it turns essentially on similar observations made for other medical treatments. Let the treatments be $i = 1, 2, \ldots, c$; under an obvious interpretation of the symbols, the conclusion is established if we allow that τ is such that $\xi_{4i+1} : \xi_{4i+2} - \xi_{4i+3} : \xi_{4i+4} = 0$ $(i = 1, 2, \ldots, c)$ entails also $\xi_1 : \xi_2 = \xi_3 : \xi_4 = 0$. The very belief in the plausibility of extending certain conclusions concerning certain medical treatments to certain others can be explained in turn by the observation of analogies in a broader and vaguer sense, and in the same way one can explain every similar belief, which manifests itself by the formulation of a "statistical law".

The same conclusions hold for laws which we are not accustomed to regard as statistical. The cases where we have no doubt that the outcome of an experiment will always be repeated in similar trials (even if it has been performed only once), are simply those where, observation of events of similar types having shown that the frequencies for each type have always been 0 or 1, one is led to expect that experiments of the new type will also have the same result, which is to say that they accord with the views of a determinist. Suppose, e.g., that we have observed a new chemical reaction: we assert not only "that happened today" but rather "that happens under such-and-such circumstances". Why? Because in the absence of specific, striking indications to the contrary, the uniformity characteristic of known reactions justifies our belief that this last case will be no exception.

In such cases we are therefore led to reason and act *as if* we shared the determinists' faith in the principle of causality, but meanwhile attributing to the idea of cause only the meaning corresponding—I think—to Hume's conception. Thus causality no longer appears as a principle which we need posit a priori if science is to be possible; it is the result of a natural process of association of ideas following the suggestive influence of certain analogies, and connected to the theory of probability, the only framework within which the analysis and explanation of this psychological process is possible.

10

Representation Theorems of the de Finetti Type for (Partially) Symmetric Probability Measures

BY GODEHARD LINK

1. INTRODUCTION

1.1. *De Finetti's philosophical program.* In his (by now) famous paper [1937] de Finetti challenges two basic notions of the objectivist approach to probability: (a) the objective, unknown probability of a certain event; (b) the independence of events. De Finetti's claim is that these two concepts can be eliminated in favor of subjectivistic terms which alone acquire a definite philosophical meaning. For illustration, let us consider the standard example of tossing a (possibly) bent coin. Let us first take the objectivist position; call E_n the event "coin falls head up on n-th trial", $\theta = P_\theta(E_n)$ the unknown probability of the occurrence of $E_n (0 < \theta < 1)$. Assuming independence we have for the event $A_{n,k}$ ("n trials, k times head"): $P_\theta(A_{n,k}) = \binom{n}{k}\theta^k(1-\theta)^{n-k}$. In the extreme case of a series of n heads the conditional probability of E_{n+1} given $A_{n,n}$ is always θ regardless of the size of n. For growing n this becomes increasingly implausible since we assumed θ to be smaller than 1. We can, however, avoid this heavy reliance on the independence model; we simply assign weights to every "hypothesis" $\theta \in [0, 1]$ and mix the corresponding

P_θ according to those weights. The resulting integral $\int_0^1 P_\theta(A)\,dq(\theta)$ with the weighing probability measure q on $[0, 1]$ yields a probability measure $P(A)$ for every $A \in \mathcal{A}(E_n)$ (the σ-algebra generated by the E_n). It can be shown that under this P past experience is no longer ignored in the evaluation of the next trial (see, for instance, Jeffrey [1971], p. 200 f.).

Now, it can be easily seen that P is *symmetric relative to* the E_n in the following sense: For all $n \in \mathbb{N}$ (the set of positive integers) we have

(1) $$P\left(\bigcap_{i=1}^n E_{\rho i}\right) = P\left(\bigcap_{i=1}^n E_i\right) =: \omega_n,$$

where ρ is any bijection from $\mathbb{N}$ onto $\mathbb{N}$ that leaves all but a finite number of integers fixed. The E_n are then said to be *exchangeable* with respect to P. (Note that, relative to P, they are no longer independent.)

At this point de Finetti takes the opposite course. All one really needs, he argues, is the notion of symmetry or exchangeability of events (which is typically realized in many important probabilistic situations), together with a subjective notion of probability, which can be defined in terms of bets. His reasons are:

(1) Unlike independence, symmetry has an immediate operational meaning, and independence can be defined in terms of it (the case in which $\omega_n = \omega_1^n$ ($n \in \mathbb{N}$)).

(2) Given the subjective symmetric probability P, de Finetti's *representation theorem* shows how the *Bernoullian* measures (i.e., those relative to which the E_n are independent) are related to P: There is a unique probability measure q on $[0, 1]$ such that the equation

(2) $$P(A) = \int_0^1 P_\theta(A)\,dq(\theta)$$

holds for all $A \in \mathcal{A}(E_n)$. That is, the subjective probability P already determines the "credibility" that is given to every possible parameter θ. (The so-called objective probability P_θ can thus be reinterpreted as the subjective symmetric probability with the point measure ε_θ as credibility over the parameter space $[0, 1]$.)

(3) By simple conditionalization on the observed data the representation theorem allows for "learning from experience" in accordance with the following intuitive principle of inductive reasoning: "A rich enough experience leads us always to consider as probable future frequencies of distributions close to those which have been observed" (de Finetti [1964], p. 142).

In carrying out de Finetti's reductionist program, the representation theorem can thus be seen to play a central role. A detailed exposition and philosophical discussion of this program can be found in Stegmüller (1973); see also Hintikka (1972).

1.2. *Partial Exchangeability.* In another paper [1938] de Finetti raises the question of how realistic the assumption of symmetry actually is. In his picture this assumption is due to a judgment of *complete analogy* between all events considered. However, there might be experimental situations in which all the events E_n look quite similar, but there is still some systematic observable difference between certain subclasses of the E_n. Take again the coin tossing example, and suppose the tosses are made by two different people, P_1 and P_2. Then we can distinguish three cases: First we may think the way P_1 and P_2 actually perform their tosses is irrelevant to the probability of the coin falling heads. Here we can treat all the tosses as exchangeable no matter who makes the trial. On the other hand, from the peculiar manner both P_1 and P_2 flip the coin, we might feel that the performance of the toss does influence the probability of "heads" in a systematic way. Now the trials are no longer exchangeable, although those of each of P_1 and P_2 are. The second case, then, is the one in which the two ways of tossing are completely different; so observation of P_1's tosses simply do not influence judgment about trials performed by P_2. Here we have two separate sequences of exchangeable events which bear no interrelations to each other. But there is a third, intermediate, case: One might observe a clear influence between, say, the technical efforts of P_1 and P_2 to produce a long series of heads. In this case the E_n again divide into two classes of separately exchangeable events; there still exists, however, a considerable dependence across classes.

De Finetti's point we tried to illustrate here is this: Suppose a chance set-up X (to use Hacking's term) is able to produce a simple dichotomy of events, E_n and CE_n, on each trial T_n conducted on X; suppose further that on each trial X takes on exactly one of k states which are considered to be relevant to the probabilistic evaluation of the model (de Finetti mentions, for instance, states of temperature and/or atmospheric pressure); finally, trials performed in the same state i are assumed to be exchangeable while there exists a recognition of some weaker dependence also between trials of two different states. The events are then called (k-*fold*) *partially exchangeable*. (For scientific applications of this notion, see Bruno [1972].)

De Finetti points out that instead of a simple sequence (ω_n) we have now a k-dimensional sequence $(\omega_{n_1,\ldots,n_k})$ of probabilities which fully characterize the distribution P relative to which the E_n are partially exchangeable. Here, $\omega_{n_1,\ldots,n_k}$ is the probability that $n = \sum_{i=1}^{n} n_i$ events all happen, where n_i of them belong to the ith *type* (i.e., the corresponding trial is performed in state i), for $1 \le i \le k$. As in the case of exchangeability, a representation of P in terms of products of Bernoullian measures can be given: For $1 \le i \le k$ and $\theta_i \in [0, 1]$, denote by $P_{\theta_1,\ldots,\theta_k}$ the probability measure that renders all the E_n independent with equal probabilities θ_i when of type i. Then, for any $A \in \mathscr{A}(E_n)$, we have

$$(3) \qquad P(A) = \int_{[0,1]^k} P_{\theta_1,\ldots,\theta_k}(A) \, dF(\theta_1, \ldots, \theta_k)$$

for some unique k-dimensional distribution function F.

We can expect (although de Finetti does not mention it) that there also exists a representation of P in the general case where P is partially symmetric relative to a sequence of random variables which take on more than just two values. Indeed, in section 4 we shall prove two versions of this fact; but see below for necessary distinctions.

1.3. *Scope of the paper.* In this paper we do not attempt to contribute to the philosophical discussion centered about de Finetti's theorem and its extensions. However, because of its impact on the subjective foundations of probability, we think that it is also necessary to be able to fully appreciate the mathematics of this theorem. To this end, we are going to exploit the basic idea (already contained in Hewitt's and Savage's key paper [1955]) to approach the notion of (partial) exchangeability through the theory of abstract convex sets. Our main tool will be the fundamental Choquet theorem about the characterization of a convex set by the set of its extreme points. Since (partially) symmetric probabilities form a convex set the extreme points of which are basically the Bernoullian measures, Choquet's result will enable us to derive six representation theorems for (partially) symmetric probability distributions; while varying in their degree of generality, they are all closely related to de Finetti's original formulations as expressed, for instance, in (2) or (3).

On a rather formal level, however, there will be a systematic difference between our presentation and the one given in the de Finetti papers referred to above. This is due to the fact that de

Finetti deals with what we shall call the *relative notion* of (partial) symmetry instead of the *absolute notion* adopted here.

In the relative case we have an arbitrary probability space $(Y, \mathscr{A}, P)$; for any integer k the probability measure P is then said to be (k-fold) *partially symmetric relative to* a sequence (X_n) of real random variables on $(Y, \mathscr{A})$ provided that the X_n divide into a k-fold infinite sequence $(X_{ij})_{1 \leq i \leq k, j \in \mathbb{N}}$ such that the following condition holds for all nonnegative integers $n_1, \ldots, n_k$ and all real numbers x_{ij} ($1 \leq i \leq k, 1 \leq j \leq n_i$):

$$(4) \qquad P\left(\bigcap_{i=1}^{k} \bigcap_{j=1}^{n_i} \{X_{i,\rho_i j} < x_{ij}\}\right) = P\left(\bigcap_{i=1}^{k} \bigcap_{j=1}^{n_i} \{X_{ij} < x_{ij}\}\right).$$

(Here, ρ_i is any "finite" permutation from $\mathbb{N}$ onto $\mathbb{N}$.) In this case the X_n are also called (k-fold) partially exchangeable with respect to P. For $k = 1$ our condition coincides with the one given in Jeffrey (1971), p. 203; P is then *symmetric relative to* the X_n. Obviously, if the X_n assume only two values, say, 0 and 1, (4) reduces to the condition (1) for partial exchangeability of events.

Now, the X_{ij} are measurable functions from Y into R (the set of real numbers). Since both range and domain are always the same, we can put the X_{ij} together to form one single function X from Y into the k-fold infinite product $(R^{\mathbb{N}})^k$ of copies of R. X is defined by the equation $X_{ij} = pr_{ij} \circ X$ ($1 \leq i \leq k, j \in \mathbb{N}$), where pr_{ij} denotes the projection mapping from $(R^{\mathbb{N}})^k$ onto the coordinate (i, j). It is known that X is measurable; so we can transplant the above measure P from Y onto $(R^{\mathbb{N}})^k$, the resulting measure P' being the image of P under X (in Halmos' terminology: $P' = PX^{-1}$). Now, P' has the property of being invariant under finite permutations of the coordinates provided that these permutations are confined to each of the k copies of $R^{\mathbb{N}}$. P' is again called partially symmetric, but reference to a sequence of random variables is no longer needed.

Thus, we shall speak of the *absolute case* if a) the probability measure P is defined on a Cartesian product of the form $(Z^{\mathbb{N}})^k$, and b) the condition (4) is expressed in terms of coordinate permutations. Note that the Bernoullian measures become some sort of simple product measures on $(R^{\mathbb{N}})^k$. (See section 2 for exact definitions.)

As an example, consider a sequence (E_n) of fully exchangeable events (this is the two-valued case for $k = 1$, where the X_n are the indicator functions of the E_n). Here, the absolute case leads us to consider the Cartesian product $\{0, 1\}^{\mathbb{N}}$ which provides the standard probabilistic model for representing the E_n. The event E_n is now the "cylinder set" $C^{(n)}(\{1\})$ in $\{0, 1\}^{\mathbb{N}}$ which is defined as the set of all sequences $a = (a_i)$ such that $a_n = 1$. Exchangeability thus means that cylinders of the above form do not change probability when their "base" $\{1\}$ is shifted from one coordinate to another, and that the same is true of finite intersections of those cylinders.

There are three reasons for dealing with the absolute case only: First, all probabilities can be calculated from the absolute case; so, for probabilistic purposes, it does not matter which case we consider. Second, condition (4) for relative partial exchangeability looks quite formidable, while the absolute case allows for a somewhat more convenient formulation. The third reason is more important: The methods to be presented here do not carry over in a trivial manner to the relative case. This is because we would have to impose some topological structure on the abstract set Y; and even then we would meet with considerable technical difficulties not present in the absolute case. So there is an essential asymmetry between the two cases (which is, or course, a quite familiar phenomenon): the transition from the relative to the absolute case is easy; but generally there is no straightforward way back.[1]

Although we are going to use quite abstract methods in this paper, we do not aim at the most general presentation possible. So we confine ourselves to products of copies of R, the set of real numbers; moreover, we avoid reference to the theory of invariant measures, which is no doubt the proper setting to deal with these matters.[2] However, as a result, we are able to keep the prerequisites to a minimum: Except for some very basic concepts from topology almost everything that is needed to apply Choquet's theorem can be found in a textbook like Bauer's (1968).

1.4. *Summary of sections 2–4.* In section 2 we first give the complete terminology we shall use for the rest of the paper. Among the notions of convexity that of a *simplex* is important; it is an extension of the more familiar concept of a simplex in finite-dimensional spaces (a simple example is a triangle in the plane). It will be needed to establish the uniqueness of our representations, because it is only when the convex set in question is a simplex that the uniqueness part of Choquet's theorem applies. (For illustration, note that every point of a triangle is the unique weighted average of the three extreme points; this is not true of a square or a circle,

---

[1] One important difficulty here lies in the fact that it is by no means clear that for an abstract set Y the set of Bernoullian measures is always nonempty.

[2] Roughly, the connection is this: Symmetric probabilities are invariant with respect to point transformations that are induced by the finite permutations of coordinates.

which do not form a simplex in the plane.) We shall conclude section 2 with a characterization of the extreme points of the set of partially symmetric probability measures on $(Z^{\mathbb{N}})^k$ (Z a Borel set in R).

Section 3 is devoted to the statement and the proof of our main theorem; it is here that Choquet's theorem is essentially used. The reason for choosing the compact set $(\tilde{R}^{\mathbb{N}})^k$ as the underlying space is this: The notion of "vague convergence" that we are going to define on the set of (finite) Baire measures is too weak to preserve quite generally the total probability mass if one goes over to the limit. Since we need this property to make sure that the set S_k of partially symmetric probability measures is closed we embed the space $(R^{\mathbb{N}})^k$ into the compact space $(\tilde{R}^{\mathbb{N}})^k$ (for compact spaces the above property is satisfied). Theorem (3.2) shows that this is only a technical move; by a simple argument we find back to any (noncompact) subspace we are interested in.

Finally, in section 4 we state a series of corollaries of the main theorem; these are representation theorems of the de Finetti type for both the partially and the fully symmetric case.

2. PREREQUISITES

2.1. *Basic terminology.* We employ the usual symbols of set theory, with 'C' for complementation and '\' for set difference. For basic measure and probability theory, see Halmos (1950) and Bauer (1968); also Stegmüller (1973). ':=' means: 'is defined as'.

Throughout the paper we use the following notation. $\mathbb{N}$: the set of positive integers i, j, k, l, m, n; $\mathbb{N}_0 := \mathbb{N} \cup \{0\}$; k will be reserved for the number of types into which the partially exchangeable random variables divide; n will often denote a sum, $n = \sum_{i=1}^{k} n_i$, when we consider the analogue to n random variables n_i of which are of type i ($1 \leq i \leq k$). We set $N_0 := 0$, $N_i := \sum_{j=1}^{i} n_j$ ($i \leq k$), so that $N_k = n$. (The n_i are elements of $\mathbb{N}_0$.) Moreover, $[0] := \varnothing$, $[n_i] := (1, \ldots, n_i)$ for $n_i > 0$ ($1 \leq i \leq k$), and $N := (n_1, \ldots, n_k)$; N will be an element of the set $\mathbb{N}_0^k \backslash \{0, \ldots, 0\}$, which we denote by $\mathcal{N}_k$. By $\rho_i (1 \leq i \leq k)$ we mean a *finite permutation* on $\mathbb{N}$, i.e., a one-to-one mapping from $\mathbb{N}$ onto $\mathbb{N}$ leaving all but a finite number of integers fixed. A k-tuple $(\rho_1, \ldots, \rho_k)$ of such permutations is abbreviated by ρ; the set of k-tuples ρ we call $\mathcal{U}_k$. We set $\rho^0 := (\rho_0, \ldots, \rho_0)$, where ρ_0 denotes the identity mapping on $\mathbb{N}$. Finally, we write $\rho\rho'$ for $\rho \circ \rho' := (\rho_1 \circ \rho_1', \ldots, \rho_k \circ \rho_k')$.

R: the set of real numbers r, s, x_i, y_i, a_i, b_i, a_{ij}, b_{ij}; x and y will be used for n-tuples of reals, $x = (x_1, \ldots, x_n)$, $y = (y_1, \ldots, y_n)$; we write $x \leqq y$ iff $x_i \leqq y_i$ $(1 \leqq i \leqq n)$. $R(r) := \{s \in R; s < r\}$ $(r \in R)$; $I := [0, 1]$ (the closed unit interval); $\tilde{R} := R \cup \{-\infty, +\infty\}$ (the extended real line).

In what follows we shall adopt the following *tilde convention*: For a symbol S, $\tilde{S}$ is defined as S except for replacing by $\tilde{R}$ every explicit or implicit occurrence of R in the definition of S.

$\mathbb{R}$: the "infinite sample space" $R^{\mathbb{N}}$, with elements $a = (a_i) = (a_1, a_2, \ldots)$; $\mathbb{R}^k$: the Cartesian product of k copies of $\mathbb{R}$ $(k \in \mathbb{N})$, with elements $a = ((a_{1j}), \ldots, (a_{kj})) = (a_{ij})$; we say that a_{ij} is in the jth *coordinate* of the ith *component* $(1 \leqq i \leqq k, j \in \mathbb{N})$. For a subset M of $\mathbb{R}^k$, we shall write $M \subseteq \mathbb{R}^k$ if M is of the form $(Z^{\mathbb{N}})^k$ with a Borel subset Z of R. (Obviously, M is a Borel set in $\mathbb{R}^k$.)

Let $\mathscr{A}$ be a σ-algebra of sets A, A_i etc. in a set Y; for $Y' \in \mathscr{A}$, $\mathscr{A} \cap Y' := \{A \cap Y'; A \in \mathscr{A}\}$ is a σ-algebra over Y'. $\mathscr{A}^k$ means the product σ-algebra of k copies of $\mathscr{A}$. Further notations are: $\mathscr{B}_1$: the standard (Borel) σ-algebra over R; $\mathscr{B}^k$: the Borel sets of $\mathbb{R}^k$ $(k \in \mathbb{N})$; $\mathscr{B} := B^1$. $\mathscr{L}(Y)$: the set of all finite measures on a set Y, with elements λ, μ, ν; for a measurable function f from $(Y, \mathscr{A})$ into $(Y', \mathscr{A}')$ we mean by λf^{-1} the *image of λ under f on* $(Y', \mathscr{A}')$.

$\Omega(Z)$: the set of probability measures on a Borel set Z in R, with elements π^1, π_i^1; $\Omega := \Omega(R)$; $P(M)$: the set of product probabilities on $M := Z^{\mathbb{N}}$ $(Z \in \mathscr{B}_1)$ of the form $\pi_i = \pi_i^1 \times \ldots \times \pi_i^1 \times \ldots$ $(\pi_i^1 \in \Omega(Z), i \in \mathbb{N})$; $P := P(\mathbb{R})$; $P_k(M^k)$: the set of product probabilities on $M^k (M \subseteq \mathbb{R})$ of the form $\pi = \pi_1 \times \ldots \times \pi_k (\pi_i \in P(M), 1 \leqq i \leqq k)$; $P_k := P_k(\mathbb{R}^k)$; Δ: the set of all one-dimensional distribution functions F, G, $\ldots$; $\mathscr{Q}$: the σ-algebra over Ω that is generated by sets of the form $\{\pi^1 \in \Omega; \pi^1(A) < r\}$ $(A \in \mathscr{B}_1, r \in R)$; for $M \subseteq \mathbb{R}^k$, $\mathscr{P}_k(M)$: the σ-algebra over $P_k(M)$ that is generated by sets of the form $\{\pi \in P_k(M); \pi(A) < r\}$ $(A \in \mathscr{B}^k \cap M, r \in R)$; $\mathscr{P}_k := \mathscr{P}_k(\mathbb{R}^k)$, $\mathscr{P} := \mathscr{P}_1$.

We need a somewhat elaborate notation for *cylinders*. As usual we define cylinder sets in $\mathbb{R}$ by

(5) $C(A_1^{(\rho 1)}, \ldots, A_n^{(\rho n)}) := \{a \in \mathbb{R}; a_{\rho i} \in A_i \ (1 \leqq i \leqq n)\}$

with $n \in \mathbb{N}_0$, $\rho \in \mathscr{U}_1$, $A_i \in \mathscr{B}_1$ $(1 \leqq i \leqq n)$. We call $B_1 := \prod_{i=1}^{n} A_i$ the *base* of the above cylinder and n the *size* $s(B_1)$ of B_1. We abbreviate the cylinder by $C_\rho(B_1)$; for $s(B_1) = 0$ we set $C_\rho(B_1) = \mathbb{R}$. We shall omit reference to ρ if it is inessential as to which coordinates contain the base (for definiteness, set $C(B_1) := C_{\rho_0}(B_1)$). Note that R^n is a special base of size n, so that $\mathbb{R} = C(R^n)$ $(n \in \mathbb{N})$.

For two bases B_1 and B_1' with $s(B_1) = n_1$ and $s(B_1') = n_2$ we define

(6) $$C(B_1, B_1') := C(A_1, \ldots, A_{n_1}, A_1', \ldots, A_{n_2}'),$$

and, by induction, $C(1B_1) := C(B_1)$, $C(nB_1) := C((n-1)B_1, B_1)$ for $n > 1$ (the base is copied $(n-1)$ times).

By a *k-base B of size $s(B)$* we mean a k-tuple $B = (B_1, \ldots, B_k)$ of bases B_i with $s(B) = (s(B_1), \ldots, s(B_k))$. We now define the notion of a *k-cylinder $D(B)$*, which is to be a subset of $\mathbb{R}^k$. Let $B = (B_1, \ldots, B_k)$ be a k-base of size $(n_1, \ldots, n_k)$; then we set for $\rho \in \mathcal{U}_k$:

(7)
$$D_\rho(B) := \prod_{i=1}^{k} C_{\rho_i}(B_i)$$

$$= C(A_{11}^{(\rho_1 1)}, \ldots, A_{1n_1}^{(\rho_1 n_1)}) \times \ldots \times C(A_{k1}^{(\rho_k 1)}, \ldots, A_{kn_k}^{(\rho_k n_k)})$$

Again, $D(B) := D_{\rho^0}(B)$; moreover, for k-bases B, B' and simple bases B_1, B_1', we set $D(B, B') := \prod_i C(B_i, B_i')$; $D(nB) := \prod_i C(nB_i)$; $D^{(i)}(B_1) := \mathbb{R}^{(1)} \times \ldots \times C^{(i)}(B_1) \times \ldots \times \mathbb{R}^{(k)}$; $D^{(i,j)}(B_i ; B_1') := D^{(i)}(B_1) \cap D^{(j)}(B_1')$ $(i \neq j)$.

Finally, if the sets A_{ij} in a k-base B are all of the form $R(x_{ij})$, we introduce a special notation for the k-cylinder $D_\rho(B)$:

(8) $$D_{\rho, N}(x) := \prod_{i=1}^{k} C(R^{(\rho_i 1)}(x_{N_{i-1}+1}), \ldots, R^{(\rho_i n_i)}(x_{N_i})),$$

where $x = (x_1, \ldots, x_n)$, $n = \sum_{i=1}^{k} n_i$, $N = (n_1, \ldots, n_k)$, $\rho = (\rho_1, \ldots, \rho_k)$. (The '$N$' in '$D_{\rho, N}(x)$' is to indicate how the vector x is distributed over the main components.)

Note that the set of k-cylinders generates $\mathcal{B}^k$ $(k \in \mathbb{N})$. We can even confine ourselves to k-cylinders generates of the special form $D_{\rho, N}(x)$. Therefore, a (probability) measure on $\mathbb{R}^k$ is already uniquely determined by defining its values on those sets.

We are now ready to state the "absolute translation" of (4); it becomes the defining condition for a *k-fold partially symmetric probability measure* τ on $(\mathbb{R}^k, \mathcal{B}^k)$:

(9) $$\tau[D_N(x)] = \tau[D_{\rho, N}(x)] \quad \text{for all } x, N, \text{ and } \rho.$$

For $k = 1$ we get the limiting case of a (fully) *symmetric* probability measure on $\mathbb{R}^1 = \mathbb{R}$. For $k \in \mathbb{N}$ and $M \subseteq \mathbb{R}^k$ we define $S_k(M)$ as the set of all k-fold partially symmetric probability measures on M; we set $S_k := S_k(\mathbb{R}^k)$, $S(M) := S_1(M)$, and $S := S(\mathbb{R})$.

2.2. *Convex sets.* We presuppose acquaintance with some very basic notions of the theory of vector spaces, such as *"vector space"*, *"(positive) linear functional"*, *"convex set"*, *"convex cone"* (see, for instance, Robertson &Robertson [1964], I, 1; II, 1, 2; or Bourbaki [1966], II, 2).

We note that the set $\mathscr{L}(M)$ of all finite measures on $M \subseteq \mathbb{R}^k$ is a (real) vector space under the operations

(10) $(\lambda + \mu)(A) := \lambda(A) + \mu(A),$

$$(\alpha\lambda)(A) := \alpha \cdot \lambda(A). \qquad (A \in \mathscr{B}^k \cap M, \alpha \in R)$$

It is easily seen that the set $S_k(M)$ is a convex subset of $\mathscr{L}(M)$: the convex combination $\alpha\tau_1 + (1-\alpha)\tau_2$ (for $\alpha \in [0, 1]$) is obviously a probability, and, by (10), the condition of partial symmetry can be played back to the τ_i.

Let L be a vector space, $K \subseteq L$ a convex set. An element $d \in K$ is called an *extreme point* of K if the equation $d = \alpha d_1 + (1-\alpha) d_2 (\alpha \in I, d_1, d_2 \in K)$ entails $\alpha = 0$ or 1, i.e. $d = d_1$ or d_2. The set of extreme points of K is denoted by $Ex(K)$.

Let K^* be the convex cone generated by K, i.e., $K^* := \{\alpha d; \alpha \geqq 0, d \in K\}$. If K is contained in a hyperplane which misses the origin then K is a *base* of K^* in the following sense: Every $d \in K^*$ can be written uniquely as $\beta c (\beta \geqq 0, c \in K)$. In this case we call K a *simplex* if the cone K^* is a lattice in its intrinsic order (this order is defined by: $c \leqq d$ if for some $e \in K^*$, $c + e = d(c, d \in K^*)$). It can be shown (see, e.g., Phelps [1966], p. 75) that this notion of a simplex coincides with the usual one for finite dimensions.

2.3. *Topology and topological vector spaces.* For quick reference of virtually all the basic concepts not explained here, see Robertson & Robertson (1964), I:2, 3; among these are: *"topology"*, *"closed set"*, *"closure"* $\bar{A}$, and *"interior"* $\mathring{A}$ of a set A, *"Hausdorff space"*, *"compact space (set)"*, *"metrizable space (set)"*, *"convergence"* with respect to a topology, *"continuous mapping"*, *"locally convex vector space"*.

A set in a Hausdorff space is called *relatively compact* if its closure is compact. Thus, a closed relatively compact set is compact. Cartesian products of compact Hausdorff spaces are compact Hausdorff (Tychonoff's theorem). Since $\tilde{R}$ is compact Hausdorff the same is true of $\tilde{\mathbb{R}}^k$. Continuous real-valued functions on compact spaces are bounded.

For the notion of a *Baire measure* see Bauer (1968), §40, p. 165 ff.; also Halmos (1950), chap. X. We note that the concepts

"Baire set (measure)" and "Borel set (measure)" coincide for metrizable spaces (Bauer [1968], p. 167).

Let $\mathcal{M}:=\mathcal{M}(\tilde{\mathbb{R}}^k)$ denote the convex cone of all (nonnegative) Baire measures on $\tilde{\mathbb{R}}^k$. The set $\mathcal{M}^1$ of probabilities on $\tilde{\mathbb{R}}^k$ is a subset of $\mathcal{M}$; indeed, $\mathcal{M}^1$ is a base for $\mathcal{M}$. We have, of course, $\tilde{S}_k \subseteq \mathcal{M}^1 \subseteq \mathcal{M}$.

Before we go on to introduce some topological properties of $\mathcal{M}$ let us state an algebraic fact about $\mathcal{M}$.

(2.1) Lemma. $\mathcal{M}$ is a lattice in its intrinsic order. To show this, it suffices to produce a least upper bound $\lambda \vee \mu$ for every pair $\lambda, \mu \in \mathcal{M}$. We are going to give an explicit definition of $\lambda \vee \mu$ which, however, involves the difference of λ and μ; since in general this difference cannot be expected to be a nonnegative set function, we shall need the notion of a *signed measure* ν and its *upper variation* ν^+ (see Halmos [1950], p. 122f.; Neveu [1969], p. 129 ff.). A signed measure is a measure that is not required to be nonnegative, but cannot take the value $-\infty$. For a signed measure ν we define the upper variation ν^+ as

(11) $$\nu^+(A):= \sup_{B \subseteq A} \nu(B),$$

where it is understood that only those sets B for which ν is defined contribute to the supremum. ν^+ is a proper, i.e., nonnegative, measure (Neveu [1969], 4.1.1., p. 129); it is plain that in case ν itself is already nonnegative we have $\nu = \nu^+$. Now we define for $\lambda, \mu \in \mathcal{M}$:

(12) $$\lambda \vee \mu := \lambda + (\mu - \lambda)^+.$$

From this we get for any $A \in \tilde{\mathcal{B}}^k$:

(13) $$(\lambda \vee \mu)(A) = \lambda(A) + \sup_{B \subseteq A} (\mu - \lambda)(B) = \lambda(A)$$

$$+ \sup_{B \subseteq A} (\mu - \lambda)(A \backslash B) = \sup_{B \subseteq A} [\lambda(B) + \mu(A \backslash B)].$$

(13) shows that $\lambda + (\mu - \lambda)^+ = \mu + (\lambda - \mu)^+$. So we have $\lambda \vee \mu - \lambda = (\mu - \lambda)^+ \geq 0$ and $\lambda \vee \mu - \mu = (\lambda - \mu)^+ \geq 0$, i.e. $\lambda \vee \mu$ is an upper bound for both λ and μ. Now take any $\nu \in \mathcal{M}$ also having this property. Then it follows for all $A, B \in \tilde{\mathcal{B}}^k$ with $B \subseteq A : \lambda(B) + \mu(A \backslash B) \leq \nu(B) + \nu(A \backslash B) = \beta(A)$, hence $\lambda \vee \mu \leq \nu$. So $\lambda \vee \mu$ is the least upper bound of λ and μ, and it is obviously an element of $\mathcal{M}$.

We now define a topology on $\mathcal{M}$. Denote by $\tilde{\mathscr{C}} := \mathscr{C}(\bar{\mathbb{R}}^k)$ the set of all continuous real-valued functions on $\bar{\mathbb{R}}^k$. For every $f \in \tilde{\mathscr{C}}$ we introduce a mapping Φ_f from $\mathcal{M}$ into R by setting

(14)
$$\Phi_f(\lambda) := \int f \, d\lambda.$$

There is a coarsest topology on $\mathcal{M}$ which renders all the Φ_f continuous; we denote it by $\mathscr{T}$. $\mathscr{T}$ is called the *vague topology* on $\mathcal{M}$ (see, for instance, Bauer [1968], p. 184). We note the following facts about $(\mathcal{M}, \mathscr{T})$:[3]

(2.2) **1.** $(\mathcal{M}, \mathscr{T})$ is a subset of the locally convex vector space $\mathcal{M} - \mathcal{M}$ (the set of all differences of two Baire measures); more precisely, $\mathscr{T}$ is derived from a locally convex topology on $\mathcal{M} - \mathcal{M}$ which is defined as above by simply dropping the restriction to $\mathcal{M}$ in (14). Note that the Φ_f are ($\mathscr{T}$-continuous) linear functionals on $\mathcal{M} - \mathcal{M}$.
2. A sequence (λ_n) of elements of $\mathcal{M}$ converges vaguely to the limit λ in $\mathcal{M}$ iff $\lim \int f \, d\lambda_n = \int f \, d\lambda$ for all $f \in \tilde{\mathscr{C}}$.
3. $(\mathcal{M}, \mathscr{T})$ is metrizable (Bauer [1968], p. 194 f.).
4. A set $H \subseteq \mathcal{M}$ is relatively compact with respect to $\mathscr{T}$ iff it is *bounded*, i.e., if $\sup_{\lambda \in H} |\int f \, d\lambda| < \infty$ for all $f \in \tilde{\mathscr{C}}$. (Bauer [1968], p. 192 f.).

Let now e be an element of a nonempty compact subset K of a locally convex vector space E, and suppose that μ is a probability measure on K. We say that μ *represents* e, or that e is the *barycenter of* μ if we have

(15)
$$f(e) = \int_K f(c) \, d\mu(c)$$

for every continuous linear functional f on E. For short, we write $e = \int c \, d\mu(c)$. If K' is a Borel subset of K then μ is said to be *supported by* K' if $\mu(K \setminus K') = 0$.

We are now ready to state Choquet's fundamental theorem about the representation of convex compact sets in a locally convex vector space. We need only the relatively simple "metrizable case" of this theorem.

---

[3] We remark that the facts listed under (2.2) follow easily from the *theory of duality* of locally convex spaces. This is because the space $\mathcal{M} - \mathcal{M}$ can be considered as the "dual" of $\mathscr{C}(\bar{\mathbb{R}}^k)$, which, as a Banach space, is a special locally convex space; so known results about duals of such spaces are applicable here. For an excellent introduction to duality theory see Robertson & Robertson (1964).

(2.3) Theorem (*Choquet*). Let E be a locally convex vector space, K a convex, compact, and metrizable subset of E. Then, for every $e \in K$ there exists a probability measure μ on K that is supported by $Ex(K)$ and represents e.

Moreover, if K is a simplex, the representing measure μ is unique.

Important references on Choquet's theory are Phelps (1966); Meyer (1966), chap. XI; Bourbaki (1965), IV, 7. For a lucid proof of (2.3) see Phelps (1966), pp. 19 ff., 70 f.

2.4. *The extreme points of* $S_k(M)$. This subsection is devoted to the characterization of the extreme points of $s_k(M)$ $(M \subset \mathbb{R}^k)$. For $k = 1$, Hewitt & Savage [1955] have already shown that $Ex(S_k(M)) = P(M)$. The method used by the authors to establish this result can easily be extended to the case $k > 1$. Since it provides some insight into the structure of the set $S_k(M)$ we find it well worthwhile to present the extended version of their proof in detail here.

The key idea is to make use of the following property of product measures $\pi \in P$ on $\mathbb{R}$. If we double the base B of a cylinder $C(B)$ in $\mathbb{R}$ the resulting cylinder $C(2B)$ will have exactly the square of the probability that π assigns to $C(B)$. Now, Hewitt & Savage show that this property is a sufficient condition for being an extreme point of P. So we have $P \subseteq Ex(S)$. The opposite inclusion is due to the fact that for a nonproduct measure σ there are cylinders C_1, C_2 which are not "independent" from each other relative to σ. These cylinders cannot have zero or unit probability, and conditionalizing σ on, say, C_1 as well as on CC_1 yields measures σ_1 and σ_2 such that $\sigma = \alpha\sigma_1 + (1 - \alpha)\sigma_2$ for some $\alpha \in I$ with $0 \neq \alpha \neq 1$. Thus σ is not an extreme point. We have, however, to make sure that both σ_1 and σ_2 are symmetric.

We are now going to extend the proof just sketched to the partially symmetric case. (For brevity, we drop the 'M' in $S_k(M)$ and $P_k(M)$ for the rest of this section.)

(2.4) Theorem. $Ex(S_k(M)) = P_k(M)$ for $M \subset \mathbb{R}^k$ $(k \in \mathbb{N})$.

Proof.   1. $P_k \subseteq Ex(S_k)$.

Lemma 1. If a $\tau \in S_k$ is such that

(16) $$\tau[D(2B)] = \{\tau[D(B)]\}^2$$

holds for all k-bases B, then τ is an extreme point of S_k.

Let $\pi = \pi_1 \times \ldots \times \pi_k$ be an element of P_k. Then it is plain that (16) is true of π.

To prove the lemma we consider a $\tau \in S_k$ which is not an extreme point of S_k. Then there are two distinct partially symmetric probabilities τ_1 and τ_2 with $\tau = \alpha\tau_1 + (1-\alpha)\tau_2$ for some α, $0 < \alpha < 1$. Since $\tau_1 \neq \tau_2$ there exists a k-cylinder $D' = D(B)$ with some k-base B such that $\tau_1(D') \neq \tau_2(D')$. We now introduce two random variables, f and g, for a simple dichotomy of events, say, $\{0\}$ and $\{1\}$, by setting $f(0) := \beta_1$, $f(1) := \beta_2$, and $g \equiv 1$ (here, β_i denotes $\tau_i(D')$, $i = 1, 2$). Assigning the probabilities α to $\{0\}$ and $1 - \alpha$ to $\{1\}$ we can apply the Cauchy–Schwarz inequality for expectations, $E^2(fg) \leq E(f^2)E(g^2)$, which amounts to

(17) $$\{\beta_1\alpha + \beta_2(1-\alpha)\}^2 < \beta_1^2\alpha + \beta_2^2(1-\alpha)$$

(The '$<$' is due to the fact that f and g are not multiples of each other; the left side of (17) is simply $\{\tau(D')\}^2$.)

Now set $D'' := \mathcal{D}(2B)$. If we can show that

(18) $$\tau'(D'') \geq \{\tau'(D')\}^2$$

for all $\tau' \in S_k$, then we have

(19) $$\tau(D'') = \alpha\tau_1(D'') + (1-\alpha)\tau_2(D'')$$
$$\geq \alpha\{\tau_1(D')\}^2 + (1-\alpha)\{\tau_2(D')\}^2$$
$$> \{\tau(D')\}^2,$$

which violates (16). So the proof of Lemma 1 will be complete if we provide the missing link (18).

Lemma 2. Let B be a k-base of size $(n_1, \ldots, n_k)$, $D' := D(B)$, $D'' := D(2B)$, $\tau \in S_k$. Then (18) holds for τ.

To show this, we define for each $i \in \mathbb{N}$ a k-cylinder D_i which is just as D' except that the k-base B is pushed $(i-1)$ times to the right (this is done, of course, simultaneously in each component). If Z is the projection of M onto each coordinate and $B_0 := \prod_{i=1}^{k} Z^{n_i}$, then D_i can be written as $D((i-1)B_0, B)$. Clearly, we have $D_1 = D'$ and $\tau(D_i) = \tau(D')$ $(i \in \mathbb{N})$, hence $\sum_{i=1}^{m} \tau(D_i) = m\tau(D')$ for all $m \in \mathbb{N}$. Now we set $f_i := \chi_{D_i}$, $f := \sum_{i=1}^{m} f_i$, and $g \equiv 1$. Application of the Cauchy–Schwarz inequality yields $\{\int f \, d\tau\}^2 \leq \int f^2 \, d\tau$, where the left side is just

$m^2\{\tau(D')\}^2$. For the right side we get:

(20)
$$\int f^2 \, d\tau = \sum_i \sum_j \int f_i f_j \, d\tau$$
$$= \sum_i \int f_i \, d\tau + m(m-1) \int f_1 f_2 \, d\tau$$
$$= m\tau(D') + m(m-1)\tau(D'').$$

So we have

(21)
$$m^2\{\tau(D')\}^2 \leqq m\tau(D') + m(m-1)\tau(D''),$$

and, by rearrangement,

(22) $$\tau(D'') \geqq \{\tau(D')\}^2 - \frac{1}{m}[\tau(D') - \tau(D'')] \geqq \{\tau(D')\}^2 - \frac{1}{m}.$$

But (22) is true for all $m \in \mathbb{N}$, whence the lemma.

2. $Ex(S_k) \subseteq P_k$.

Let τ be an element of $S_k \backslash P_k$. Then we distinguish two possible cases:

(a) There is a main component i in which τ is not a product measure, i.e. there exists a pair of two simple bases, B_1 and B_1' such that

(23) $$\tau[D^{(i)}(B_1 \times B_1')] \neq \tau[D^{(i)}(B_1)] \cdot \tau[D^{(i)}(B_1')];$$

(b) τ is not a product measure "across components", i.e. there are $i \neq j$ such that for some simple bases B_1, B_1', we have

(24) $$\tau[D^{(i,j)}(B_1; B_1')] \neq \tau[D^{(i)}(B_1)] \cdot \tau[D^{(j)}(B_1')].$$

Now, in either case, $\tau[D^{(i)}(B_1)]$ cannot be 0 or 1. Abbreviating $D^{(i)}(B_1)$ by E and $D^{(i)}(B_1')$ (resp. $D^{(j)}(B_1')$) by F, we can see this as follows: The sets $E \cap F$ on the left side of both (23) and (24) are subsets of E; so E cannot have zero probability without rendering $\tau(E \cap F)$ zero as well. On the other hand, $\tau(E) \neq 1$; otherwise we would have $\tau(CE) = 0$, hence $\tau(CE \cap F) = 0$, which would contradict $\tau(E \cap F) < \tau(F)$ because of $\tau(F) = \tau(E \cap F) + \tau(CE \cap F)$.

Thus, we can define two probabilities, τ_1 and τ_2, by

(25)
$$\tau_1(A) = \frac{1}{\tau(E)} \tau(E \cap T_i A)$$
$$\tau_2(A) = \frac{1}{\tau(CE)} \tau(CE \cap T_i A)$$

for all $A \in \mathcal{B}^k \cap M$; here, T_i denotes the shift to the right of $s(B_1)$ coordinates in the ith component. It is plain that both τ_1 and τ_2 are partially symmetric probabilities. Moreover, $\tau(A) = \tau(T_iA)$ (this is true for k-cylinders, which generate $\mathcal{B}^k \cap M$, so it follows for any A); thus we see that $\tau = \tau(E)\tau_1 + (1 - \tau(E))\tau_2$, so τ is not an extreme point of S_k.

3. THE MAIN THEOREM

Recall that, by our tilde convention, we have $\tilde{\mathbb{R}}^k = (\tilde{R}^{\mathbb{N}})^k$, $\tilde{\mathcal{B}}^k$: the Borel sets of $\tilde{\mathbb{R}}^k$ $(k \geqq 1)$; $\tilde{S}_k = S_k(\tilde{\mathbb{R}}^k)$, $\tilde{P}_k = P_k(\tilde{\mathbb{R}}^k)$, $\tilde{\mathcal{P}}_k$: the σ-algebra over $\tilde{P}_k$ corresponding to $\mathcal{P}_k$; $\tilde{\mathcal{C}} = \mathcal{C}(\tilde{\mathbb{R}}^k)$.

(3.1) Theorem. For every $\tau \in \tilde{S}_k$ there is a unique probability measure μ on $(\tilde{P}_k, \tilde{\mathcal{P}}_k)$ such that

(26) $$\tau(A) = \int_{\tilde{P}_k} \pi(A)\, d\mu(\pi) \qquad (A \in \tilde{\mathcal{B}}^k).$$

Proof. We are going to verify the conditions of theorem (2.3) for the convex set $\tilde{S}_k$ in the vague topology $\mathcal{T}$. Since $(\mathcal{M}, \mathcal{T})$ is metrizable (2.2,3) the same is true of $\tilde{S}_k \subseteq \mathcal{M}$. Also, $\tilde{S}_k$ is obviously bounded: For every $\tau \in \tilde{S}_k$ we have $|\int f\, d\tau| \leqq \sup |f| \cdot \tau(\tilde{\mathbb{R}}^k) = \sup |f|$, which is finite for every $f \in \tilde{\mathcal{C}}$, hence $\sup_{\tau \in S_k} |\int f\, d\tau| < \infty (f \in \tilde{\mathcal{C}})$. However, a $\mathcal{T}$-bounded set is relatively compact (2.2,4), so $\tilde{S}_k$ is relatively compact. $\tilde{S}_k$ will be compact if it is closed. To show this, we take a sequence (τ_n) in $\tilde{S}_k$ with the vague limit τ. Since the indicator function $\chi_{\tilde{\mathbb{R}}^k}$ is an element of $\tilde{\mathcal{C}}$, we have

(27) $$\tau(\tilde{\mathbb{R}}^k) = \int \chi_{\tilde{\mathbb{R}}^k}\, d\tau = \lim \int \chi_{\tilde{\mathbb{R}}^k}\, d\tau_n = \lim \tau_n(\tilde{\mathbb{R}}^k) = 1,$$

so τ is a probability.[4]

We establish the symmetry of τ by approximation. It can be shown (Bauer [1968], p. 190) that $\lim \tau_n(A) = \tau(A)$ for every Borel set A such that $\tau(\bar{A} \backslash \mathring{A}) = 0$ ($\bar{A} \backslash \mathring{A}$ is the topological boundary of A). So the partial symmetry carries over to the limit τ for k-cylinders $D_{\rho,N}(x)$ such that there is no τ-probability mass on the points $a \in \tilde{\mathbb{R}}^k$ with $a_{i,(\rho,j)} = x_{N_i+j}$ $(1 \leqq j \leqq n_i; 1 \leqq i \leqq k)$, $\rho = (\rho_1, \ldots, \rho_k) \in \mathcal{U}_k$. But this means that the n-dimensional distribution

---

[4] Notice that for this step the compactness of $\tilde{\mathbb{R}}^k$ is essential. For a noncompact underlying space Y, which is usually assumed to be only "locally compact", the vague topology is defined in terms of a proper subclass of $\mathcal{C}(Y)$ to which χ_Y does not belong any more (see Bauer [1968], pp. 172, 182).

function $F_{\rho,N}(x_1, \ldots, x_n) := \tau[D_{\rho,N}(x)]$ is continuous at $x = (x_1, \ldots, x_n)$ (see, for instance, Bauer [1968], p. 191, for the case $n = 1$; intuitively, there is no increase in probability at those points). Now, for every distribution function F, the set Con (F) of points at which F is continuous is dense in $\tilde{R}^n$; so points of discontinuity can be approximated by those of continuity. For any $\rho \in \mathcal{U}_k$, let (y_m) be a sequence in R^n such that $y_m \in \mathrm{Con}\,(F_N) \cap \mathrm{Con}\,(F_{\rho,N})$, $y_1 \leqq y_2 \leqq \ldots \leqq x$, and $x = \lim\limits_m y_m$. Then, since a distribution function is continuous from the left, the following equation holds:

(28) $\tau(D_{\rho,N}(x)] = F_{\rho,N}(x_1, \ldots, x_n) = \lim\limits_m F_{\rho,N}(y_{m1}, \ldots, y_{mn})$

$$= \lim\limits_m \tau[D_{\rho,N}(y_m)];$$

especially, we have $\tau[D_N(x)] = \lim\limits_m \tau[D_N(y_m)]$. Now, by assumption, $\tau[D_N(y_m)] = \tau[D_{\rho,N}(y_m)]$ $(m \in \mathbb{N})$, hence

(29) $$\tau[D_N(x)] = \tau[D_{\rho,N}(x)].$$

It follows that τ is partially symmetric. Thus, $\tilde{S}_k$ contains all its vague adherent points, and so, by definition, $\tilde{S}_k$ is closed.

We now apply theorem (2.3) and conclude that for each $\tau \in \tilde{S}_k$ there is a probability measure μ on $\tilde{S}_k$ which is supported by $Ex(\tilde{S}_k)$ and which represents τ. But $Ex(\tilde{S}_k) = \tilde{P}_k$ (Theorem 2.4), so the probability mass of μ is concentrated on $\tilde{P}_k$. Therefore we can take μ to be a probability measure over $(\tilde{P}_k, \mathcal{A})$, where $\mathcal{A}$ denotes the vague Baire sets of $\tilde{P}_k$ (recall that since $\tilde{P}_k$ is metrizable every Borel set is a Baire set; we speak of "vague" Baire sets because $\tilde{P}_k$ carries the vague topology induced by $\mathcal{T}$). The following lemma claims that $\mathcal{A} = \tilde{\mathcal{P}}_k$. (Cf. Hewitt & Savage [1955], p. 481.)

Lemma 1. $\mathcal{A} = \tilde{\mathcal{P}}_k$.

Proof. By definition, $\mathcal{A}$ is the smallest σ-algebra such that all functions $f \in \mathcal{C}(\tilde{P}_k)$ are $\mathcal{A} - \mathcal{B}_1$-measurable, i.e., $f^{-1}[R(r)] \in \mathcal{A}$ for every $r \in \tilde{R}$. However, the functions Φ_f defined in (14) are elements of $\mathcal{C}(\tilde{P}_k)$ when restricted to $\tilde{P}_k$, so we have $\Phi_f^{-1}[R(r)] = \{\pi; \int f\, d\pi < r\}(f \in \tilde{\mathcal{C}})$. Now we observe that $\tilde{\mathcal{B}}^k$ is generated by the open "F_σ-sets" of $\tilde{R}^k$ (Bauer [1968], 40.3 and 40.2, p. 167). Let A be such a set; then there exists a monotone sequence (f_n) in $\tilde{\mathcal{C}}$ such that $\chi_A = \sup f_n$ (Bauer [1968], 40.2, p. 167, and 39.2, p. 159). By Levi's

224   STUDIES IN INDUCTIVE LOGIC AND PROBABILITY

theorem (Bauer [1968], 11.4, p. 51) it follows with $\Phi_A := \Phi_{\chi_A}$:

(30) $\pi(A) = \Phi_A(\pi) = \int (\sup f_n) \, d\pi = \sup \Phi_{f_n}(\pi).$

So from $\{\pi; \Phi_{f_n}(\pi) < r\} \in \mathscr{A}$ $(n \in \mathbb{N})$ we get $\{\pi; \pi(A) < r\} \in \mathscr{A}$ $(r \in \tilde{R})$, thus $\tilde{\mathscr{P}}_k \subseteq \mathscr{A}$. On the other hand, the functions g_A are $\tilde{\mathscr{P}}_k$-measurable (by definition). Therefore, the same is true of polynomials of such functions, which form a subalgebra $\mathscr{S}$ of the (Banach) algebra $\mathscr{C}(\tilde{P}_k)$ (note that, as $\tilde{S}_k$, $\tilde{P}_k$ is closed, hence compact). $\mathscr{S}$ "separates" points of $\tilde{P}_k$ and contains the constant functions (the constant polynomials). By the Stone-Weierstrass theorem (Dieudonné [1960], p. 131) $\mathscr{S}$ is dense in $\mathscr{C}(\tilde{P}_k)$. Since limits of measurable functions are again measurable, every $f \in \mathscr{C}(\tilde{P}_k)$ is $\tilde{\mathscr{P}}_k$-measurable, which proves the inclusion $\mathscr{A} \subseteq \tilde{\mathscr{P}}_k$.

To complete the existence part of the main proof consider again an open F_σ-set $A \in \tilde{\mathscr{B}}^k$ and a monotone sequence (f_n) in $\tilde{\mathscr{C}}$ with $\chi_A = \sup f_n$. Then (30) holds for all $\tau \in \tilde{S}_k$. However, (Φ_{f_n}) is a monotone sequence of $\mathscr{T}$-continuous linear functionals on $\mathscr{M} - \mathscr{M}$, and so, applying Levi's theorem twice, we get for any $\tau \in \tilde{S}_k$ and its representing measure μ:

(31) $\tau(A) = \sup \Phi_{f_n}(\tau) = \sup \int_{\tilde{P}_k} \Phi_{f_n}(\pi) \, d\mu(\pi)$

$= \int_{\tilde{P}_k} \sup \Phi_{f_n}(\pi) \, d\mu(\pi)$

$= \int_{\tilde{P}_k} \Phi_A(\pi) \, d\mu(\pi) = \int_{\tilde{P}_k} \pi(A) \, d\mu(\pi).$

But this is equation (26).

Finally we show that μ is unique. This is done in the following lemma.

Lemma 2. $\tilde{S}_k$ is a simplex.

Proof. We must show that the subcone $\tilde{S}_k^* \subseteq \mathscr{M}$ (i.e., the set of all partially symmetric Baire measures on $\mathbb{R}^k$) is a lattice in the usual ordering. Let τ_1 and τ_2 be elements of $\tilde{S}_k^*$. Then we have only to make sure that the least upper bound $\tau_1 \vee \tau_2$ in $\mathscr{M}$ is itself partially symmetric. In view of (12), this in turn amounts to the claim that whenever τ is a partially symmetric, signed measure the upper variation τ^+ is again partially symmetric.

To establish this, we define for every $\rho \in \mathscr{U}_k$ a transformation $T_\rho : \tilde{\mathbb{R}}^k \to \tilde{\mathbb{R}}^k$ by $T_\rho[(a_{ij})] := (a_{i,(\rho^{-1}j)})$. Obviously, T_ρ is one-to-one and onto, with $T_\rho^{-1}(D_{\rho'}(B)) = D_{\rho\rho'}(B)$ for every k-cylinder $D_{\rho'}(B)$ and $\rho' \in \mathcal{U}_k$ (in what follows we omit 'B' for brevity). Since $\tau(D_{\rho'}) = \tau(D_{\rho\rho'})$ and $\tau[T_\rho^{-1}(D_{\rho'})] = \tau(D_{\rho\rho'}) = \tau(D_{\rho'})$, we have $\tau = \tau T_\rho^{-1}$ for all $\rho \in \mathcal{U}_k$. Now the partial symmetry of τ^+ is obtained by the following chain of equations which holds for every k-cylinder D and $\rho \in \mathcal{U}_k$ (note that, trivially, $B = T_\rho^{-1} T_\rho B$ and $C = T_\rho T_\rho^{-1} C$):

(32) $\tau^+(D_\rho) = \tau^+(T_\rho^{-1} D) = \sup\limits_{B \subseteq T_\rho^{-1} D} \tau(B) = \sup\limits_{T_\rho B \subseteq D} \tau(T_\rho B) = \sup\limits_{C \subseteq D} \tau(C)$

$$= \tau^+(D).$$

This concludes the proof of the main theorem. ∎

For the next section we need the following simple theorem.

(3.2) Theorem. Suppose $M \subseteq \tilde{\mathbb{R}}^l$ (i.e., $M = (Z^\mathbb{N})^k$ for some Borel set Z in $\tilde{R}$). Then for every $\tau \in S_k(M)$ there exists a unique probability measure μ on $(P_k(M), \mathcal{P}_k(M))$ which represents τ.

Proof. Let τ be an element of $S_k(M)$. We identify τ with that $\tilde{\tau} \in \tilde{S}_k$ which coincides with τ on M and assigns zero probability to $\mathscr{C}M$. By the main theorem there is a unique μ on $(\tilde{P}_k, \tilde{\mathcal{P}}_k)$ representing $\tilde{\tau}$. Now it remains to observe that the set $U = \{\pi \in \tilde{P}_k ; \pi(\mathscr{C}M) > 0\}$ is of zero measure with respect to μ; we then can identify μ with a probability measure on $(P_k(M), \mathcal{P}_k(M))$ which represents τ. However,

$$U = \bigcup_{n=1}^\infty A_n \quad \text{with} \quad A_n = \left\{ \pi \in \tilde{P}_k ; \pi(\mathrm{CM}) > \frac{1}{n} \right\},$$

and

(33) $0 = \tilde{\tau}(\mathrm{CM}) = \int_{P_k(M)} \pi(\mathrm{CM}) \, d\mu(\pi) + \int_{\mathrm{CP}_k(M) \backslash A_n} \cdots + \int_{A_n} \cdots.$

But this means that we have

(34) $$0 = \int_{A_n} \pi(\mathrm{CM}) \, d\mu(\pi) \geq \frac{1}{n} \mu(A_n) \geq 0,$$

thus $\mu(A_n) = 0$ for all $n \in \mathbb{N}$, and $\mu(U) = 0$. ∎

4. DE FINETTI REPRESENTATIONS

In the present section we shall derive from the main theorem various formulations of representation theorems of the de Finetti type for (partially) symmetric probability distributions.

(4.1) Theorem (*Partial symmetry; the general case*). For every $\tau \in S_k$ there is a unique probability measure μ on $(P_k, \mathcal{P}_k)$ representing τ.

Proof. We apply (3.2) with $M = \mathbb{R}^k$. ∎

In his paper (1938) de Finetti mentions two limiting cases of partial exchangeability. First, there may be no interdependence between types. In our absolute formulation we then have a $\tau \in S_k$ which is simply the product of k symmetric measures $\sigma_1, \ldots, \sigma_k$ on $\mathbb{R}$. Accordingly, the representing measure μ is a product measure $\mu_1 \times \ldots \times \mu_k$ where μ_i separately represents $\sigma_i (1 \leq i \leq k)$.

The second case is that of total exchangeability or symmetry. Here we have $k = 1$, and (4.1) yields the absolute counterpart of de Finetti's 1937 representation.

(4.2) Theorem (*Symmetry; the general case*). For every symmetric probability σ on $\mathbb{R}$ there is a unique probability measure μ on $(P, \mathcal{P})$ representing σ.

We are now going to state analogues of (4.1) and (4.2) in terms of distribution functions. As above let $N = (n_1, \ldots, n_k)$ be a k-tuple of nonnegative integers with $n = \sum n_i > 0$, and again call $\mathcal{N}_k^1$ the set of such N. By F_N we mean a distribution function of dimension n. F_N is called (*k-fold*) *partially symmetric* if for all permutations ρ_i confined to $[n_i] \subseteq \mathbb{N}_0$ and $\rho = (\rho_1, \ldots, \rho_k)$ the following equation holds:

(35) $$F_N(x_1, \ldots, x_n) = F_{\rho,N}(x_1, \ldots, x_n),$$

where $F_{\rho,N}(x_1, \ldots, x_n) := F_N(x_{N_0 + \rho_1 1}, \ldots, x_{N_0 + \rho_1 n_1}, \ldots, x_{N_{k-1} + \rho_k 1}, \ldots, x_{N_{k-1} + \rho_k n_k})$. Further we call the family $(F_N)_{N \in \mathcal{N}_k}$ *k-consistent* if for any $\rho \in \mathcal{U}_k$ and for any i, $1 \leq i \leq k$,

(36) $$F_N(x_1, \ldots, x_n) = F_{N^{(i)}}(y_1, \ldots, y_{n+1}),$$

with $N^{(i)} := (n_1, \ldots, n_i + 1, \ldots, n_k)$ and

(37) $$y_j := \begin{cases} x_j \ (1 \leq j \leq N_i) \\ \infty \ (j = N_i + 1) \\ x_{j-1} \ (N_i + 1 < j < n). \end{cases}$$

Note that the family (F_n) typically contains more than one function for each dimension $n > 1$.

(4.3) Theorem (*Partially symmetric distribution functions*). Let $(F_N)_{N \in \mathcal{N}_k}$ be a k-consistent family of k-fold partially symmetric distribution functions. Then there exists a unique probability measure Q on $(\Delta^k, \mathcal{D}^k)$ such that for all $n \in \mathbb{N}$ with $\sum n_i = n$ and for all $x, \ldots, x_n \in R$ the following equation holds:

$$(38) \quad F_N(x_1, \ldots, x_n)$$
$$= \int_{\Delta^k} \prod_{i=1}^k G_i(x_{N_{i-1}+1}) \cdot \ldots \cdot G_i(x_{N_i}) \, dQ(G_1, \ldots, G_k)$$

Proof. We define a set function τ on $\mathbb{R}^k$ by

$$(39) \quad \tau[D_{\rho,N}(x)] := F_N(x_1, \ldots, x_n)$$

for every $N = (n_1, \ldots, n_k)$, $n = \sum n_i$, $x \in R^n$, and $\rho \in \mathcal{U}_k$. The compatibility conditions (35) and (36) imply that this definition is indeed meaningful. Although the theorem of Kolmogorov is usually formulated for symmetric distribution functions only, a check of the proof[5] shows that it carries through also for the τ given here. So τ is an (obviously partially symmetric) probability on $\mathbb{R}^k$. By (4.1) τ can be written as an integral, $\tau(A) = \int_{P_k} \pi(A) \, d\mu(\pi)$, for all $A \in \mathcal{B}^k$, and with $\pi = \pi_1 \times \ldots \times \pi_k$. Now we observe that there are bijections $\Phi : \pi_1 \times \ldots \times \pi_k \to (\pi_1^1, \ldots, \pi_k^1)$ between P_k and Ω^k and $\psi : (\pi_1^1, \ldots, \pi_k^1) \to (G_{\pi_1^1}, \ldots, G_{\pi_k^1})$ between Ω^k and Δ^k. By inspection, we can see that Φ is $\mathcal{P}_k - \mathcal{Q}^k$-measurable, and that ψ is $\mathcal{Q}^k - \mathcal{D}^k$-measurable. Therefore, by the theorem on transformations of integrals, we can transplant the unique measure μ via $\mu\Phi^{-1}$ into the unique probability measure $Q := \mu(\psi \circ \Phi)^{-1}$ on $(\Delta^k, \mathcal{D}^k)$. Taking for A in (4.1) the k-cylinder $D_N(x)$ we then have:

$$(40) \quad F_N(x_n, \ldots, x_n) = \tau[D_N(x)]$$

$$= \int_{P_k} \prod_{i=1}^k \pi_i[C(R(x_{N_{i-1}+1}), \ldots, R(x_{N_i}))] \, d\mu(\pi_1 \times \ldots \times \pi_k)$$

$$= \int_{\Omega^k} \prod_{i=1}^k \pi_i^1[R(x_{N_{i-1}+1})] \cdot \ldots \cdot \pi_i^1[R(x_{N_i})] \, d(\mu\Phi^{-1})(\pi_1^1, \ldots, \pi_k^1)$$

$$= \int_{\Delta^k} \prod_{i=1}^k G_i(x_{N_{i-1}+1}) \cdot \ldots \cdot G_i(x_{N_i}) \, dQ(G_1, \ldots, G_k).$$

This is the desired result. ∎

---

[5] See, for instance, Richter (1966), p. 209 f.

For completeness, we shall write down as an own theorem the special case $k = 1$, which gives representations for symmetric distribution functions. We remark that it can be arrived at by treating exchangeability in terms of conditional independence (cf. Loève [1963], p. 364 f., Jeffrey [1971], p. 217, and especially Bühlmann [1960]). Bühlmann's result (op. cit., p. 4) has only to be integrated over to yield the form given here.

(4.4) Theorem (*Symmetric distribution functions*). Let (F_n) be a consistent family of symmetric distribution functions. Then there exists a unique probability Q on $(\Delta, \mathcal{D})$ such that for all $n \in \mathbb{N}$ and for all $x_1, \ldots, x_n \in R$,

$$(41) \qquad F_n(x_1, \ldots, x_n) = \int_\Delta G(x_1) \ldots G(x_n) \, dQ(G).$$

Let us finally consider the special case where the partially exchangeable random variables take on the values 0 and 1 only. This is the case of a family of partially exchangeable events considered by de Finetti in [1938]. In our absolute presentation we have to specialize theorem (3.2) to that subspace of $\tilde{\mathbb{R}}^k$ which contains but the elements 0 and 1 in each of the k-*fold* infinitely many coordinates. Thus, $M = (\{0, 1\}^\mathbb{N})^k =: M_2$. For every i, $1 \leq i \leq k$, let π_{θ_i} be the unique probability on $\{0, 1\}^\mathbb{N}$ defined as follows:

$$(42) \qquad \pi_{\theta_i} := \pi^1_{\theta_i} \times \ldots \times \pi^1_{\theta_i} \times \ldots \quad \text{with} \quad \pi^1_{\theta_i}(\{1\}) := \theta_i \qquad (\theta_i \in I).$$

Further, set $\pi_{\theta_1, \ldots, \theta_k} := \pi_{\theta_1} \times \ldots \times \pi_{\theta_k}$. We can then derive the following theorem.

(4.5) Theorem (*Partial symmetry; the two-valued case*).   For every $\tau \in S(M_2)$ there is exactly one probability measure μ on $(I^k, \mathcal{B}^k_1 \cap I^k)$ such that for all $A \in \mathcal{B}^k \cap M_2$,

$$(43) \qquad \tau(A) = \int_{I^k} \pi_{\theta_1, \ldots, \theta_k}(A) \, d\mu(\theta_1, \ldots, \theta_k).$$

Proof.   First we apply theorem (3.2) with $M = M_2$. This gives us a representing measure μ for τ, defined on $(P_k(M_2), \mathcal{P}_k(M_2))$. However, each $\pi = \pi_1 \times \ldots \times \pi_k \in P_k(M_2)$ is uniquely determined by the values θ_i $(1 \leq i \leq k)$ that the one-dimensional counterpart π^1_i of π_i assigns to the set $\{1\}$. Therefore the function $\Phi': \pi_{\theta_1} \times \ldots \times \pi_{\theta_k} \to (\theta_1, \ldots, \theta_k)$ bijectively maps $P_k(M_2)$ onto I^k. Moreover, Φ' is

$\mathscr{P}_k(M_2) - \mathscr{B}_1^k \cap I^k$-measurable; this is because a Cartesian product of the form $\prod_i \{\theta_i \,; \theta_i < r_i\}$ has as inverse image under Φ' the set $\prod_i \{\pi_{\theta_i} \,; \pi_{\theta_i}[C\{1\})] < r_i\}$ which is in $\mathscr{P}_k(M_2)$. So we can transform μ into its image under Φ', and, keeping the notation for the representing measure, this yields (43).

Suppose now that (E_{ij}) is a sequence of k-fold partially exchangeable events with respect to a probability p such that the E_{ij} $(j \in \mathbb{N}, i$ fixed) belong to the same type i. Let us see how we can calculate from (43) the probability $\omega_{l_1,\ldots,l_k}^{(n_1,\ldots,n_k)}$ of the simultaneous realization of exactly l_i events of type i out of n_i of type i $(1 \leqq i \leqq k, \sum_i n_i = n)$. We consider one particular arrangement $E_1, \ldots, E_n$ of these n events such that the intersection

$$\textbf{(44)}\quad E := \bigcap_{i=1}^{k} E_{N_{i-1}+1} \cap \ldots \cap E_{N_{i-1}+l_i} \cap CE_{N_{i-1}+l_i+1} \cap \ldots \cap CE_{N_i}$$

is the set in the probability of which we are interested. By the random variable $X = (\chi_{E_{ij}})$ E is transformed into a k-cylinder $D(B)$ of M_2 with $B = (B_1, \ldots, B_k)$, $B_i = \{1\}^{l_i} \times \{0\}^{n_i - l_i}$ $(1 \leqq i \leqq k)$. For $\tau := pX^{-1}$ we then have with some unique probability μ:

$$\textbf{(45)}\quad \tau[D(B)] = \int_{I^k} \pi_{\theta_1}, \ldots, \theta_k[D(B)] \, d\mu(\theta_1, \ldots, \theta_k)$$

$$= \int_{I^k} \pi_{\theta_1}[C(B_1)] \cdot \ldots \cdot \pi_{\theta_k}[C(B_k)] \, d\mu(\theta_1, \ldots, \theta_k)$$

$$= \int_{I^k} \theta_1^{l_1}(1-\theta_1)^{n_1-l_1} \cdot \ldots \cdot \theta_k^{l_k}(1-\theta_k)^{n_k-l_k} \, d\mu(\theta_1, \ldots, \theta_k).$$

If we now disregard the arrangement within types we have to multiply the last integral by the product of binomial coefficients, $\binom{n_1}{l_1} \ldots \binom{n_k}{l_k}$, which is de Finetti's formula in (1938).

We conclude with an absolute formulation of de Finetti's original representation theorem about (fully) exchangeable events (cf. equation (2)). The proof is now obvious.

(4.6) Theorem (*Symmetry; the two-valued case*). For every symmetric probability σ on $J := \{0, 1\}^{\mathbb{N}}$ there is a unique probability measure μ over I such that for all $A \in \mathscr{B} \cap J$,

$$\textbf{(46)}\quad \sigma(A) = \int_0^1 \pi_\theta(A) \, d\mu(\theta).$$

230   STUDIES IN INDUCTIVE LOGIC AND PROBABILITY

ACKNOWLEDGMENT

This work was supported by the Deutsche Forschungsgemein-
schaft, Bonn–Bad Godesberg. It is part of a D.F.G. research program that was carried out at the Philosophisches Seminar II, University of Munich. I wish to thank Professor W. Stegmüller, Munich,
who invited me to join this program, and Professor R. Jeffrey for
including the present paper in this volume. Moreover, I am indebted
to H. W. v. Weizsäcker, Munich, for helpful discussions and a
critical reading of the manuscript.

REFERENCES

Bauer, H. (1968) *Wahrscheinlichkeitstheorie und Grundzüge der Mass-
theorie.* Berlin.
Bourbaki, N. (1965) *Intégration.* Paris.
——— (1966) *Espaces vectoriels topologiques,* chap. 1 et 2. Paris.
Bruno, Angelo (1972) *On the Notion of Partial Exchangeability,* in de
Finetti,. *Probability, Induction and Statistics.*
Bühlmann, H. (1960) *Austauschbare stochastische Variablen und ihre
Grenzwertsätze.* University of California Publications in Statistics, 3, 1:
1–36.
Dieudonné, J. (1960) *Foundations of Modern Analysis.* New York.
de Finetti, B., (1937) "La prévision: ses lois logiques, ses sources subjectives". *Annales de l'Institut Henri Poincaré,* 7: 1–68.
——— (1938) "Sur la condition d'"équivalence partielle"", in *Act. Sci. Ind.*
No. 739: Colloque consacré à la théorie des probabilités, VIième
partie, 5–18. Paris.
——— (1964) *Foresight: Its Logical Laws, Its Subjective Sources,* (English
translation of de Finetti [1937]), in Kyburg and Smokler, *Studies in
Subjective Probability.* New York.
——— (1972) *Probability, Induction and Statistics.* London, New York.
——— (1979) "On the Condition of 'Partial Exchangeability'" (article
9 above).
Halmos, P. (1950) *Measure Theory.* Princeton.
Hewitt, E. and Savage, L. (1955) "Symmetric Measures on Cartesian
Products". *Trans. Amer. Math. Soc.,* 80: 470–501.
Hintikka, J. (1972) "Unknown Probabilities, Bayesianism, and de Finetti's
Representation Theorem". *Boston Studies in the Philosophy of Sci-
ence.* VIII: 325–341.
Jeffrey, R. (1971) "Probability Measures and Integrals", (article 3 here).
Loève, M. (1963) *Probability Theory.* Princeton.
Meyer, P. A. (1966) *Probability and Potentials.* Waltham, Mass.
Neveu, J. (1969) *Mathematische Grundlagen der Wahrscheinlichkeitstheorie.*
München and Wien.
Phelps, R. (1966) *Lectures on Choquet's Theorem.* New York.
Richter, H. (1966) *Wahrscheinlichkeitstheorie.* Berlin, Heidelberg, New
York.

Robertson, A, and Robertson, W. (1964) *Topological Vector Spaces*. Cambridge.
Stegmüller, W. (1973) *Probleme und Resultate der Wissenschaftstheorie und Analytischen Philosophie*, Band IV: Personelle und statistische Wahrscheinlichkeit. Berlin, Heidelberg, New York.

11

De Finetti's Generalizations of Exchangeability

BY PERSI DIACONIS AND DAVID FREEDMAN

1. INTRODUCTION

De Finetti has written about partial exchangeability in his articles of 1938 (translated in this volume) and 1959, Section 9.6.2 (translated in de Finetti 1974). Both treatments are rich sources of ideas which take many readings to digest. This article gives examples of partial exchangeability that we understand well enough to put into crisp mathematical terms. All results in Sections 2–5 involve random quantities taking only two values. We follow de Finetti by giving results for finite as well as infinite sequences. In Section 2 we review exchangeability. In Section 3 we present examples of partially exchangeable sequences—2×2 tables and Markov chains—and give general definitions. In Section 4 a finite form of de Finetti's theorem is presented. Section 5 gives some infinite versions of de Finetti's theorem and a counterexample which shows that the straightforward generalization from the exchangeable case sketched by de Finetti is not possible. The last section contains comments about the practical implications of partial exchangeability. We also discuss the closely related work of P. Martin-Löf on repetitive structures.

2. EXCHANGEABILITY

We begin with the case of exchangeability. Consider the following experiment: A coin is spun on a table. We will denote heads by

1 and tails by 0. The experiment is to be repeated ten times. A subjectivist believes he can assign probabilities to the $2^{10} = 1024$ possible outcomes by looking at the coin and thinking about what he knows. There are *no* a priori restrictions on the probabilities assigned save that they are nonnegative and sum to 1. Even with so simple a problem, assigning over a thousand probabilities is not a simple task. De Finetti has called attention to exchangeability as a possible simplifying assumption. With an exchangeable probability two sequences of length 10 with the same number of ones are assigned the same probability. Thus, the probability assignment is symmetric, or invariant under changes in order. Another way to say this is that only the number of ones in the ten trials matters, not the location of the ones. If believed, the symmetry assumption reduces the number of probabilities to be assigned from 1024 to 11—the probability of no ones through the probability of ten ones.

It is useful to single out certain extreme exchangeable probability assignments. Though it is unrealistic, we might be sure there will be exactly one head in the ten spins. The assumption of exchangeability forces each of the ten possible sequences with a single one in it to be equally likely. The distribution is just like the outcome of ten draws without replacement from an urn with one ball marked 1 and nine balls marked 0—the ball marked 1 could be drawn at any stage and must be drawn at some time. There are 11 such extremal urns corresponding to sure knowledge of exactly i one outcomes in the ten draws where i is a fixed number between zero and ten. The first form of de Finetti's theorem follows from these observations:

(1)   Finite form of de Finetti's theorem

Every exchangeable probability assignment on sequences of length N is a unique mixture of draws without replacement from the $N+1$ extremal urns.

By a mixture of urns we simply mean a probability assignment over the $N+1$ possible urns. Any exchangeable assignment on sequences of length N can be realized by first choosing an urn and then drawing without replacement until the urn is empty.

This form of the result has been given by de Finetti (1938), (1974), and by many other writers on the subject: Diaconis (1977), Ericson (1973), Heath and Sudderth (1976), Hewitt and Savage (1955), and Kendall (1967).

The extremal urns, representing certain knowledge of the total number of ones, seem like unnatural probability assignments in most cases. While such situations arise (for example, when drawing a sample from a finite population), the more usual situation is that of the coin. While we are only considering ten spins, in principle it seems possible to extend the ten to an arbitrarily large number. In this case there is a stronger form of (1) which restricts the probability assignment within the class of exchangeable assignments.

(2)   Infinite form of de Finetti's theorem

Every exchangeable probability assignment which can be extended to a probability assignment on infinite sequences of zeros and ones has the following representations:

$$(3)\quad P(j \text{ ones in } k \text{ trials}) = \binom{k}{j}\int_0^1 p^j(1-p)^{k-j}\,d\mu(p)$$

for a uniquely determined measure μ.

Note that (3) holds for every k with the same μ. Equation (3) says that exchangeable probability assignments which can be extended have the special form of mixtures of independent and identically distributed coin tossing. We have more to say about this interpretation in Remark 1 of Section 6.

Not all exchangeable measures on sequences of length k can be extended to exchangeable sequences of length $n > k$. For example, sampling without replacement from an urn with k balls in it cannot be extended to $k+1$ trials. Necessary and sufficient conditions for extension are found in de Finetti (1969), Crisma (1971), and Diaconis (1977). The requirement that an exchangeable sequence of length k be infinitely extendable seems out of keeping with de Finetti's general program of restricting attention to finite samples. An appropriate finite version of (3) is given by Diaconis and Freedman (1978a). We show that if an exchangeable probability on sequences of length k is extendable to an exchangeable probability on sequences of length $n > k$, then (3) almost holds in the sense that there is a measure μ such that for any set $A \subset \{0, 1, 2, \ldots, k\}$,

$$(4)\quad \left| P\left\{ \begin{array}{c} \text{number of ones in} \\ k \text{ trials is in } A \end{array} \right\} - \sum_{j \in A}\binom{k}{j}\int_0^1 p^j(1-p)^{k-j}\,d\mu(p) \right| \leq \frac{2k}{n},$$

uniformly in n, k, and A.

For example, it is easy to imagine the spins of the coin as the first ten spins in a series of 1000 spins. This yields a bound of .02 on the right side of (4).

Both of the results (3) and (4) imply that for many practical purposes instead of specifying a probability assignment on the number of ones in n trials it is equivalent to specify a prior measure μ on the unit interval. Much of de Finetti's discussion in his papers on partial exchangeability is devoted to reasonable choices of μ. The paper by A. Bruno (1964) is also devoted to this important problem. We will not discuss the choice of a prior further but rather restrict attention to generalization of (2), (3), and (4) to partially exchangeable probability assignments.

3.   EXAMPLES OF PARTIAL EXCHANGEABILITY

In many situations exchangeability is not believable or does not permit incorporation of other relevant data. Here are two examples which will be discussed further in Sections 4 and 5.

Example—2×2 tables

Consider zero/one outcomes in a medical experiment with n subjects. We are told each subject's sex and if each subject was given a treatment or was in a control group. In some cases, a reasonable symmetry assumption is the following kind of partial exchangeability: regard all the treated males as exchangeable with one another but not with the subjects in the other three categories; likewise for the other categories. Thus, two sequences of zeros and ones of length n which had the same number of ones in each of the four categories would be assigned the same probability. For example, if $n = 10$, each of the three sequences below must be assigned the same probability.

Trial	1	2	3	4	5	6	7	8	9	10
Sex	M	M	M	F	F	M	M	F	F	F
Treatment/Control	T	T	T	T	T	C	C	C	C	C
1	1	0	1	0	1	1	1	0	1	0
2	0	1	1	0	1	1	1	0	0	1
3	0	1	1	1	0	1	1	1	0	0

In this example, there are three treated males, two treated females, two control males, and three control females. The data from each of the three sequences can be summarized in a 2×2 table which records the number of one outcomes in each group. Each of the three sequences leads to the same table.

$$\text{T} \quad \text{C}$$

(5)

	T	C
M	2	2
F	1	1

Example—Markov dependence

Consider an experiment in which a thumbtack is placed on the floor and given an energetic flick with the fingers. We record a one if the tick lands point upward and a zero if it lands point to the floor. For simplicity suppose the tack starts point to the floor. If after each trial the tack were reset to be point to the floor, exchangeability might be a tenable assumption. If each flick of the tack was given from the position in which the tack just landed, then the result of each trial may depend on the result of the previous trial. For example, there is some chance the tack will slide across the floor without ever turning. It does not seem reasonable to think of a trial depending on what happened two or more trials before. A natural notion of symmetry here is to say that if two sequences of zeros and ones of length n which both begin with zero have the same number of transitions: zero to zero, zero to one, one to zero, and one to one, they should both be assigned the same probability. For example, if $n = 10$, any of the following three sequences would be assigned the same probability.

Trial	1	2	3	4	5	6	7	8	9	10
1	0	1	0	1	1	0	0	1	0	1
2	0	1	0	1	0	0	1	1	0	1
3	0	0	1	0	1	0	1	0	1	1

Each sequence begins with a zero and has the same transition matrix

$$\text{to}$$
$$0 \quad 1$$

(6)

		0	1
from	0	1	4
	1	3	1

It turns out that there are 16 different sequences starting with zero that have this transition matrix.

A general definition of partial exchangeability that includes these examples involves the notion of a *statistic:* A function from the sequences of length n into a set X. A probability assignment P on sequences of length n is *partially exchangeable for a statistic T* if

$$T(x) = T(y) \quad \text{implies} \quad P(x) = P(y)$$

where x and y are sequences of length n. Freedman (1962) and Lauritzen (1974) have said that P was summarized by T in this situation.

In the case of exchangeability the statistic T is the number of ones. Two sequences with the same number of ones get assigned the same probability by an exchangeable probability. This definition is equivalent to the usual one of permutation invariance. In the case of 2×2 tables the statistic T is the 2×2 table (5). In the Markov example the statistic T is the matrix of transition counts (6) along with the outcome of the first trial.

Such examples can easily be combined and extended. For instance, two stage Markov dependence with additional information such as which experimenter reported the trial and the time of day being given. De Finetti (1938), (1974, Section 9.6.2), Martin-Löf (1970), (1974), and Diaconis and Freedman (1978a,b,c) give further examples. In remark 4 of Section 6 we discuss a more general definition of partial exchangeability.

4. FINITE FORMS OF DE FINETTI'S THEOREM

There is a simple analog of Theorem (1) for partially exchangeable sequences of length n. We will write 2^n for the set of sequences of zeros and ones of length n. Let $T : 2^n \rightarrow X$ be a statistic taking values $t_1, t_2, \ldots, t_k$. Let $S_i = \{x \in 2^n : T(x) = t_i\}$ and suppose S_i contains n_i elements. Let P_i be the probability assignment on 2^n which picks a sequence $x \in 2^n$ by choosing an x from S_i uniformly—e.g., with probability $1/n_i$. Then P_i is partially exchangeable with respect to T. In terms of these definitions we now state

(7) Finite form of de Finetti's theorem

Every probability assignment P on 2^n which is partially exchangeable with respect to T is a unique mixture of the extreme measures P_i. The mixing weights are $w_i = P\{x : T(x) = t_i\}$.

In the language of convex sets, the set of partially exchangeable probabilities with respect to T forms a simplex with extreme points P_i. Theorem (7) seems trivial but in practice a more explicit description of the extreme measures P_i—like the urns in (1)—can be difficult. We now explore this for the examples of Section 3.

(8) Example—2×2 tables

Suppose we know there are: a treated males, b untreated males, c treated females, and d untreated females with $a + b + c + d = n$. The sufficient statistic is the 2×2 table with entries which are the number of ones in each of the four groups.

$$\begin{array}{cc} & T \quad U \\ M & \begin{pmatrix} i & j \\ k & l \end{pmatrix} \\ F & \end{array} \quad \text{where} \quad \begin{array}{cc} 0 \le i \le a, & 0 \le j \le b \\ 0 \le k \le c, & 0 \le l \le d. \end{array}$$

There are $(a+1) \times (b+1) \times (c+1) \times (d+1)$ possible values of the matrix. An extreme partially exchangeable probability can be thought of as follows: Fix a possible matrix. Make up four urns. In the first urn, labeled TM (for treated males), put i balls marked one and $a - i$ balls marked zero. Similarly, construct urns labeled UM, TF, and UF. To generate a sequence of length n given the labels (Sex and Treated/Untreated) draw without replacement from the appropriate urns. This scheme generates all sequences $x \in 2^n$ with the given matrix $\begin{pmatrix} i & j \\ k & l \end{pmatrix}$ equiprobably. Theorem (7) says that any partially exchangeable probability assignment on 2^n is a unique mixture of such urn schemes. If a, b, c, and d all tend to infinity, the binomial approximation to the hypergeometric distribution will lead to the appropriate infinite version of de Finetti's theorem as stated in Section 5.

(9) Example—Markov chains

For simplicity, assume we have a sequence of length $n + 1$ that begins with a zero. The sufficient statistic is $T = \begin{pmatrix} t_{00} & t_{01} \\ t_{10} & t_{11} \end{pmatrix}$ where t_{ij} is the number of i to j transitions. A counting argument shows that there are $\binom{n}{2} + 1$ different values of T possible. Here is an urn model which generates all sequences of length $n + 1$ with a fixed transition matrix T equiprobably. Form two urns U_0 and U_1 as follows: Put t_{ij} balls marked j into urns U_i. It is now necessary to make an adjustment to make sure the process doesn't run into trouble. There are two cases possible:

Case 1. If $t_{01} = t_{10}$, remove a zero from U_1.

Case 2. If $t_{01} = t_{10} + 1$, remove a one from U_0.

To generate a sequence of length $n + 1$, let $X_1 = 0$. Let X_2 be the result of a draw from U_{X_1}; and, in general, let X_i be the result of a draw without replacement from urn $U_{X_{i-1}}$. If the sequence generated ever forces a draw from an empty urn, make a forced transition to the other urn. The adjustment made above guarantees that such a forced jump can only be made once from either urn and that the process generates all sequences of length $n + 1$ that start with zero and have transition matrix T with the same probability. Theorem (7) says that every probability assignment on sequences of length $n + 1$ which is partially exchangeable for the transition matrix T is a unique mixture of the $\binom{n}{2} + 1$ different urn processes described above. Again, the binomial approximation to the hypergeometric will lead to an infinite form of de Finetti's theorem in certain cases. This is further discussed in Sections 5 and 6.

Determining when a simple urn model such as the ones given above can be found to describe the extreme partially exchangeable probabilities may be difficult. For instance, we do not known how to extend the urn model for Markov chains to processes taking three values.

5.   INFINITE FORMS OF DE FINETTI'S THEOREM

Let us examine the results and problems for infinite sequences in the two examples.

(10)   Example—2 × 2 tables

Let $X_1, X_2, X_3, \ldots$ be an infinite sequence of random variables each taking values 0 or 1. Suppose each trial is labeled as Male or Female and as Treated or Untreated and that the number of labels in each of the four possible categories (M, U), (M, T), (F, U), (F, T) is infinite. Suppose that for each n the distribution of $X_1, X_2, \ldots, X_n$ is partially exchangeable with respect to the sufficient statistic that counts the number of zeros and the number of ones for each label. Thus, $T_n = (a_1, b_1, a_2, b_2, a_3, b_3, a_4, b_4)$ where, for example, a_1 is the number of ones labeled (M, U), b_1 is the number of zeros labeled (M, U), a_2 is the number of ones labeled (M, T), b_2 is the number of zeros labeled (M, T) and so on. Then there is a unique probability distribution μ such that for every n and each sequence $x_1, x_2, \ldots, x_n$

(11) $P(X_1 = x_1, \ldots, X_n = x_n) = \int \sum_{i=1}^{4} p_i^{a_i}(1 - p_i)^{b_i} \, d\mu(p_1, p_2, p_3, p_4).$

where a_i, b_i are the values of $T_n(x_1, x_2, \ldots, x_n)$. The result can be proved by passing to the limit in the urn model of Section 4. A different proof is given in G. Link's chapter in this volume.

(12)   Example—Markov chains

Let $X_1, X_2, \ldots$ be an infinite sequence of random variables each taking values 0 or 1. For simplicity assume $X_1 = 0$. Suppose that for each n the joint distribution of $X_1, \ldots, X_n$ is partially exchangeable with respect to the matrix of transition counts. Suppose that the following recurrence condition is satisfied

(13) $P(X_n = 0 \text{ infinitely often}) = 1.$

Then there is a unique probability distribution μ such that for every n, and each sequence $x_2, x_3, \ldots, x_n$ of zeros and ones

(14)
$$P(X_1 = 0, X_2 = x_2, \ldots, X_n = x_n)$$
$$= \int p_{11}^{t_{11}}(1 - p_{11})^{t_{10}} p_{00}^{t_{00}}(1 - p_{00})^{t_{01}} \, d\mu(p_{11}, p_{00})$$

where t_{ij} are the four entries of the transition matrix of $x_1, x_2, \ldots, x_n$.

De Finetti appears to state (pp. 218–219 of de Finetti [1974]) that the representation (14) is valid for every partially exchangeable probability assignment in this case. Here is an example to show that the representation (14) need not hold in the absence of the recurrence condition (13). Consider the probability assignment which goes 001111111 . . . (all ones after two zeros) with probability one. This probability assignment is partially exchangeable and not representable in the form (14). It is partially exchangeable because, for any n, the first n symbols of this sequence form the only sequence with transition matrix $\begin{pmatrix} 1 & 1 \\ 0 & n-3 \end{pmatrix}$. To see that it is not representable in the form (14), write p_k for the probability that the last zero occurs at trial k ($k = 1, 2, 3, \ldots$). For a mixture of Markov chains the numbers p_k can be represented as

(15) $$p_k = c \int_0^1 p_{00}^k (1 - p_{00}) \, d\mu(p_{00}) \qquad k = 1, 2, \ldots,$$

where c is the probability mass the mixing distribution puts on $p_{11} = 1$. The representation (15) implies that the numbers p_k are decreasing. For the example $001111111\ldots$, $p_1 = 0$, $p_2 = 1$, $p_3 = p_4 = \ldots = 0$. So this example doesn't have a representation as a mixture of Markov chains. A detailed discussion of which partially exchangeable assignments are mixtures of Markov chains is in Diaconis and Freedman (1978b).

When can we hope for representations like (3), (11), and (14) in terms of averages over a naturally constructed "parameter space"?

The theory we have developed for such representations still uses the notation of a statistic T. Generally, the statistic will depend on the sample size n and one must specify the way the different T_n's interrelate. Freedman (1962b) introduced the notion of S structures—roughly, from the value of $T_n(x_1, x_2, \ldots, x_n)$ and $T_m(x_{n+1}, x_{n+2}, \ldots, x_{n+m})$ one can compute $T_{n+m}(x_1, x_2, \ldots, x_{n+m})$. Lauritzen (1973) compares S-structure with several other ways of linking together sufficient statistics. We have worked with a somewhat different notion in Diaconis and Freedman (1978c) and developed a theory general enough to include a wide variety of statistical models.

De Finetti sketches out what appears to be a general theory in terms of what he calls the *type* of an observation. In de Finetti (1938) he only gives examples which generalize the examples of 2×2 tables. Here things are simple. In the example there are four types of observations depending on the labels (M, U), (M, T), (F, U), (F, T). In general, for each i we observe the value of another variable giving information like sex, time of day, and so on. An analog of (11) clearly holds in these cases. In de Finetti (1974), Section 9.6.2, the type of an observation is allowed to depend on the outcome of past observations like in our Markov chain example. In this example there are three types of observations—observations X_i that follow a 0 are of type zero; observations X_i that follow a 1 are of type one; and the first observation X_1 is of type 2. For the original case of exchangeability there is only one type.

In attempting to define a general notion of type we thought of trying to define a *type function* $t_n : 2^n \rightarrow \{1, 2, \ldots, r\}^n$ which assigns each symbol in a string a "type" depending only on past symbols. If there are r types, then it is natural to consider the statistic $T_n(x_1, \ldots, x_n) = (a_1, b_1, \ldots, a_r, b_r)$, where a_i is the number of ones of type i and b_i is the number of zeros of type i. We suppose that the type functions t_n were chosen so that the statistics T_n had what Lauritzan (1973) has called Σ structure—T_{n+1} can be computed from T_n and x_{n+1}. Under these circumstances we hoped that a probability P which was partially exchangeable with respect to the T_n's would have a representation of the form

$$(16) \quad P\{X_1 = x_1, \ldots, X_n = x_n\} = \int \prod_{i=1}^{n} p_i^{a_i}(1 - p_i)^{b_i} \, d\mu(p_1, \ldots, p_r)$$

for some measure μ.

The following contrived counterexample indicates the difficulty. There will be two types of observations. However, there will be some partially exchangeable probabilities which fail to have the representation (16), even though the number of observations of each type becomes infinite.

Example. A computer scientist is observing a sequence of zeros and ones $X_0, X_1, X_2, X_3, \ldots$. He knows that one of 3 possible mechanisms generate the process:

- All the positions are exchangeable.
- The even positions $X_0, X_2, X_4, \ldots$, are exchangeable with each other and the odd positions are generated by reading off a fixed reference sequence x of zeros and ones.
- The even positions $X_0, X_2, X_4, \ldots$, are exchangeable with each other and the odd positions are generated by reading off the complement $\bar{x}$ (the complement has $\bar{x}_j = 1 - x_j$).

The scientist knows the reference sequence is $x = 11101110 \ldots$. *He thus keeps track of two types of* X_i. If i is odd and all the preceding X_j with j odd lead to a sequence which matches x or $\bar{x}$, he calls i of type 1. In particular, X_1 and X_3 are always of type 1. He counts the number of zeros and ones of each type. Let $T_n = (a_1, b_1, a_2, b_2)$ be the type counts at time n. Any process of the kind described above is partially exchangeable for these T_n. Moreover, the sequence T_n has Σ structure. Now consider the process which is fair coin tossing on the even trials and equals the ith coordinate of x on trial $2i - 1$. The number of zeros and ones of each type becomes infinite for this process. However, the process cannot be represented in the form (16).

The class of all processes with these T_n's is studied in Diaconis and Freedman (1978c) where the extreme points are determined.

We do not know for which type functions the representation (16) will hold. Some cases when parametric representation is possible have been determined by Martin-Löf (1970, 1974) and Lauritzen (1976). A general theory of partial exchangeability and more examples are in Diaconis and Freedman (1978c).

6.   CONCLUDING REMARKS

1. Some Bayesians are willing to talk about "tossing a coin with unknown p". For them, de Finetti's theorem can be interpreted as follows: If a sequence of events is exchangeable, then it is like the successive tosses of a p-coin with unknown p. Other Bayesians do not accept the idea of p coins with unknown p: de Finetti is a prime example. Writers on subjective probability have suggested that de Finetti's theorem bridges the gap between the two positions. We have trouble with this synthesis and the following quote (de Finetti 1976) indicates that de Finetti has reservations about it:

> The sensational effect of this concept (which went well beyond its intrinsic meaning) is described as follows in Kyburg and Smokler's preface to the collection *Studies in subjective probability* which they edited (pp. 13–14).

> In a certain sense the most important concept in the subjective theory is that of "exchangeable events". Until this was introduced (by de Finetti (1931)) the subjective theory of probability remained little more than a philosophical curiosity. None of those for whom the theory of probability was a matter of knowledge or application paid much attention to it. But, with the introduction of the concept of "*equivalence*" or "*symmetry*" or "*exchangeability*", as it is now called, a way was discovered to link the notion of subjective probability with the classical problem of statistical inference.

It does not seem to us that the theorem explains the idea of a coin with unknown p. The main point is this: Probability assignments involving mixtures of coin tossing were used by Bayesians long before de Finetti. The theorem gives a characterizing feature of such assignments—exchangeability—which can be thought about in terms involving only opinions about observable events.

The connection between mixtures and exchangeable probability assignments allows a subjectivist to interpret some of the classical calculations involving mixtures. For example, consider Laplace's famous calculation of the chance that the Sun will rise tomorrow given that it has risen on $n-1$ previous days. Laplace took a uniform prior on $[0, 1]$ and calculated the chance as the posterior mean of the unknown parameter:

p(Sun rises tomorrow | Has risen on $n-1$ previous days.)

$$= \frac{\int_0^1 p^n \, dp}{\int_0^1 p^{n-1} \, dp} = \frac{n}{n+1}.$$

The translation of this calculation is as follows: Let X_i be one if the Sun rises on day i, zero otherwise. Laplace's uniform mixture of coin tossing is exchangeable and

$$P(X_1 = 1, \ldots, X_k = 1) = \frac{1}{k+1} \qquad k = 1, 2, 3, \ldots.$$

With this allocation,

$$P(X_n = 1 \mid X_1 = 1, \ldots, X_{n-1} = 1) = \frac{P(X_1 = 1 \ldots X_n = 1)}{P(X_1 = 1, \ldots, X_{n-1} = 1)} = \frac{n}{n+1}.$$

A similar interpretation can be given to any calculation involving averages over a parameter space.

2. The exchangeable form of de Finetti's theorem (1) is also a useful computational device for specifying probability assignments. The result is more complicated and much less useful in the case of real valued variables. Here there is no natural notion of a parameter p. Instead, de Finetti's theorem says real valued exchangeable variables, $\{X_i\}_{i=1}^{\infty}$, are described as follows: There is a prior measure π on the space of all probability measures on the real line such that

$$P(X_1 \in A_1, \ldots, X_n \in A_n) = \int \prod_{i=1}^{n} p(X_i \in A_i) \, d\pi(p). \quad \text{The space of all}$$

probability measures on the real line is so large that it is difficult for subjectivists to describe personally meaningful distributions on this space. Ferguson (1974) contains examples of the various attempts to choose such a prior. Thus, for real valued variables de Finetti's theorem is far from an explanation of the type of parametric estimation—involving a family of probability distributions parametrized by a finite dimensional parameter space—that Bayesians from Bayes and Laplace to Lindley have been using in real statistical problems.

In some cases, more restrictive conditions than exchangeability are reasonable to impose, and do single out tractable classes of distributions. Here are some examples adapted from Freedman (1962a, b).

Example: (Scale mixtures of normal variables)

When can a sequence of real valued variables $\{X_i\}$ $1 \leq i < \infty$ be represented as a scale mixture of normal variables

$$(19) \qquad P(X_1 \leq t_1, \ldots, X_n \leq t_n) = \int_0^\infty \prod_{i=1}^n \Phi(\sigma t_i)\, d\pi(\sigma)$$

where $\Phi(t) = \dfrac{1}{\sqrt{2\pi}} \int_{-\infty}^t e^{-t^2/2}\, dt$?

In Freedman (1963) it is shown that a necessary and sufficient condition for (19) to hold is that for each n the joint distribution of $X_1, X_2, \ldots, X_n$ be rotationally symmetric. This result is related to the derivation of Maxwell's distribution for velocity in a Monatomic Ideal Gas (Khinchin [1949], Chap. VI).

Example: (Poisson distribution)

Let X_i $1 \leq i < \infty$ take integer values. In Freedman (1962) it is shown that a necessary and sufficient condition for X_i to have a representation as a mixture of Poisson variables,

$$P(X_1 = a_1, \ldots, X_n = a_n) = \int_0^\infty \prod_{i=1}^n e^{-\lambda} \frac{\lambda^{a_i}}{a_i!}\, d\pi(\lambda)$$

is as follows: For every n the joint distribution of $X_1, X_2, \ldots, X_n$ given $S_n = \sum_{i=1}^n X_i$ must be multinomial; like the joint distribution of S_n balls dropped at random into n boxes.

Many further examples and some general theory are given in Diaconis and Freedman (1978c).

3. De Finetti's generalizations of partial exchangeability are closely connected to recent work of P. Martin-Löf. Martin-Löf does not seem to work in a Bayesian context, rather he takes the notion of sufficient statistic as basic and from this constructs the joint distribution of the process in much the same way as de Finetti. Martin-Löf connects the conditional distribution of the process with

the microcanonical distributions of statistical mechanics. The idea is to specify the conditional distribution of the observations given the sufficient statistics. In this paper, and in Martin-Löf's work, the conditional distribution has been chosen as uniform. We depart from this assumption in Diaconis and Freedman (1978c) as we have in the example of mixtures of Poisson distributions. The families of conditional distributions we work with still "project" in the right way. This projection property allows us to use the well developed machinery of Gibbs states as developed by Lanford (1973), Fölmer (1974), and Preston (1977).

Martin-Lof's work appears most clearly spelled out in a set of mimeographed lecture notes (Martin-Löf [1970]), unfortunately available only in Swedish. A technical treatment of part of this may be found in Martin-Löf (1974). Further discussion of Martin-Lof's ideas are in Lauritzen (1973), (1975) and the last third of Tjur (1974).

These references contain many new examples of partially exchangeable processes and their extreme points. We have tried to connect Martin-Löf's treatment to the general version of de Finetti's theorem we have derived in Diaconis and Freedman (1978c).

4. In this paper we have focused on generalizations of exchangeability involving a statistic. A more general extension involves the idea of invariance with respect to a collection of transformations of the sample space into itself. This contains the idea of partial exchangeability with respect to a statistic since we can consider the class of all transformations leaving the statistic invariant. A typical case which cannot be neatly handled by a finite dimensional statistic is de Finetti's theorem for zero/one matrices. Here the distribution of the doubly infinite random matrix is to be invariant under permutations of the rows and columns. David Aldous has recently identified the extreme points of these matrices and shown that no representation as mixture of finite parameter processes is possible.

5. Is exchangeability a natural requirement on subjective probability assignments? It seems to us that much of its appeal comes from the (forbidden?) connection with coin tossing. This is most strikingly brought out in the thumbtack, Markov chain example. If someone were thinking about assigning probability to 10 flips of the tack and had never heard of Markov chains it seems unlikely that they would hit on the appropriate notion of partial exchangeability.

from the connection with Markov chains with unknown transition probabilities. A feeling of naturalness only appears after experience and reflection.

BIBLIOGRAPHY

Bruno, A. (1964). "On the notion of partial exchangeability". *Giorn. Ist. It. Attuari*, **27**, 174–196. Translated in Chapter 10 of de Finetti (1974).
Crisma, L. (1971). "Sulla proseguibilità di processi scambiabili", *Rend. Matem. Trieste* **3**, 96–124.
Diaconis, P. (1977). "Finite forms of de Finetti's theorem on exchangeability", *Synthese* **36**, 271–281.
Diaconis, P. and Freedman, D. (1978*a*). "Finite exchangeable sequences". To appear *Ann. Prob.*
———. (1978*b*). "De Finetti's theorem for Markov chains". To appear *Ann. Prob.*
———. (1978*c*). "Partial exchangeability and sufficiency". In preparation
Ericson, W. (1973). "A Bayesian approach to two-stage sampling", Technical Report No. 26, Department of Statistics, University of Michigan, Ann Arbor.
Feller, W. (1971). *An Introduction to Probability Theory and Its Applications.* Vol. 2, 2d ed. New York: Wiley.
Ferguson, T. (1974). "Prior distributions on spaces of probability measures", *Ann. Stat.* **2**, 615–629.
De Finetti, B. (1937). "La prevision: ses Lois Logiques ses sources subjectives", *Ann. Inst. H. Poincaré* (Paris), **7**, 1–68. Translated in Kyburg and Smokler (1964).
———. (1938). "Sur la condition d'equivalence partielle" (Colloque Geneve, 1937). *Act. Sci. Ind.* **739**, 5–18, Herman, Paris. Translated in this volume.
———. (1959). "La probabilita e la statistica nei rapporti con l'induzione, secondo i dwersi punti di vista". In *Corso C.I.M.E. su Induzione e Statistica.* Rome: Cremones. Translated as Chapter 9 of de Finetti (1974).
———. (1969). "Sulla proseguibilità di processi aleatori scambiabili", *Rend. Matem. Trieste,* **1**, 53–67.
———. (1974). *Probability, Induction and Statistics.* New York: Wiley.
———. (1976). "Probability: Beware of falsifications"! *Scientia* **111**, 283–303.
Föllmer, H. (1974). "Phase transitions and Martin boundary", *Springer Lecture Notes in Mathematics* **465**, 305–317. New York: Springer-Verlag.
Freedman, D. (1962*a*). "Mixtures of Markov processes", *Ann. Math. Stat.* **33**, 114–118.
———. (1962*b*). "Invariants under mixing which generalize de Finetti's theorem", *Ann. Math. Stat.* **33**, 916–923.
Heath, D., and Sudderth, W. (1976). "De Finetti's theorem on exchangeable variables", *American Statistician* **30**, 188–189.
Kendall, D. (1967). "On finite and infinite sequences of exchangeable events", *Studia Sci. Math. Hung.* **2**, 319–327.

Khinchin, A. (1949). *Mathematical Foundations of Statistical Mechanics.* New York: Dover.

Kyburg, H. E., and Smokler, H. E. (1964). *Studies in Subjective Probability.* New York: Wiley.

Lanford, O. E. (1975). "Time evolutions of large classical systems, Theory and Applications". *Springer Lecture Notes in Physics* **38.** New York: Springer-Verlag.

Lauritzen, S. L. (1973). "On the interrelationships among sufficiency, total sufficiency, and some related concepts", Institute of Math. Stat., University of Copenhagen.

———. (1975). "General exponential models for discrete observations", *Scand. J. Statist.* **2,** 23–33.

Martin-Löf, P. (1970). *Statistiska Modeller,* Antechningar från seminarer läsaret, 1969–70, uturbetade of R. Sundberg, Institutionen för Matematisk Statistik, Stockholms Universitet.

———. (1973). "Repetitive structures and the relation between canonical and microcanonical distributions in statistics and statistical mechanics". *In Proc. Conference on Foundational Questions in Statistical Inference,* Department of Theoretical Statistics, University of Aarhus–Barndorf–Nielsen, ed. P. Bluesild and G. Schon.

Preston, C. (1976). "Random Fields", *Springer Lecture Notes in Mathematics* **534.** New York: Springer-Verlag.

Tjur, T. (1974). "Conditional probability distributions", Lecture Notes 2, Institute of Mathematical Statistics, University of Copenhagen.

12

The Structure of Probabilities Defined on First-order Languages

BY JENS ERIK FENSTAD

The fundamental question of "applied" probability theory is simply this: Under which circumstances can the notion of probability be applied? Are probabilities objective or physical quantities, or certain kinds of indices which are used to express opinions or estimates in a coherent way? Must one always base a probability estimate upon previously observed frequencies?

No formal inquiry can answer these questions. But a formal or logical analysis may shed some light on what possibilities there are. And this is precisely our concern in this paper. What we intend to discuss is the following problem: What are the possible interpretations of the notion of probability?

This question is of central importance in the epistemological analysis of the idea of probability. It may be pursued on different levels and in many directions. We indend to show that there is a role for the formal apparatus of logic in this analysis.

More precisely, we are interested in a representation theory for the notion of probability. And as any representation theory it must start out from a fixed frame. In our case we assume that a probability function is defined on a suitable formal language and we then proceed to describe a representation of it in terms of probability measures defined on models (i.e., "possible worlds") associated in a canonical way with the language. And a representation theorem gives a classification of all possibilities, i.e., a general scheme for interpreting *any* notion of probability as long as it satisfies the formal rules of the calculus. And, we must add, only as long as it fits into the formal frame chosen as starting point for our investigations.

Remarks 1. Except for an improvement in the proof of the representation theorem due to Th. Eisele [3] there are no new technical results beyond my previous papers [5]–[8].

   2. A somewhat different application of logic to probability theory has been pursued by H. Gaifman [9] and D. Scott and P. Kraus [16]. It is perhaps fair to say that their aim has primarily been to extend the mathematical theory of probability using tools and ideas from logic, whereas the aim of our investigations has been to understand the present theory by some use of concepts and methods from logic.

PROBABILITY FUNCTIONS DEFINED ON
FIRST ORDER LANGUAGES.

   A probability function c on a first order language L is a mapping from formulas in L to the interval $[0, 1]$ satisfying the (usual) requirements:

$c(p \vee q) + c(p \wedge q) = c(p) + c(q)$.
$c(\daleth p) = 1 - c(p)$.
$c(p) = c(q)$, if p and q are logically equivalent in L.
$c(p) = 1$, if p is provable in L.

p and q are here arbitrary formulas of L. c is thus defined both for sentences and formulas with free variables. Let $p(x)$ be a formula of L with one free variable x; p then expresses a property of or condition on the individual x. $c(p(x))$ then represents the probability of the property p.

   Let S be the space of all models M for L. There are various ways in which S can be considered as a well-defined mathematical object. Let q be any sentence of L, we define

$$S(q) = \{M \in S \mid q \text{ is true in } M\}.$$

The completeness theorem of first order logic tells us that two sentences q_1 and q_2 are logically equivalent in L, if and only if $S(q_1) = S(q_2)$. We may therefore without ambiguity define a set function λ by

$$\lambda(S(q)) = c(q).$$

A second consequence of the completeness theorem is that the space of models S can be made into a compact topological space (in the usual Stone-topology). Hence λ can be extended to a countably additive probability measure on the σ-algebra generated by the sets $S(q)$, where q is a sentence of L. We may conclude: Any probability c on L induces a σ-additive probability measure on S.

These remarks are but prefatory to the following representation theory. So far we have been working within a Boolean frame. However, there is one point we wish to stress. The model concept for L is a precise technical counterpart of the vague, but heuristically important idea of a "possible world". In elementary probability theory the notion of "urn" is used in illustrative examples, in statistical contexts it is more usual to talk about "populations". Sometimes these concepts are used to "explain" the notion of probability. Clearly, these concepts are very special cases of the general notion of model. And the general representation theorem will have an obvious connection with the usual heuristics of urns and populations.

We should also note that our use of model here is static or time independent. Given a property $p(x)$, a model M for L specifies a "universe" of individuals some of which have the property p, some do not. There is no connection between the various models in S. In particular, we cannot in the present framework discuss how the property p changes over time. However, using ideas which are current in the model theory of intentional logics, it may be possible to extend the present analysis to take care of this aspect.

A formal language gives preciseness, but it also enforces a large measure of rigidity. H. Jeffreys in his well-known book [12] also starts out with probability assignments to sentences in some unspecified language. Very soon his sentences appear in the form "$dx\,d\theta$" and other various similar shapes. If the syntax is left indeterminate, this is hardly objectionable. But then one loses the precise notion of model or "possible world". We hope that the following representation theory shows that it may be useful to keep to a fixed even if somewhat rigid formal frame.

A FIRST VERSION OF THE REPRESENTATION THEOREM.

Starting from a given probability function c on L we derived a probability measure λ on S. Define for each formula p of L a measure λ_p on S by

$$\lambda_p(S(q)) = c(p \wedge q).$$

It is easily seen that λ_p is absolutely continuous with respect to λ, hence by the Radon-Nikodym theorem it can be represented as

$$\lambda_p(B) = \int_B f_p(M) \, d\lambda(M),$$

for all B in the σ-algebra generated by the sets $S(q)$, where f_p is the Radon–Nikodym derivative of λ_p. An immediate calculation then gives

$$\mathbf{c}(p) = \mathbf{c}(p \wedge 1) = \lambda_p(S) = \int_S f_p(M) \, d\lambda(M),$$

where 1 denotes some logically provable sentence of L.

If the language L is countable, it is possible to choose the functions f_p such that for all $M \in S$

$$0 \leq f_p(M) \leq 1.$$

$$f_p(M) = 1 \qquad f_{1p}(M) = 0, \quad \text{if } p \text{ is provable.}$$

$$f_{p \vee q}(M) + f_{p \wedge q}(M) = f_p(M) + f_q(M).$$

To proceed further we have to look a bit closer on the interplay between language and model. Let M be a model for L and let X_M be the domain of individuals in M. As usual let X_M^ω be the countable cartesian product. A sequence $x = \langle x_n \rangle \in X_M^\omega$ satisfies a formula $p(v_{i_1}, \ldots, v_{i_n})$ of L in M, if $p(x_{i_1}, \ldots, x_{i_n})$ (i.e., p with the variables $v_{i_1}, \ldots, v_{i_n}$ interpreted as the elements $x_{i_1}, \ldots, x_{i_n}$ from X_M) is true in M. This is no definition, but may be sufficient explanation to make sense of the following definition: where p is a formula of L and $M \in S$, we define

$$p[M] = \{x \in X_M^\omega \mid x \quad \text{satisfies} \quad p \quad \text{in} \quad M\}.$$

No extensive analysis should be necessary to convince oneself that it seems reasonable to try to define a measure μ_M on subsets $p[M]$ of X_M^ω by interchanging parameter and variable in the Radon–Nikodym derivative $f_p(M)$. We want to define μ_M by setting

$$\mu_M(p[M]) = f_p(M).$$

But is this legitimate? Does $p[M] = \varnothing$ imply that $f_p(M) = 0$, which is necessary in order to make μ_M well-defined?

At this point we may use the theory of strong liftings [11]. The functions f may be divided into equivalence classes by identifying functions which are equal almost everywhere. A strong lifting ρ is a map from functions to functions giving a consistent way of picking representatives which preserves the algebraic and order structure on the space of functions and, most importantly, is the identity on the continuous functions. We may therefore, given any choice of Radon–Nikodym derivative f_p, define μ_M by

$$\mu_M(p[M]) = \rho(f_p(M)),$$

where ρ is a strong lifting, which by the general theory [11] will exist if the language L is countable.

The properties of f_p listed above are now provable. It remains to verify that μ_M is well defined. So assume that $p[M] = \varnothing$. Let $\exists p$ denote the existential closure of p. Then obviously $\exists p$ is not true in M. Since $\exists p$ is a sentence, $f_{\exists p}$ is equal almost everywhere to the characteristic function $\chi_{\exists p}$ of the set $S(\exists p)$. Note that $\chi_{\exists p}(M) = 0$, since $\exists p$ is not true in M. We now get

$$\mu_M(p[M]) \leqq \mu_M(\exists p[M]) = \rho(f_{\exists p}(M)) = \rho(\chi_{\exists p}(M)),$$

since $f_{\exists p}$ and $\chi_{\exists p}$ are equivalent. But $\chi_{\exists p}$ is continuous, so $\rho(\chi_{\exists p}(M)) = \chi_{\exists p}(M)$, since ρ is a strong lifting; hence $\mu_M(p[M]) = 0$. Putting things together we obtain the following result:

Theorem. Let L be a countable first-order language and $\mathbf{c}$ a probability function on L. There exists a σ-additive probability measure λ on the space S of all models for L, and for each model $M \in S$ a probability function μ_M, such that for all formulas p of L

$$\mathbf{c}(p) = \int_S \mu_M(p[M]) \, d\lambda(M).$$

Remark. The idea of using the Radon–Nikodym theorem and a first version of the representation theorem is due to J. Łos [13]. However, his proof was not entirely complete; it was not verified that the definition $\mu_M(p[M]) = f_p(M)$ can be made legitimate by a suitable choice of f_p. The missing verification was supplied in my paper [5]. The idea of using strong liftings to solve the problem is due to Th. Eisele [3].

RELATIVE FREQUENCIES IN MODELS.

In our formalism a conjunction

$$\bigwedge_{i=1}^{n} p(v_i) = p(v_1) \wedge p(v_2) \wedge \ldots \wedge p(v_n),$$

where $p(v)$ is a property (i.e. a formula with one free variable v), describes a sample (with replacement) of n individuals, all having the property p. In a model M

$$\left(\bigwedge_{i=1}^{n} p(v_i)\right)[M]$$

will (essentially) denote the set of all n-tuples $\langle x_1, \ldots, x_n \rangle$ from X_M which satisfy p. Thus μ_M may be thought of as a kind of "sample" probability.

We will pursue this idea, but to do so we need some further assumptions. First we introduce some notational devices. We assume that L contains the sign of equality. Next there shall be formulas k_n, $n < \omega$, each having v_1 as its only free variable, such that

(A) $\exists v_1[k_n(v_1) \wedge \forall v_2[k_n(v_2) \to v_1 = v_2]]$

is valid in L for all n, i.e., k_n determines in each model a unique individual. Further, for each $N < \omega$ we let t_N be the following sentence

(B) $t_N = \exists v_1 \ldots \exists v_N \left[\bigwedge_{i < j} v_1 \neq v_j \wedge \forall v_{N+1} \left[\bigvee_{i=1}^{N} v_i = v_{N+1} \right] \right]$,

which says that there exist exactly N individuals. Finally we want to express that if a model M has N individuals, they are named by $k_1, \ldots, k_N$. Since each k_n names some individual in M, we have simply to assume that $k_1, \ldots, k_N$ name different individuals

(C) $t_N \to \bigwedge_{i < j} \forall v_1 [\neg k_i(v_1) \vee \neg k_i(v_1)]$.

We next introduce an assumption on **c** which goes beyond the purely notational, but which follows naturally from the idea of the measures μ_M as sampling measures.

(I) $\mathbf{c}\left(\bigwedge_{i=1}^{k} k_{n_i}(v_i) \wedge q\right) = \mathbf{c}\left(\bigwedge_{i=1}^{k} k_{m_i}(v_i) \wedge q\right)$,

for all sentences q and all sequences $n_1, \ldots, n_k$ and $m_1, \ldots, m_k$. Basically (I) says that on any hypothesis q every sample of k individuals shall count equally in determining the probabilities.

Let M be a finite model for L. It follows from (I) that

$$\mu_M(k_{n_1}(v_1)[M] \cap \ldots \cap k_{n_k}(v_n)[M])$$

$$= \mu_M(k_{m_1}(v_1)[M] \cap \ldots \cap k_{m_k}(v_k)[M])$$

for all sequences $n_1, \ldots, n_k$ and $m_1, \ldots, m_k$. By a simple counting and symmetry argument using (A)–(C) it first follows that

$$\mu_M(k_{n_i}(v_i)[M]) = \operatorname{card}(X_M)^{-1},$$

and further that

$$\mu_M(k_{n_1}(v_1)[M] \cap \ldots \cap k_{n_k}(v_n)[M])$$
$$= \mu_M(k_{n_1}(v_1)[M]) \cdot \ldots \cdot \mu_M(k_{n_k}(v_n)[M]),$$

which implies that μ_M for each finite model M as a measure on the product space X_M^ω is the product of the (normalized) counting measure on the factor spaces X_M. With an obvious definition of the relative frequency of p in a finite model M, which we will denote by $fr(p, M)$, it follows that for finite M

$$\mu_M(p[M]) = fr(p, M).$$

Our next assumption is a kind of generalized finiteness assumption. For any set of sentences B of L we can define $\mathbf{c}(B) = \lambda\left(\bigcap_{q \in B} S_q\right)$. Our condition is now

(II) Let B be a set of sentences of L and assume that $\mathbf{c}(B) > 0$. Then there is a finite model M of L such that each sentence $q \in B$ is true in M.

Is (II) a reasonable assumption? We will return to this question in a later section. At this point we will make two applications.

But first we note that from (I) and (II) it follows that for all formulas p of L

$$\mathbf{c}(p) = \int_{S_0} fr(p, M) \, d\lambda(M),$$

where S_0 is the space of *finite* models for L. Thus (II) implies that all λ-mass is concentrated on S_0, i.e., $\lambda(S - S_0) = 0$, and (I) says that $\mu_M(p[M])$ for $M \in S_0$ is the relative frequencies of the property p in M. It is this we will make explicit in two simple examples.

Example 1. Consider the random variable X on S_0 defined by $X(M) = fr(p, M)$. Its expected value is clearly $\mathbf{c}(p)$, hence by the usual strong law of large numbers:

Let L be a countable language satisfying (A)–(C), let $\mathbf{c}$ be any probability function on L satisfying (I) and (II). If $p(v)$ is any property of L, then

$$\frac{1}{n} \sum_{i=1}^{n} fr(p, M_i) \to \mathbf{c}(p)$$

for almost all sequences $M_1, M_2, \ldots$ of finite models for L.

"Almost all" is here understood relative to the measure λ. The result is a kind of consistency requirement. It tells us that by committing ourselves to a particular probability function c on L, we have imposed on the space of finite models a measure or "weight function" λ such that the probability $c(p)$ for any property p is the limit of "observed frequencies", where we observe models (or "nature" presents models to us) according to the distribution λ.

Example 2. For any property $p(v)$ of L, let $p^\epsilon(v) = p(v)$ if $\epsilon = 1$, and $p^\epsilon(v) = \rceil p(v)$ if $\epsilon = 0$. The formula

$$p_r^{(n)} = \bigvee_{(\epsilon_1,...,\epsilon_n)} p^{\epsilon_1}(v_1) \wedge \ldots \wedge p^{\epsilon_n}(v_n),$$

where the disjunction is taken over all n-tuples $(\epsilon_1, \ldots, \epsilon_n)$ consisting of exactly r 1's and $n-r$ 0's, expresses that r out of n observed individuals has the property p. A simple calculation gives

$$c(p_r^{(n)}) = \binom{n}{r} \int_{S_0} fr(p, M)^r \cdot (1 - fr(p, M))^{n-r} \, d\lambda(M).$$

If we define the distribution function Φ by

$$\Phi(\xi) = \lambda(\{M \in S_0 \mid fr(p, M) \leq \xi\})$$

we can rewrite the result as

$$c(p_r^{(n)}) = \binom{n}{r} \int_0^1 \xi^r \cdot (1 - \xi)^{n-r} \, d\Phi(\xi).$$

(Note that Φ depends on p, whereas λ does not.) Thus the general representation theorem gives under the added assumptions (I)–(II) a representation similar to the one obtained from de Finetti's theorem for exchangeable events [1].

CONDITIONAL PROBABILITY FUNCTIONS.

The finiteness condition (II) implies that the measure λ is concentrated on S_0, the space of finite models. But $S_0 = \bigcup S(t_N)$, a union of disjoint sets, so $\lambda(S_0) = \sum \lambda(S(t_N))$. This means that $\lambda(S(t_N))$ must converge to 0 when N increases. (The same applies whenever $\lambda(S_0) > 0$). But is this reasonable?

If we are willing to express an opinion about the "size of the universe", then assumption (II) could be defended. But if we are not willing to commit ourselves on this point, there are problems in interpreting our formalism.

The problem is, of course, the old one of uniform priors over infinite (discrete, noncompact) spaces. Such priors do not exist. It is therefore necessary to proceed with a more delicate analysis. And this can be obtained through the use of conditional probability functions.

We will consider a conditional probability $c(p \mid q)$, where p can be any formula of L, but q is supposed to belong to a special class of sentences L_0. In order to treat one important example in some detail we will assume in the sequel that L_0 consists of all finite disjunctions of sentences of the type t_N. Part of the following theory can be developed under more general conditions. In particular, a different choice of L_0 could be used to tie our analysis up with the recent work of Hintikka [10] on inductive logic.

The function $c(p \mid q)$ shall satisfy the usual axioms for conditional probabilities, e.g., for q constant $c(\cdot \mid q)$ shall satisfy the ordinary axioms for a probability function on L. We further suppose that $c(t \mid t) = 1$. Finally, if $t_1, t_2 \in L_0$ and $t_1 \rightarrow t_2$ is L provable, then $c(t_1 \mid t_2) > 0$ and

$$c(p \mid t_1) = \frac{c(p \wedge t_1 \mid t_2)}{c(t_1 \mid t_2)},$$

for all formulas p of L.

Let S_0 be the space of finite models and $S_0(q)$ be those finite models in which q is true. Adding a representation theorem of Renyi [15] to our previous analysis we obtain the following result: There exists a σ-finite measure λ on S_0 such that $0 < \lambda(S(t_N)) < \infty$ for all N, and such that

$$c(q \mid t_N) = \frac{\lambda(S_0(q) \cap S(t_N))}{\lambda(S(t_N))}$$

for all *sentences* q of L.

From this we get for all *formulas* p in L that

$$c(p \mid t_N) = \frac{1}{\lambda(S(t_N))} \cdot \int_{S(t_N)} \mu_M(p[M]) \, d\lambda(M).$$

If we keep the notational conventions (A)–(C) and the symmetry condition (I), we may once more conclude that $\mu_M(p[M]) = fr(p, M)$.

Again, for the sake of simplicity, we shall restrict attention to the case of "simple sampling", i.e., consider one property $p(v)$. The general representation can then be written in the following simple form

$$c(p \mid t_N) = \sum_{r=0}^{n} \frac{r}{n} \cdot \lambda_r^{(N)},$$

where

$$\lambda_r^{(N)} = \lambda \left(\left\{ M \in S(t_N) \mid fr(p, M) = \frac{r}{n} \right\} \right) \Big/ \lambda(S(t_N))..$$

Notice that the numbers $\lambda_0^{(N)}, \ldots, \lambda_N^{(N)}$ define an atomic probability distribution Φ_N on the interval $[0, 1]$ by

$$\Phi_N(t) = \sum_{r \leq t \cdot N} \lambda_r^{(N)}.$$

The symmetry condition (I) determined μ_M for finite models M. We shall now introduce an assumption on λ, which is basically identical to de Finetti's condition of exchangeability [1], and which is intimately related to the notion of a sufficient statistics.

Let t_N^r be a sentence which says that there are N individuals and exactly r of them have the property p. We now assume that it is only the number, r, of individuals that have the property p that counts, and that the particular distribution of p over the N individuals is irrelevant. This means that λ is uniform on the set of models satisfying t_N^r. And since each model of N elements can be thought of as derived from a model with $N+1$ elements in which the extra element may or may not have the property p, it follows that our second condition can be expressed in the form:

(I*) $$\frac{\mathbf{c}(t_N^r \mid t_N)}{\binom{N}{r}} = \frac{\mathbf{c}(t_{N+1}^{r+1} \mid t_{N+1})}{\binom{N+1}{r+1}} + \frac{\mathbf{c}(t_{N+1}^r \mid t_{N+1})}{\binom{N+1}{r}}.$$

Remark. $\mathbf{c}(t_N^r \mid t_N)$ which is equal to $\lambda_r^{(N)}$ is the weight given to the set of models satisfying t_N^r. Since individuals in models are named by "constants" $k_1, \ldots, k_N$, there are exactly $\binom{N}{r}$ models satisfying t_N^r, hence the above form of (I*). It can also be expressed in the following equivalent form

$$\lambda_r^{(N)} = \frac{r+1}{N+1} \cdot \lambda_{r+1}^{(N+1)} + \frac{N-r+1}{N+1} \cdot \lambda_r^{(N+1)}.$$

The assumption (I*) has the following important consequence: the sequence of distribution functions Φ_N, $N = 1, 2, \ldots$, converges to a probability distribution Φ concentrated on $[0, 1]$, which means that we obtain an absolute probability function $\mathbf{c}^*$ on L derived from the family of conditional probability functions $\mathbf{c}(\cdot \mid t_N)$, $N = 1, 2, \ldots$ (For some details of the proof see [6]).

In particular we derive the usual integral representation for the probability $\mathbf{c}^*$, e.g.,

$$\mathbf{c}^*(p_r^{(n)}) = \binom{n}{r} \int_0^1 \xi^r \cdot (1 - \xi)^{n-r} \, d\Phi(\xi).$$

Note that Φ depends on the property p, whereas λ only depends on L.

Remark. The analysis above seems related to a recent study of P. Martin-Löf [14] on repetitive structures. Th. Eisele has pursued these ideas in a not yet published study [4].

CONCLUDING REMARKS.

The starting point for our final analysis was a conditional probability function defined on a first order language L. We feel that this is a natural setting. In the first stage there were no ad hoc mathematical assumptions, the probability function is finitely additive and no conditions of measurability were imposed. (Compare de Finetti [2] chap. 9 for a discussion of similar points.)

From the conditional probabilities we derived a σ-finite measure on the space of models. Compactness of the model space, which is a consequence of the completeness theorem for first order logic, implies that the derived measure is σ-additive. Thus the measure theory enters in the second stage as a tool for analyzing the given probability function.

The first symmetry condition (I) determines the "sample probabilities" μ_M as relative frequencies in models. The second condition (I*) establishes a connection between $c(\cdot \mid t_N)$ and $c(\cdot \mid t_{N'})$ for different N and N'. This leads to a convergence result and a limit probability c^* with the associated integral representation formulas of de Finetti type. We tend to believe that such formulas represent a kind of natural limit to what can be obtained through a formal analysis. The λ or Φ distribution cannot be further specified unless extra assumptions are added. But the representation theorems, nevertheless, give a general scheme for interpreting *any* notion of probability as long as it satisfies the formal rules of the calculus.

BIBLIOGRAPHY.

[1] De Finetti, B. "Foresight: Its Logical Laws, Its Subjective Sources", in *Studies in Subjective Probability*. Ed. Kyburg and Smokler. New York: John Wiley, 1964. Pp. 95–158.

[2] ———. *Probability, Induction and Statistics*, New York: John Wiley, 1972.

[3] Eisele, Th. "On the representation of polyadic measures". Unpublished.

[4] ———. "Wahrscheinlichkeitslogik, aufgefasst als eine repetitive Struktur". unpublished

[5] Fenstad, J. E. "Representations of Probabilities Defined on First Order Languages", in *Sets, Models and Recursion Theory*, Ed. Crossley. Amsterdam: North-Holland, 1967. Pp. 156–172.

[6] ———. "The Structure of Logical Probabilities", *Synthese* 18 (1968), 1–23.

[7] ———. "Logikk og Sannsynlighet" (in Norwegian), Nordisk Mat. Tidskrift 17 (1969), 71–81.

[8] ———. "Remarks on Logic and Probability", in *Logical Theory and Semantic Analysis.* Ed. Stenlund, Dordrecht: D. Reidel, 1974. Pp. 193–197.

[9] Gaifman, H. "Concerning measures on first-order calculi", *Israel Journal Math.* 2 (1964), 1–18.

[10] Hintikka, J., and Niiniluoto, I. "An Axiomatic Foundation for the Logic of Inductive Generalization". Art. 7 above.

[11] Ionescu Tulcea, A., and Ionescu Tulcea, C. *Topics in the Theory of Lifting.* Ergebniss d. Math. und ihrer Grenzgebiete. Vol. 48. Heidelberg: Springer Verlag, 1969.

[12] Jeffreys, H. *Theory of Probability.* 3d ed. Oxford: Oxford University Press, 1961.

[13] Łos, J., "Remarks on Foundation of Probability", in *Proceedings of the International Congress of Mathematicians.* Stockholm, 1962. Pp. 225–229.

[14] Martin-Löf, P., "Repetitive Structures", in *Proc. Conference on Foundational Questions on Statistical Inference,* Department of Theoretical Statistics, University of Aarhus, ed. P. Bluesild and G. Schon, Barndorf-Nielsen.

[15] Renyi, A. "On a New Axiomatic Theory of Probability," *Acta Math. Acad. Sci. Hungarica* 6 (1955), 285–335.

[16] Scott, D., and Krauss, P. "Assigning probabilities to logical formulas", in *Aspects of Inductive Logic.* Ed. Hintikka and Suppes, Amsterdam: North-Holland, 1966. Pp. 219–264.

13

A Subjectivist's Guide to Objective Chance

BY DAVID LEWIS

INTRODUCTION

We subjectivists conceive of probability as the measure of reasonable partial belief. But we need not make war against other conceptions of probability, declaring that where subjective credence leaves off, there nonsense begins. Along with subjective credence we should believe also in objective chance. The practice and the analysis of science require both concepts. Neither can replace the other. Among the propositions that deserve our credence we find, for instance, the proposition that (as a matter of contingent fact about our world) any tritium atom that now exists has a certain chance of decaying within a year. Why should we subjectivists be less able than other folk to make sense of that?

Carnap (1945) did well to distinguish two concepts of probability, insisting that both were legitimate and useful and that neither was at fault because it was not the other. I do not think Carnap chose quite the right two concepts, however. In place of his "degree of confirmation", I would put *credence* or *degree of belief*; in place of his "relative frequency in the long run", I would put *chance* or *propensity*, understood as making sense in the single case. The division of labor between the two concepts will be little changed by these replacements. Credence is well suited to play the role of Carnap's probability$_1$, and chance to play the role of probability$_2$.

Given two kinds of probability, credence and chance, we can have hybrid probabilities of probabilities. (Not "second order probabilities", which suggests one kind of probability self-applied.) Chance of credence need not detain us. It may be partly a matter of chance what one comes to believe, but what of it? Credence about chance is more important. To the believer in chance, chance is a proper subject to have beliefs about. Propositions about chance will enjoy various degrees of belief, and other propositions will be believed to various degrees conditionally upon them.

As I hope the following questionnaire will show, we have some very firm and definite opinions concerning reasonable credence about chance. These opinions seem to me to afford the best grip we have on the concept of chance. Indeed, I am led to wonder whether anyone *but* a subjectivist is in a position to understand objective chance!

QUESTIONNAIRE

First question. A certain coin is scheduled to be tossed at noon today. You are sure that this chosen coin is fair: it has a 50% chance of falling heads and a 50% chance of falling tails. You have no other relevant information. Consider the proposition that the coin tossed at noon today falls heads. To what degree should you now believe that proposition?

Answer. 50%, of course.

(Two comments. (1) It is abbreviation to speak of the coin as fair. Strictly speaking, what you are sure of is that the entire "chance setup" is fair: coin, tosser, landing surface, air, and surroundings together are such as to make it so that the chance of heads is 50%. (2) Is it reasonable to think of coin-tossing as a genuine chance process, given present-day scientific knowledge? I think so: consider, for instance, that air resistance depends partly on the chance making and breaking of chemical bonds between the coin and the air molecules it encounters. What is less clear is that the toss could be designed so that you could reasonably be sure that the chance of heads is 50% exactly. If you doubt that such a toss could be designed, you may substitute an example involving radioactive decay.)

Next question. As before, except that you have plenty of seemingly relevant evidence tending to lead you to expect that the coin will fall heads. This coin is known to have a displaced center of mass, it has been tossed 100 times before with 86 heads, and many duplicates of it have been tossed thousands of times with about 90% heads. Yet you remain quite sure, despite all this evidence, that the chance of heads this time is 50%. To what degree should you believe the proposition that the coin falls heads this time?

Answer. Still 50%. Such evidence is relevant to the outcome by way of its relevance to the proposition that the chance of heads is 50%, not in any other way. If the evidence somehow fails to diminish your certainty that the coin is fair, then it should have no effect on the distribution of credence about outcomes that accords with that certainty about chance. To the extent that uncertainty about outcomes is based on certainty about their chances, it is a stable, resilient sort of uncertainty—new evidence won't get rid of it. (The term "resiliency" comes from Skyrms [1977]; see also Jeffrey [1965], §12.5.)

Someone might object that you could not reasonably remain sure that the coin was fair, given such evidence as I described and no contrary evidence that I failed to mention. That may be so, but it doesn't matter. Canons of reasonable belief need not be counsels of perfection. A moral code that forbids all robbery may also prescribe that if one nevertheless robs, one should rob only the rich. Likewise it is a sensible question what it is reasonable to believe about outcomes if one is unreasonably stubborn in clinging to one's certainty about chances.

Next question. As before, except that now it is afternoon and you have evidence that became available after the coin was tossed at noon. Maybe you know for certain that it fell heads; maybe some fairly reliable witness has told you that it fell heads; maybe the witness has told you that it fell heads in nine out of ten tosses of which the noon toss was one. You remain as sure as ever that the chance of heads, just before noon, was 50% To what degree should you believe that the coin tossed at noon fell heads?

Answer. Not 50%, but something not far short of 100%. Resiliency has its limits. If evidence bears in a direct enough way on the outcome—a way that may nevertheless fall short of outright implication—then it may bear on your beliefs about outcomes otherwise than by way of your beliefs about the chances of the outcomes. Resiliency under all evidence whatever would be extremely unreasonable. We can only say that degrees of belief about outcomes that are based on certainty about chances are resilient under *admissible* evidence. The previous question gave examples of admissible evidence; this question gave examples of inadmissible evidence.

Last question. You have no inadmissible evidence; if you have any relevant admissible evidence, it already has had its proper effect on your credence about the chance of heads. But this time, suppose you are not sure that the coin is fair. You divide your belief among three alternative hypotheses about the chance of heads, as follows.

You believe to degree 27% that the chance of heads is 50%.
You believe to degree 22% that the chance of heads is 35%.
You believe to degree 51% that the chance of heads is 80%.

Then to what degree should you believe that the coin falls heads?

Answer. $(27\% \times 50\%) + (22\% \times 35\%) + (51\% \times 80\%)$; that is, 62%. Your degree of belief that the coin falls heads, conditionally on any one of the hypotheses about the chance of heads, should equal your unconditional degree of belief if you were sure of that hypothesis. That in turn should equal the chance of heads according to the hypothesis: 50% for the first hypothesis, 35% for the second, and 80% for the third. Given your degrees of belief that the coin falls heads, conditionally on the hypotheses, we need only apply the standard multiplicative and additive principles to obtain our answer.

THE PRINCIPAL PRINCIPLE

I have given undefended answers to my four questions. I hope you found them obviously right, so that you will be willing to take them as evidence for what follows. If not, do please reconsider. If so, splendid—now read on.

It is time to formulate a general principle to capture the intuitions that were forthcoming in our questionnaire. It will resemble familiar principles of direct inference except that (1) it will concern chance, not some sort of actual or hypothetical frequency, and (2) it will incorporate the observation that certainty about chances—or conditionality on propositions about chances—makes for resilient degrees of belief about outcomes. Since this principle seems to me to capture all we know about chance, I call it

The Principal Principle.   Let C be any reasonable initial credence function. Let t be any time. Let x be any real number in the unit interval. Let X be the proposition that the chance, at time t, of A's holding equals x. Let E be any proposition compatible with X that is admissible at time t. Then

$$C(A/XE) = x.$$

That will need a good deal of explaining. But first I shall illustrate the principle by applying it to the cases in our questionnaire.

Suppose your present credence function is $C(-/E)$, the function that comes from some reasonable initial credence function C by conditionalizing on your present total evidence E. Let t be the time of the toss, noon today, and let A be the proposition that the coin tossed today falls heads. Let X be the proposition that the chance at noon (just before the toss) of heads is x. (In our questionnaire, we mostly considered the case that x is 50%.) Suppose that nothing in your total evidence E contradicts X; suppose also that it is not yet noon, and you have no foreknowledge of the outcome, so everything that is included in E is entirely admissible. The conditions of the Principal Principle are met. Therefore $C(A/XE)$ equals x. That is to say that x is your present degree of belief that the coin falls heads, conditionally on the proposition that its chance of falling heads is x. If in addition you are sure that the chance of heads is x—that is, if $C(X/E)$ is one—then it follows also that x is your present unconditional degree of belief that the coin falls heads. More generally, whether or not you are sure about the chance of heads, your unconditional degree of belief that the coin falls heads is given by summing over alternative hypotheses about chance:

$$C(A/E) = \sum_x C(X_x/E)C(A/X_xE) = \sum_x C(X_x/E)x,$$

where X_x, for any value of x, is the proposition that the chance at t of A equals x.

Several parts of the formulation of the Principal Principle call for explanation and comment. Let us take them in turn.

THE INITIAL CREDENCE FUNCTION C

I said: let C be any reasonable initial credence function. By that I meant, in part, that C was to be a probability distribution over (at least) the space whose points are possible worlds and whose regions (sets of worlds) are propositions. C is a nonnegative, normalized, finitely additive measure defined on all propositions.

The corresponding conditional credence function is defined simply as a quotient of unconditional credences:

$$C(A/B) =_{df} C(AB)/C(B).$$

I should like to assume that it makes sense to conditionalize on any but the empty proposition. Therefore I require that C is *regular*: $C(B)$ is zero, and $C(A/B)$ is undefined, only if B is the empty proposition, true at no worlds. You may protest that there are too many alternative possible worlds to permit regularity. But that is so only if we suppose, as I do not, that the values of the function C are restricted to the standard reals. Many propositions must have infinitesimal C-values, and $C(A/B)$ often will be defined as a quotient of infinitesimals, each infinitely close but not equal to zero. (See Bernstein and Wattenberg [1969].) The assumption that C is regular will prove convenient, but it is not justified only as a convenience. Also it is required as a condition of reasonableness: one who started out with an irregular credence function (and who then learned from experience by conditionalizing) would stubbornly refuse to believe some propositions no matter what the evidence in their favor.

In general, C is to be reasonable in the sense that if you started out with it as your initial credence function, and if you always learned from experience by conditionalizing on your total evidence, then no matter what course of experience you might undergo your beliefs would be reasonable for one who had undergone that course of experience. I do not say what distinguishes a reasonable from an unreasonable credence function to arrive at after a given course of experience. We do make the distinction, even if we cannot analyze it; and therefore I may appeal to it in saying what it means to require that C be a reasonable initial credence function.

I have assumed that the method of conditionalizing is *one* reasonable way to learn from experience, given the right initial credence function. I have not assumed something more controversial: that it is the *only* reasonable way. The latter view may also be right (the cases where it seems wrong to conditionalize may all be cases where one departure from ideal rationality is needed to compensate for another) but I shall not need it here.

(I said that C was to be a probability distribution over *at least* the space of worlds; the reason for that qualification is that sometimes one's credence might be divided between different possibilities within a single world. That is the case for someone who is sure what sort of world he lives in, but not at all sure who and when and where in the world he is. In a fully general treatment of credence it would be well to replace the worlds by something like the "centered worlds" of Quine [1969], and the propositions by something corresponding to properties. But I shall ignore these complications here.)

THE REAL NUMBER x

I said: let x be any real number in the unit interval. I must emphasize that "x" is a quantified variable; it is not a schematic letter that may freely be replaced by terms that designate real numbers in the unit interval. For fixed A and t, "the chance, at t, of

A's holding" is such a term; suppose we put it in for the variable x. It might seem that for suitable C and E we have the following: if X is the proposition that the chance, at t, of A's holding equals the chance, at t, of A's holding—in other words, if X is the necessary proposition—then

$$C(A/XE) = \text{the chance, at } t, \text{ of } A\text{'s holding.}$$

But that is absurd. It means that if E is your present total evidence and $C(-/E)$ is your present credence function, then if the coin is in fact fair—whether or not you think it is!—then your degree of belief that it falls heads is 50%. Fortunately, that absurdity is not an instance of the Principal Principle. The term "the chance, at t, of A's holding" is a nonrigid designator; chance being a matter of contingent fact, it designates different numbers at different worlds. The context "the proposition that . . .", within which the variable "x" occurs, is intensional. Universal instantiation into an intensional context with a nonrigid term is a fallacy. It is the fallacy that takes you, for instance, from the true premise "For any number x, the proposition that x is nine is noncontingent" to the false conclusion "The proposition that the number of planets is nine is noncontingent". See Jeffrey (1970) for discussion of this point in connection with a relative of the Principal Principle.

I should note that the values of "x" are not restricted to the standard reals in the unit interval. The Principal Principle may be applied as follows: you are sure that some spinner is fair, hence that it has infinitesimal chance of coming to rest at any particular point; therefore (if your total evidence is admissible) you should believe only to an infinitesimal degree that it will come to rest at any particular point.

THE PROPOSITION X

I said: let X be the proposition that the chance, at time t, of A's holding equals x. I emphasize that I am speaking of objective, single-case chance—not credence, not frequency. Like it or not, we have this concept. We think that a coin about to be tossed has a certain chance of falling heads, or that a radioactive atom has a certain chance of decaying within the year, quite regardless of what anyone may believe about it and quite regardless of whether there are any other similar coins or atoms. As philosophers we may well find the concept of objective chance troublesome, but that is no excuse to deny its existence, its legitimacy, or its indispensability. If we can't understand it, so much the worse for us.

Chance and credence are distinct, but I don't say they are unrelated. What is the Principal Principle but a statement of their relation? Neither do I say that chance and frequency are unrelated, but they are distinct. Suppose we have many coin tosses with the same chance of heads (not zero or one) in each case. Then there is some chance of getting any frequency of heads whatever; and hence some chance that the frequency and the uniform single-case chance of heads may differ, which could not be so if these were one and the same thing. Indeed the chance of difference may be infinitesimal if there are infinitely many tosses, but that is still not zero. Nor do hypothetical frequencies fare any better. There is no such thing as *the* infinite sequence of outcomes, or *the* limiting frequency of heads, that *would* eventuate if some particular coin toss were somehow repeated forever. Rather there are countless sequences, and countless frequencies, that *might* eventuate and would have some chance (perhaps infinitesimal) of eventuating. (See Jeffrey [1977], Skyrms [1977], and the discussion of "might" counter-factuals in Lewis [1973].)

Chance is not the same thing as credence or frequency; this is not yet to deny that there might be some roundabout way to analyze chance in terms of credence or frequency. I would only ask that no such analysis be accepted unless it is compatible with the Principal Principle. We shall consider how this requirement bears on the prospects for an analysis of chance, but without settling the question of whether such an analysis is possible.

I think of chance as attaching in the first instance to propositions: the chance of an event, an outcome, etc., is the chance of truth of the proposition that holds at just those worlds where that event, outcome, or whatnot occurs. (Here I ignore the special usage of "event" to simply mean "proposition".) I have foremost in mind the chances of truth of propositions about localized matters of particular fact—a certain toss of a coin, the fate of a certain tritium atom on a certain day—but I do not say that those are the only propositions to which chance applies. Not only does it make sense to speak of the chance that a coin will fall heads on a particular occasion; equally it makes sense to speak of the chance of getting exactly seven heads in a particular sequence of eleven tosses. It is only caution, not any definite reason to think otherwise, that stops me from assuming that chance of truth applies to any proposition whatever. I shall assume, however, that the broad class of propositions to which chance of truth applies is closed under the Boolean operations of conjunction (intersection), disjunction (union), and negation (complementation).

We ordinarily think of chance as time-dependent, and I have made that dependence explicit. Suppose you enter a labyrinth at 11:00 A.M., planning to choose your turn whenever you come to a branch point by tossing a coin. When you enter at 11:00, you may have a 42% chance of reaching the center by noon. But in the first half hour you may stray into a region from which it is hard to reach the center, so that by 11:30 your chance of reaching the center by noon has fallen to 26%. But then you turn lucky; by 11:45 you are not far from the center and your chance of reaching it by noon is 78%. At 11:49 you reach the center; then and forevermore your chance of reaching it by noon is 100%.

Sometimes, to be sure, we omit reference to a time. I do not think this means that we have some timeless notion of chance. Rather, we have other ways to fix the time than by specifying it explicitly. In the case of the labyrinth we might well say (before, after, or during your exploration) that your chance of reaching the center by noon is 42%. The understood time of reference is the time when your exploration begins. Likewise we might speak simply of the chance of a certain atom's decaying within a certain year, meaning the chance at the beginning of that year. In general, if A is the proposition that something or other takes place within a certain interval beginning at time t, then we may take a special interest in what I shall call the *endpoint chance* of A's holding: the chance at t, the beginning of the interval in question. If we speak simply of the chance of A's holding, not mentioning a time, it is this endpoint chance—the chance at t of A's holding—that we are likely to mean.

Chance also is world-dependent. Your chance at 11:00 of reaching the center of the labyrinth by noon depends on all sorts of contingent features of the world: the structure of the labyrinth and the speed with which you can walk through it, for instance. Your chance at 11:30 of reaching the center by noon depends on these things, and also on where in the labyrinth you then are. Since these things vary from world to world, so does your chance (at either time) of reaching the center by noon. Your chance at noon of reaching the center by noon is one at the worlds where you have reached the center; zero at all others, including those worlds where you do not explore the labyrinth at all, perhaps because you or it do not exist. (Here I am speaking loosely, as if I believed that you and the labyrinth could inhabit several worlds at once. See Lewis [1968] for the needed correction.)

We have decided this much about chance, at least: it is a function of three arguments. To a proposition, a time, and a world it assigns a real number. Fixing the proposition A, the time t, and the number x, we have our proposition X; it is the proposition that holds at all and only those worlds w such that this function assigns to A, t, and w the value x. This is the proposition that the chance, at t, of A's holding is x.

THE ADMISSIBLE PROPOSITION E

I said: let E be any proposition that is admissible at time t. Admissible propositions are the sort of information whose impact on credence about outcomes comes entirely by way of credence about the chances of those outcomes. Once the chances are given outright, conditionally or unconditionally, evidence bearing on them no longer matters. (Once it is settled that the suspect fired the gun, the discovery of his fingerprints on the trigger adds nothing to the case against him.) The power of the Principal Principle depends entirely on how much is admissible. If nothing is admissible it is vacuous. If everything is admissible it is inconsistent. Our question-naire suggested that a great deal is admissible, but we saw examples also of inadmissible information. I have no definition of admissibility to offer, but must be content to suggest sufficient (or almost suffi-cient) conditions for admissibility. I suggest that two different sorts of information are generally admissible.

The first sort is historical information. If a proposition is entirely about matters of particular fact at times no later than t, then as a rule that proposition is admissible at t. Admissible information just before the toss of a coin, for example, includes the outcomes of all previous tosses of that coin and others like it. It also includes every detail—no matter how hard it might be to discover—of the structure of the coin, the tosser, other parts of the setup, and even anything nearby that might somehow intervene. It also includes a great deal of other information that is completely irrelevant to the outcome of the toss.

A proposition is *about* a subject matter—about history up to a certain time, for instance—if and only if that proposition holds at both or neither of any two worlds that match perfectly with respect to that subject matter. (Or we can go the other way: two worlds match perfectly with respect to a subject matter if and only if every proposition about that subject matter holds at both or neither.) If our world and another are alike point for point, atom for atom, field for field, even spirit for spirit (if such there be) throughout the past and up until noon today, then any proposition that distinguishes the two cannot be entirely about the respects in which there is no difference. It cannot be entirely about what goes on no later than noon today. That is so even if its linguistic expression makes no overt mention of later times; we must beware lest information about the future is hidden in the predicates, as in "Fred was mortally wounded at 11:58". I doubt that any linguistic test of aboutness will work without circular restrictions on the language used. Hence it seems best to take either "about" or "perfect match with respect to" as a primitive.

Time-dependent chance and time-dependent admissibility go together. Suppose the proposition A is about matters of particular fact at some moment or interval t_A, and suppose we are concerned with chance at time t. If t is later than t_A, then A is admissible at t. The Principal Principle applies with A for E. If X is the proposition that the chance at t of A equals x, and if A and X are compatible, then

$$1 = C(A/XA) = x.$$

Put contrapositively, this means that if the chance at t of A, according to X, is anything but one, then A and X are incompatible. A implies that the chance at t of A, unless undefined, equals one. What's past is no longer chancy. The past, unlike the future, has no chance of being any other way than the way it actually is. This temporal asymmetry of chance falls into place as part of our conception of the past as "fixed" and the future as "open"— whatever that may mean. The asymmetry of fixity and of chance may be pictured by a tree. The single trunk is the one possible past that has any present chance of being actual. The many branches are the many possible futures that have some present chance of being actual. I shall not try to say here what features of the world justify our discriminatory attitude toward past and future possibilities,

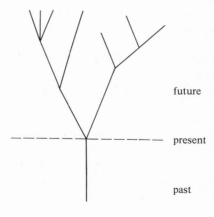

future

present

past

reflected for instance in the judgment that historical information is admissible and similar information about the future is not. But I think they are contingent features, subject to exception and absent altogether from some possible worlds.

That possibility calls into question my thesis that historical information is invariably admissible. What if the commonplace de facto asymmetries between past and future break down? If the past lies far in the future, as we are far to the west of ourselves, then it cannot simply be that propositions about the past are admissible and propositions about the future are not. And if the past contains seers with foreknowledge of what chance will bring, or time travelers who have witnessed the outcome of coin tosses to come, then patches of the past are enough tainted with futurity so that historical information about them may well seem inadmissible. That is why I qualified my claim that historical information is admissible, saying only that it is so "as a rule". Perhaps it is fair to ignore this problem in building a case that the Principal Principle captures our common opinions about chance, since those opinions may rest on a naive faith that past and future cannot possibly get mixed up. Any serious physicist, if he remains at least open-minded both about the shape of the cosmos and about the existence of chance processes, ought to do better. But I shall not; I shall carry on as if historical information is admissible without exception.

Besides historical information, there is at least one other sort of admissible information: hypothetical information about chance itself. Let us return briefly to our questionnaire and add one further supposition to each case. Suppose you have various opinions about what the chance of heads would be under various hypotheses about the detailed nature and history of the chance setup under consideration. Suppose further that you have similar hypothetical opinions about other chance setups, past, present, and future. (Assume that these opinions are consistent with your admissible historical information and your opinions about chance in the present case.) It seems quite clear to me—and I hope it does to you also—that these added opinions do not change anything. The correct answers to the questionnaire are just as before. The added opinions do not bear in any overly direct way on the future outcomes of chance processes. Therefore they are admissible.

We must take care, though. Some propositions about future chances do reveal inadmissible information about future history, and these are inadmissible. Recall the case of the labyrinth: you enter at 11:00, choosing your turns by chance, and hope to reach the center by noon. Your subsequent chance of success depends on the point you have reached. The proposition that at 11:30 your chance of success has fallen to 26% is not admissible information at 11:00; it is a giveaway about your bad luck in the first half hour. What is admissible at 11:00 is a conditional version: if you were to reach a certain point at 11:30, your chance of success would then be 26%. But even some conditionals are tainted: for instance, any conditional that could yield inadmissible information about future chances by *modus ponens* from admissible historical propositions. Consider also the truth-functional conditional that if history up to 11:30 follows a certain course, then you will have a 98% chance of becoming a monkey's uncle before the year is out. This conditional closely resembles the denial of its antecedent, and is inadmissible at 11:00 for the same reason.

I suggest that conditionals of the following sort, however, are admissible; and indeed admissible at all times. (1) The consequent is a proposition about chance at a certain time. (2) The antecedent is a proposition about history up to that time; and further, it is a complete proposition about history up to that time, so that it either implies or else is incompatible with any other proposition about history up to that time. It fully specifies a segment, up to the given time, of some possible course of history. (3) The conditional is made from its consequent and antecedent not truth-functionally, but rather by means of a strong conditional operation of some sort. This might well be the counterfactual conditional of Lewis (1973); but various rival versions would serve as well, since many differences do not matter for the case at hand. One feature of my treatment will be needed, however: if the antecedent of one of our conditionals holds at a world, then both or neither of the conditional and its consequent hold there.

These admissible conditionals are propositions about how chance depends (or fails to depend) on history. They say nothing, however, about how history chances to go. A set of them is a theory about the way chance works. It may or may not be a complete theory, a consistent theory, a systematic theory, or a credible theory. It might be a miscellany of unrelated propositions about what the chances would be after various fully specified particular courses of events. Or it might be systematic, compressible into generalizations to the effect that after any course of history with property J there would follow a chance distribution with property K. (For instance, it might say that any coin with a certain structure would be fair.) These generalizations are universally quantified conditionals about single-case chance; if lawful, they are probabilistic laws in the sense of Railton (1978). (I shall not consider here what would make them lawful; but see Lewis [1973], §3.3, for a treatment that could cover laws about chance along with other laws.) Systematic theories of chance are the ones we can express in language, think about, and believe to substantial degrees. But a reasonable initial credence function does not reject any possibility out of hand. It assigns some nonzero credence to any consistent theory of chance, no matter how unsystematic and incompressible it is.

Historical propositions are admissible; so are propositions about the dependence of chance on history. Combinations of the two, of course, are also admissible. More generally, we may assume that any Boolean combination of propositions admissible at a time also is admissible at that time. Admissibility consists in keeping out of a forbidden subject matter—how the chance processes turned out—and there is no way to break into a subject matter by making Boolean combinations of propositions that lie outside it.

There may be sorts of admissible propositions besides those I have considered. If so, we shall have no need of them in what follows.

This completes an exposition of the Principal Principle. We turn next to an examination of its consequences. I maintain that they include all that we take ourselves to know about chance.

THE PRINCIPLE REFORMULATED

Given a time t and world w, let us write P_{tw} for the *chance distribution* that obtains at t and w. For any proposition A, $P_{tw}(A)$ is the chance, at time t and world w, of A's holding. (The domain of P_{tw} comprises those propositions for which this chance is defined.)

Let us also write H_{tw} for the *complete history* of world w up to time t: the conjunction of all propositions that hold at w about matters of particular fact no later than t. H_{tw} is the proposition that holds at exactly those worlds that perfectly match w, in matters of particular fact, up to time t.

Let us also write T_w for the *complete theory of chance* for world w: the conjunction of all the conditionals from history to chance, of the sort just considered, that hold at w. Thus T_w is a full specification, for world w, of the way chances at any time depend on history up to that time.

Taking the conjunction $H_{tw}T_w$, we have a proposition that tells us a great deal about the world w. It is nevertheless admissible at time t, being simply a giant conjunction of historical propositions that are admissible at t and conditionals from history to chance that are admissible at any time. Hence the Principal Principle applies:

$$C(A/XH_{tw}T_w) = x$$

when C is a reasonable initial credence function, X is the proposition that the chance at t of A is x, and $H_{tw}T_w$ is compatible with X.

Suppose X holds at w. That is so if and only if x equals $P_{tw}(A)$. Hence we can choose such an X whenever A is in the domain of P_{tw}. $H_{tw}T_w$ and X both hold at w, therefore they are compatible. But further, $H_{tw}T_w$ implies X. The theory T_w and the history H_{tw} together are enough to imply all that is true (and contradict all that is false) at world w about chances at time t. For consider the strong conditional with antecedent H_{tw} and consequent X. This conditional holds at w, since by hypothesis its antecedent and consequent hold there. Hence it is implied by T_w, which is the conjunction of all conditionals of its sort that hold at w; and this conditional and H_{tw} yield X by *modus ponens*. Consequently the conjunction $XH_{tw}T_w$ simplifies to $H_{tw}T_w$. Provided that A is in the domain of P_{tw}, so that we can make a suitable choice of X, we can substitute $P_{tw}(A)$ for x, and $H_{tw}T_w$ for $XH_{tw}T_w$, in our instance of the Principal Principle. Therefore we have

The Principal Principle Reformulated. Let C be any reasonable initial credence function. Then for any time t, world w, and proposition A in the domain of P_{tw}

$$P_{tw}(A) = C(A/H_{tw}T_w).$$

In words: the chance distribution at a time and a world comes from any reasonable initial credence function by conditionalizing on the complete history of the world up to the time, together with the complete theory of chance for the world.

This reformulation enjoys less direct intuitive support than the original formulation, but it will prove easier to use. It will serve as our point of departure in examining further consequences of the Principal Principle.

CHANCE AND THE PROBABILITY CALCULUS

A reasonable initial credence function is, among other things, a probability distribution: a nonnegative, normalized, finitely additive measure. It obeys the laws of mathematical probability theory. There are well-known reasons why that must be so if credence is to rationalize courses of action that would not seem blatantly unreasonable in some circumstances.

Whatever comes by conditionalizing from a probability distribution is itself a probability distribution. Therefore a chance distribution is a probability distribution. For any time t and world w, P_{tw} obeys the laws of mathematical probability theory. These laws carry over from credence to chance via the Principal Principle. We have no need of any independent assumption that chance is a kind of probability.

Observe that although the Principal Principle concerns the relationship between chance and credence, some of its consequences concern chance alone. We have seen two such consequences. (1) The thesis that the past has no present chance of being otherwise than it actually is. (2) The thesis that chance obeys the laws of probability. More such consequences will appear later.

CHANCE AS OBJECTIFIED CREDENCE

Chance is objectified subjective probability in the sense of Jeffrey (1965), §12.7. Jeffrey's construction (omitting his use of sequences of partitions, which is unnecessary if we allow infinitesimal credences) works as follows. Suppose given a partition of logical space: a set of mutually exclusive and jointly exhaustive propositions. Then we can define the *objectification* of a credence function, with respect to this partition, at a certain world, as the probability distribution that comes from the given credence function by conditionalizing on the member of the given partition that holds at the given world. Objectified credence is credence conditional on the truth—not the whole truth, however, but exactly as much of it as can be captured by a member of the partition without further subdivision of logical space. The member of the partition that holds depends on matters of contingent fact, varying from one world to another; it does not depend on what we think (except insofar as our thoughts are relevant matters of fact) and we may well be ignorant or mistaken about it. The same goes for objectified credence.

Now consider one particular way of partitioning. For any time t, consider the partition consisting of the propositions $H_{tw}T_w$ for all worlds w. Call this the *history-theory partition* for time t. A member of this partition is an equivalence class of worlds with respect to the relation of being exactly alike both in respect of matters of particular fact up to time t and in respect of the dependence of chance on history. The Principal Principle tells us that the chance distribution, at any time t and world w, is the objectification of any reasonable credence function, with respect to the history-theory partition for time t, at world w. Chance is credence conditional on the truth—*if* the truth is subject to censorship along the lines of the history-theory partition, and *if* the credence is reasonable.

Any historical proposition admissible at time t, or any admissible conditional from history to chance, or any admissible Boolean combination of propositions of these two kinds—in short, any sort of admissible proposition we have considered—is a disjunction of members of the history-theory partition for t. Its borders follow the lines of the partition, never cutting between two worlds that the partition does not distinguish. Likewise for any proposition about chances at t. Let X be the proposition that the chance at t of A is x, let Y be any member of the history-theory partition for t, and let C be any reasonable initial credence function. Then, according to our reformulation of the Principal Principle, X holds at all worlds in Y if $C(A/Y)$ equals x, and at no worlds in Y otherwise. Therefore X is the disjunction of all members Y of the partition such that $C(A/Y)$ equals x.

We may picture the situation as follows. The partition divides space into countless tiny squares. In each square there is a black region where A holds and a white region where it does not. Now blur the focus, so that divisions within the squares disappear from view. Each square becomes a gray patch in a broad expanse covered with varying shades of gray. Any maximal region of uniform shade is a proposition specifying the chance of A. The darker the shade, the higher is the uniform chance of A at the worlds in the region. The worlds themselves are not gray—they are black or white, worlds where A holds or where it doesn't—but we cannot focus on single worlds, so they all seem to be the shade of gray that covers their region. Admissible propositions, of the sorts we have considered, are regions that may cut across the contours of the shades of gray. The conjunction of one of these admissible propositions and a proposition about the chance of A is a region of uniform shade, but not in general a maximal uniform region. It consists of some, but perhaps not all, the members Y of the partition for which $C(A/Y)$ takes a certain value.

We derived our reformulation of the Principal Principle from the original formulation, but have not given a reverse derivation to show the two formulations equivalent. In fact the reformulation may be weaker, but not in any way that is likely to matter. Let C be a reasonable initial credence function; let X be the proposition that the chance at t of A is x; let E be admissible at t (in one of the ways we have considered) and compatible with X. According to the reformulation, as we have seen, XE is a disjunction of incompatible propositions Y, for each of which $C(A/Y)$ equals x. If there are only finitely many Y's, it would follow that $C(A/XE)$ also equals x. But the implication fails in certain cases with infinitely many Y's (and indeed we would expect the history-theory partition to be infinite) so we cannot quite recover the original formulation in this way. The cases of failure are peculiar, however, so the extra strength of the original formulation in ruling them out seems unimportant.

KINEMATICS OF CHANCE

Chance being a kind of probability, we may define conditional chance in the usual way as a quotient (leaving it undefined if the denominator is zero):

$$P_{tw}(A/B) =_{df} P_{tw}(AB)/P_{tw}(B).$$

To simplify notation, let us fix on a particular world—ours, as it might be—and omit the subscript 'w'; let us fix on some particular reasonable initial credence function C, it doesn't matter which; and let us fix on a sequence of times, in order from earlier to later, to be called $1, 2, 3, \ldots$ (I do not assume they are equally spaced.) For any time t in our sequence, let the proposition I_t be the complete history of our chosen world in the interval from time t to time $t+1$ (including $t+1$ but not t). Thus I_t is the set of worlds that match the chosen world perfectly in matters of particular fact throughout the given interval.

A complete history up to some time may be extended by conjoining complete histories of subsequent intervals. H_2 is $H_1 I_1$, H_3 is $H_1 I_1 I_2$, and so on. Then by the Principal Principle we have:

$$P_1(A) = C(A/H_1 T),$$
$$P_2(A) = C(A/H_2 T) = C(A/H_1 I_1 T) = P_1(A/I_1),$$
$$P_3(A) = C(A/H_3 T) = C(A/H_1 I_1 I_2 T) = P_2(A/I_2) = P_1(A/I_1 I_2),$$

$$\cdot$$
$$\cdot$$
$$\cdot$$

and in general

$$P_{t+n+1}(A) = P_t(A/I_t \ldots I_{t+n}).$$

In words: a later chance distribution comes from an earlier one by conditionalizing on the complete history of the interval in between.

The evolution of chance is parallel to the evolution of credence for an agent who learns from experience, as he reasonably might, by conditionalizing. In that case a later credence function comes from an earlier one by conditionalizing on the total increment of evidence gained in the interval in between. For the evolution of chance we simply put the world's chance distribution in place of the agent's credence function, and the totality of particular fact about a time in place of the totality of evidence gained at that time.

In the interval from t to $t+1$ there is a certain way that the world will in fact develop: namely, the way given by I_t. And at t, the last moment before the interval begins, there is a certain chance that the world will develop in that way: $P_t(I_t)$, the endpoint chance of I_t. Likewise for a longer interval, say from time 1 to time 18. The world will in fact develop in the way given by $I_1 \ldots I_{17}$, and the endpoint chance of its doing so is $P_1(I_1 \ldots I_{17})$. By definition of conditional chance

$$P_1(I_1 \ldots I_{17}) = P_1(I_1) \cdot P_1(I_2/I_1) \cdot P_1(I_3/I_1 I_2) \ldots P_1(I_{17}/I_1 \ldots I_{16}),$$

and by the Principal Principle, applied as above,

$$P_1(I_1 \ldots I_{17}) = P_1(I_1) \cdot P_2(I_2) \cdot P_3(I_3) \ldots P_{17}(I_{17}).$$

In general, if an interval is divided into subintervals, then the endpoint chance of the complete history of the interval is the product of the endpoint chances of the complete histories of the subintervals.

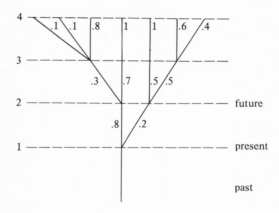

Earlier we drew a tree to represent the temporal asymmetry of chance. Now we can embellish the tree with numbers to represent the kinematics of chance. Take time 1 as the present. Worlds—those of them that are compatible with a certain common past and a certain common theory of chance—lie along paths through the tree. The numbers on each segment give the endpoint chance of the course of history represented by that segment, for any world that passes through that segment. Likewise, for any path consisting of several segments, the product of numbers along the path gives the endpoint chance of the course of history represented by the entire path.

CHANCE OF FREQUENCY

Suppose that there is to be a long sequence of coin tosses under more or less standardized conditions. The first will be in the interval between time 1 and time 2, the second in the interval between 2 and 3, and so on. Our chosen world is such that at time 1 there is no chance, or negligible chance, that the planned sequence of tosses will not take place. And indeed it does take place. The outcomes are given by a sequence of propositions $A_1, A_2, \ldots$. Each A_t states truly whether the toss between t and $t+1$ fell heads or tails. A conjunction $A_1 \ldots A_n$ then gives the history of outcomes for an initial segment of the sequence.

The endpoint chance $P_1(A_1 \ldots A_n)$ of such a sequence of outcomes is given by a product of conditional chances. By definition of conditional chance,

$$P_1(A_1 \ldots A_n)$$
$$= P_1(A_1) \cdot P_1(A_2/A_1) \cdot P_1(A_3/A_1A_2) \ldots P_1(A_n/A_1 \ldots A_{n-1}).$$

Since we are dealing with propositions that give only incomplete histories of intervals, there is no general guarantee that these factors equal the endpoint chances of the A's. The endpoint chance of A_2, $P_2(A_2)$, is given by $P_1(A_2/I_1)$; this may differ from $P_1(A_2/A_1)$ because the complete history I_1 includes some relevant information that the incomplete history A_1 omits about chance occurrences in the first interval. Likewise for the conditional and endpoint chances pertaining to later intervals.

Even though there is no general guarantee that the endpoint chance of a sequence of outcomes equals the product of the endpoint chances of the individual outcomes, yet it may be so if the world is right. It may be, for instance, that the endpoint chance of A_2 does not depend on those aspects of the history of the first interval that are omitted from A_1—it would be the same regardless. Consider the class of all possible complete histories up to time 2 that are compatible both with the previous history H_1 and with the outcome A_1 of the first toss. These give all the ways the omitted aspects of the first interval might be. For each of these histories, some strong conditional holds at our chosen world that tells what the chance at 2 of A_2 would be if that history were to come about. Suppose all these conditionals have the same consequent: whichever one of the alternative histories were to come about, it would be that X, where X is the proposition that the chance at 2 of A_2 equals x. Then the conditionals taken together tell us that the endpoint chance of A_2 is independent of all aspects of the history of the first interval except the outcome of the first toss.

In that case we can equate the conditional chance $P_1(A_2/A_1)$ and the endpoint chance $P_2(A_2)$. Note that our conditionals are of the sort implied by T, the complete theory of chance for our chosen world. Hence A_1, H_1, and T jointly imply X. It follows that A_1H_1T and XA_1H_1T are the same proposition. It also follows that X holds at our chosen world, and hence that x equals $P_2(A_2)$. Note also that A_1H_1T is admissible at time 2. Now, using the Principal Principle first as reformulated and then in the original formulation, we have

$$P_1(A_2/A_1) = C(A_2/A_1H_1T) = C(A_2/XA_1H_1T) = x = P_2(A_2).$$

If we also have another such battery of conditionals to the effect that the endpoint chance of A_3 is independent of all aspects of the history of the first two intervals except the outcomes A_1 and A_2 of the first two tosses, and another battery for A_4, and so on, then the multiplicative rule for endpoint chances follows:

$$P_1(A_1 \ldots A_n) = P_1(A_1) \cdot P_2(A_2) \cdot P_3(A_3) \ldots P_n(A_n).$$

The conditionals that constitute the independence of endpoint chances mean that the incompleteness of the histories $A_1, A_2, \ldots$ doesn't matter. The missing part wouldn't make any difference.

We might have a stronger form of independence. The endpoint chances might not depend on *any* aspects of history after time 1, not even the outcomes of previous tosses. Then conditionals would hold at our chosen world to the effect that if any complete history up to time 2 which is compatible with H_1 were to come about, it would be that X (where X is again the proposition that the chance at 2 of A_2 equals x). We argue as before, leaving out A_1: T implies the conditionals, H_1 and T jointly imply X, H_1T and XH_1T are the same, X holds, x equals $P_2(A_2)$, H_1T is admissible at 2; so, using the Principal Principle in both formulations, we have

$$P_1(A_2) = C(A_2/H_1T) = C(A_2/XH_1T) = x = P_2(A_2).$$

Our strengthened independence assumption implies the weaker independence assumption of the previous case, wherefore

$$P_1(A_2/A_1) = P_2(A_2) = P_1(A_2).$$

If the later outcomes are likewise independent of history after time 1, then we have a multiplicative rule not only for endpoint chances but also for unconditional chances of outcomes at time 1:

$$P_1(A_1 \ldots A_n) = P_1(A_1) \cdot P_1(A_2) \cdot P_1(A_3) \ldots P_1(A_n).$$

Two conceptions of independence are in play together. One is the familiar probabilistic conception: A_2 is independent of A_1, with respect to the chance distribution P_1, if the conditional chance $P_1(A_2/A_1)$ equals the unconditional chance $P_1(A_2)$; equivalently, if the chance $P_1(A_1A_2)$ of the conjunction equals the product $P_1(A_1) \cdot P_1(A_2)$ of the chances of the conjuncts. The other conception involves batteries of strong conditionals with different antecedents and the same consequent. (I consider this to be *causal* independence, but that's another story.) The conditionals need not have anything to do with probability; for instance, my beard does not depend on my politics since I would have such a beard whether I were Republican, Democrat, Prohibitionist, Libertarian, Socialist Labor, or whatever. But one sort of consequent that can be independent of a range of alternatives, as we have seen, is a consequent about single-case chance. What I have done is to use the Principal Principle to parlay battery-of-conditionals independence into ordinary probabilistic independence.

If the world is right, the situation might be still simpler; and this is the case we hope to achieve in a well-conducted sequence of chance trials. Suppose the history-to-chance conditionals and the previous history of our chosen world give us not only independence (of the stronger sort) but also uniformity of chances: for any toss in our sequence, the endpoint chance of heads on that toss would be h (and the endpoint chance of tails would be $1-h$) no matter which of the possible previous histories compatible with H_1 might have come to pass. Then each of the A_t's has an endpoint chance of h if it specifies an outcome of heads, $1-h$ if it specifies an outcome of tails. By the multiplicative rule for endpoint chances,

$$P_1(A_1 \dots A_n) = h^{fn} \cdot (1-h)^{(n-fn)}$$

where f is the frequency of heads in the first n tosses according to $A_1 \dots A_n$.

Now consider any other world that matches our chosen world in its history up to time 1 and in its complete theory of chance, but not in its sequence of outcomes. By the Principal Principle, the chance distribution at time 1 is the same for both worlds. Our assumptions of independence and uniformity apply to both worlds, being built into the shared history and theory. So all goes through for this other world as it did for our chosen world. Our calculation of the chance at time 1 of a sequence of outcomes, as a function of the uniform single-case chance of heads and the length and frequency of heads in the sequence, goes for any sequence, not only for the sequence $A_1, A_2, \dots$ that comes about at our chosen world.

Let F be the proposition that the frequency of heads in the first n tosses is f. F is a disjunction of propositions each specifying a sequence of n outcomes with frequency f of heads; each disjunct has the same chance at time 1, under our assumptions of independence and uniformity; and the disjuncts are incompatible. Multiplying the number of these propositions by the uniform chance of each, we get the chance of obtaining some or other sequence of outcomes with frequency f of heads:

$$P_1(F) = \frac{n! \cdot h^{fn} \cdot (1-h)^{(n-fn)}}{(fn)! \cdot (n-fn)!}.$$

The rest is well known. For fixed h and n, the right-hand side of the equation peaks for f close to h; the greater is n, the sharper is the peak. If there are many tosses, then the chance is close to one that the frequency of heads is close to the uniform single-case chance of heads. The more tosses, the more stringent we can be about what counts as "close". That much of frequentism is true; and that much is a consequence of the Principal Principle, which relates chance not only to credence but also to frequency.

On the other hand, unless h is zero or one, the right-hand side of the equation is nonzero. So, as already noted, there is always some chance that the frequency and the single-case chance may differ as badly as you please. That objection to frequentist analyses also turns out to be a consequence of the Principal Principle.

EVIDENCE ABOUT CHANCES

To the subjectivist who believes in objective chance, particular or general propositions about chances are nothing special. We believe them to varying degrees. As new evidence arrives, our credence in them should wax and wane in accordance with Bayesian confirmation theory. It is reasonable to believe such a proposition, like any other, to the degree given by a reasonable initial credence function conditionalized on one's present total evidence.

If we look at the matter in closer detail, we find that the calculations of changing reasonable credence involve *likelihoods:* credences of bits of evidence conditionally upon hypotheses. Here the Principal Principle may act as a useful constraint. Sometimes when the hypothesis concerns chance and the bit of evidence concerns the outcome, the reasonable likelihood is fixed, independently of the vagaries of initial credence and previous evidence. What is more, likelihoods are fixed in such a way that observed frequencies tend to confirm hypotheses according to which these frequencies differ not too much from uniform chances.

To illustrate, let us return to our example of the sequence of coin tosses. Think of it as an experiment, designed to provide evidence bearing on various hypotheses about the single-case chances of heads. The sequence begins at time 1 and goes on for at least n tosses. The evidence gained by the end of the experiment is a proposition F to the effect that the frequency of heads in the first n tosses was f. (I assume that we use a mechanical counter that keeps no record of individual tosses. The case in which there is a full record, however, is little different. I also assume, in an unrealistic simplification, that no other evidence whatever arrives during the experiment.) Suppose that at time 1 your credence function is $C(-/E)$, the function that comes from our chosen reasonable initial credence function C by conditionalizing on your total evidence E up to that time. Then if you learn from experience by conditionalizing, your credence function after the experiment is $C(-/FE)$. The impact of your experimental evidence F on your beliefs, about chances or anything else, is given by the difference between these two functions.

Suppose that before the experiment your credence is distributed over a range of alternative hypotheses about the endpoint chances of heads in the experimental tosses. (Your degree of belief that none of these hypotheses is correct may not be zero, but I am supposing it to be negligible and shall accordingly neglect it.) The hypotheses agree that these chances are uniform, and each independent of the previous course of history after time 1; but they disagree about what the uniform chance of heads is. Let us write G_h for the hypothesis that the endpoint chances of heads are uniformly h. Then the credences $C(G_h/E)$, for various h's comprise the *prior distribution* of credence over the hypotheses; the credences $C(G_h/FE)$ comprise the *posterior distribution*; and the credences $C(F/G_hE)$ are the likelihoods. Bayes's Theorem gives the posterior distribution in terms of the prior distribution and the likelihoods:

$$C(G_h/FE) = \frac{C(G_h/E) \cdot C(F/G_hE)}{\sum_h [C(G_h/E) \cdot C(F/G_hE)]}.$$

(Note that "h" is a bound variable of summation in the denominator of the right hand side, but a free variable elsewhere.) In words: to get the posterior distribution, multiply the prior distribution by the likelihood function and renormalize.

In talking only about a single experiment, there is little to say about the prior distribution. That does indeed depend on the vagaries of initial credence and previous evidence.

Not so for the likelihoods. As we saw in the last section, each G_h implies a proposition X_h to the effect that the chance at 1 of F equals x_h, where x_h is given by a certain function of h, n, and f. Hence $G_h E$ and $X_h G_h E$ are the same proposition. Further, $G_h E$ and X are compatible (unless $G_h E$ is itself impossible, in which case G_h might as well be omitted from the range of hypotheses). E is admissible at 1, being about matters of particular fact—your evidence—at times no later than 1. G_h also is admissible at 1. Recall from the last section that what makes such a proposition hold at a world is a certain relationship between that world's complete history up to time 1 and that world's history-to-chance conditionals about the chances that would follow various complete extensions of that history. Hence any member of the history-theory partition for time 1 either implies or contradicts G_h; G_h is therefore a disjunction of conjunctions of admissible historical propositions and admissible history-to-chance conditionals. Finally, we supposed that C is reasonable. So the Principal Principle applies:

$$C(F/G_h E) = C(F/X_h G_h E) = x_h.$$

The likelihoods are the endpoint chances, according to the various hypotheses, of obtaining the frequency of heads that was in fact obtained.

When we carry the calculation through, putting these implied chances for the likelihoods in Bayes's theorem, the results are as we would expect. An observed frequency of f raises the credences of the hypotheses G_h with h close to f at the expense of the others; the more sharply so, the greater is the number of tosses. Unless the prior distribution is irremediably biased, the result after enough tosses is that the lion's share of the posterior credence will go to hypotheses putting the single-case chance of heads close to the observed frequency.

CHANCE AS A GUIDE TO LIFE

It is reasonable to let one's choices be guided in part by one's firm opinions about objective chances or, when firm opinions are lacking, by one's degrees of belief about chances. *Ceteris paribus*, the greater chance you think a lottery ticket has of winning, the more that ticket should be worth to you and the more you should be disposed to chose it over other desirable things. Why so?

There is no great puzzle about why credence should be a guide to life. Roughly speaking, what makes it be so that a certain credence function is *your* credence function is the very fact that you are disposed to act in more or less the ways that it rationalizes. (Better: what makes it be so that a certain reasonable initial credence function and a certain reasonable system of basic intrinsic values are both yours is that you are disposed to act in more or less the ways that are rationalized by the pair of them together, taking into account the modification of credence by conditionalizing on total evidence; and further, you would have been likewise disposed if your life history of experience, and consequent modification of credence, had been different; and further, no other such pair would fit your dispositions more closely.) No wonder your credence function tends to guide your life. If its doing so did not accord to some considerable extent with your dispositions to act, then it would not be your credence function. You would have some other credence function, or none.

If your present degrees of belief are reasonable—or at least if they come from some reasonable initial credence function by conditionalizing on your total evidence—then the Principal Principle applies. Your credences about outcomes conform to your firm beliefs and your partial beliefs about chances. Then the latter guide your life because the former do. The greater chance you think the ticket has of winning, the greater should be your degree of belief that it will win; and the greater is your degree of belief that it will win, the more, *ceteris paribus*, it should be worth to you and the more you should be disposed to choose it over other desirable things.

PROSPECTS FOR AN ANALYSIS OF CHANCE

Consider once more the Principal Principle as reformulated:

$$P_{tw}(A) = C(A/H_{tw}T_w).$$

Or in words: the chance distribution at a time and a world comes from any reasonable initial credence function by conditionalizing on the complete history of the world up to the time, together with the complete theory of chance for the world.

Doubtless it has crossed your mind that this has at least the form of an analysis of chance. But you may well doubt that it is informative as an analysis; that depends on the distance between the analysandum and the concepts employed in the analysans.

Not that it has to be informative *as an analysis* to be informative. I hope I have convinced you that the Principal Principle is indeed informative, being rich in consequences that are central to our ordinary ways of thinking about chance.

There are two different reasons to doubt that the Principal Principle qualifies as an analysis. The first concerns the allusion in the analysans to reasonable initial credence functions. The second concerns the allusion to complete theories of chance. In both cases the challenge is the same: could we possibly get any independent grasp on this concept, otherwise than by way of the concept of chance itself? In both cases my provisional answer is: most likely not, but it would be worth trying. Let us consider the two problems in turn.

It would be natural to think that the Principal Principle tells us nothing at all about chance, but rather tells us something about what makes an initial credence function be a reasonable one. To be reasonable is to conform to objective chances in the way described. Put this strongly, the response is wrong: the Principle has consequences, as we noted, that are about chance and not at all about its relationship to credence. (They would be acceptable, I trust, to a believer in objective single-case chance who rejects the very idea of degree of belief.) It tells us more than nothing about chance. But perhaps it is divisible into two parts: one part that tells us something about chance, another that takes the concept of chance for granted and goes on to lay down a criterion of reasonableness for initial credence.

Is there any hope that we might leave the Principal Principle in abeyance, lay down other criteria of reasonableness that do not mention chance, and get a good enough grip on the concept that way? It's a lot to ask. For note that just as the Principal Principle yields some consequences that are entirely about chance, so also it yields some that are entirely about reasonable initial credence. One such consequence is as follows. There is a large class of propositions such that if Y is any one of the these, and C_1 and C_2 are any two reasonable initial credence functions, then the functions that come from C_1 and C_2 by conditionalizing on Y are exactly the same. (The large class is, of course, the class of members of history-theory partitions for all times.) That severely limits the ways that reasonable initial credence functions may differ, and so shows that criteria adequate to pick them out must be quite strong. What might we try? A reasonable initial credence function ought to (1) obey the laws of mathematical probability theory; (2) avoid dogmatism, at least by never assigning zero credence to possible propositions and perhaps also by never assigning infinitesimal credence to certain kinds of possible propositions; (3) make it possible to learn from experience by having a built-in bias in favor of worlds where the future in some sense resembles the past; and perhaps (4) obey certain carefully

restricted principles of indifference, thereby respecting certain sym-
metries. Of these, criteria (1)–(3) are all very well, but surely not yet
strong enough. Given C_1 satisfying (1)–(3), and given any proposition Y that holds at more than one world, it will be possible to
distort C_1 very slightly to produce C_2, such that $C_1(-/Y)$ and
$C_2(-/Y)$ differ but C_2 also satisfies (1)–(3). It is less clear what (4)
might be able to do for us. Mostly that is because (4) is less clear
simpliciter, in view of the fact that it is not possible to obey too many
different restricted principles of indifference at once and it is hard to
give good reasons to prefer some over their competitors. It also
remains possible, of course, that some criterion of reasonableness
along different lines than any I have mentioned would do the trick.

I now turn to our second problem: the concept of a complete
theory of chance. In saying what makes a certain proposition be the
complete theory of chance for a world (and for any world where it
holds), I gave an explanation in terms of chance. Could these same
propositions possibly be picked out in some other way, without
mentioning chance?

The question turns on an underlying metaphysical issue. A
broadly Humean doctrine (something I would very much like to
believe if at all possible) holds that all the facts there are about the
world are particular facts, or combinations thereof. This need not be
taken as a doctrine of analyzability, since some combinations of
particular facts cannot be captured in any finite way. It might be
better taken as a doctrine of supervenience: if two worlds match
perfectly in all matters of particular fact, they match perfectly in all
other ways too—in modal properties, laws, causal connections,
chances, and so on. It seems that if this broadly Humean doctrine
is false, then chances are a likely candidate to be the fatal counter-
instance. And if chances are not supervenient on particular fact,
then neither are complete theories of chance. For the chances at a
world are jointly determined by its complete theory of chance
together with propositions about its history, which latter plainly are
supervenient on particular fact.

If chances are not supervenient on particular fact, then neither
chance itself nor the concept of a complete theory of chance could
possibly be analyzed in terms of particular fact, or of anything
supervenient thereon. The only hope for an analysis would be to use
something in the analysans which is itself not supervenient on
particular fact. I cannot say what that something might be.

How might chance, and complete theories of chance, be supervenient on particular fact? Could something like this be right: the
complete theory of chance for a world is that one of all possible

complete theories of chance that somehow best fits the global pattern of outcomes and frequencies of outcomes? It could not. For consider any such global pattern, and consider a time long before the pattern is complete. At that time, the pattern surely has some chance of coming about and some chance of not coming about. There is surely some chance of a very different global pattern coming about; one which, according to the proposal under consideration, would make true some different complete theory of chance. But a complete theory of chance is not something that could have some chance of coming about or not coming about. By the Principal Principle,

$$P_{tw}(T_w) = C(T_w/H_{tw}T_w) = 1.$$

If T_w is something that holds in virtue of some global pattern of particular fact that obtains at world w, this pattern must be one that has no chance at any time (at w) of not obtaining. If w is a world where many matters of particular fact are the outcomes of chance processes, then I fail to see what kind of global pattern this could possibly be.

But there is one more alternative. I have spoken as if I took it for granted that different worlds have different history-to-chance conditionals, and hence different complete theories of chance. Perhaps this is not so: perhaps all worlds are exactly alike in the dependence of chance on history. Then the complete theory of chance for every world, and all the conditionals that comprise it, are necessary. They are supervenient on particular fact in the trivial way that what is noncontingent is supervenient on anything—no two worlds differ with respect to it. Chances are still contingent, but only because they depend on contingent historical propositions (information about the details of the coin and tosser, as it might be) and not also because they depend on a contingent theory of chance. Our theory is much simplified if this is true. Admissible information is simply historical information; the history-theory partition at t is simply the partition of alternative complete histories up to t; for any reasonable initial credence function C

$$P_{tw}(A) = C(A/H_{tw}),$$

so that the chance distribution at t and w comes from C by conditionalizing on the complete history of w up to t. Chance is reasonable credence conditional on the whole truth about history up to a time. The broadly Humean doctrine is upheld, so far as chances are concerned: what makes it true at a time and a world that something has a certain chance of happening is something about matters of particular fact at that time and (perhaps) before.

What's the catch? For one thing, we are no longer safely exploring the consequences of the Principal Principle, but rather engaging in speculation. For another, our broadly Humean speculation that history-to-chance conditionals are necessary solves our second problem by making the first one worse. Reasonable initial credence functions are constrained more narrowly than ever. Any two of them, C_1 and C_2, are now required to yield the same function by conditionalizing on the complete history of any world up to any time. Put it this way: according to our broadly Humean speculation (and the Principal Principle) if I were perfectly reasonable and knew all about the course of history up to now (no matter what that course of history actually is, and no matter what time is now) then there would be only one credence function I could have. Any other would be unreasonable.

It is not very easy to believe that the requirements of reason leave so little leeway as that. Neither is it very easy to believe in features of the world that are not supervenient on particular fact. But if I am right, that seems to be the choice. I shall not attempt to decide between the Humean and the anti-Humean variants of my approach to credence and chance. The Principal Principle doesn't.

BIBLIOGRAPHY

Bernstein, Allen R., and Frank Wattenberg. (1969). "Non-Standard Measure Theory", in *Applications of Model Theory of Algebra, Analysis, and Probability*. Ed. W. Luxemburg. New York: Holt, Reinhart & Winston.

Carnap, Rudolf. (1945). "The Two Concepts of Probability", *Philosophy and Phenomenological Research* **5**, 513–532.

Jeffrey, Richard C. (1965). *The Logic of Decision*. New York: McGraw-Hill.

———. (1970). Review of articles by David Miller et al., *Journal of Symbolic Logic*, **35**, 124–127.

———. (1977). "Mises Redux", in *Basic Problems in Methodology and Linguistics: Proceedings of the Fifth International Congress of Logic, Methodology and Philosophy of Science, Part III*. Ed. R. Butts and J. Hintikka. Dordrecht: D. Reidel.

Lewis, David. (1968). "Counterpart Theory and Quantified Modal Logic", *Journal of Philosophy* **65**, 113–126.

———. (1973). *Counterfactuals*. Oxford: Blackwell.

Mellor, D. H. (1971). *The Matter of Chance*. Cambridge: Cambridge University Press.

Quine, W. V. (1969). "Propositional Objects", in *Ontological Relativity and Other Essays*. New York: Columbia University Press.

Railton, Peter. (1978). "A Deductive-Nomological Model of Probabilistic Explanation", *Philosophy of Science* **45**, 202–226.

Skyrms, Brian. (1977). "Resiliency, Propensities, and Casual Necessity", *Journal of Philosophy* **74**, 704–713.

NOTE

I am grateful to several people for valuable discussions of this material, especially John Burgess, Nancy Cartwright, Richard Jeffrey, Peter Railton, and Brian Skyrms. I am also much indebted to Mellor (1971), which presents a view very close to mine; exactly how close, I am not prepared to say.

14

A Note on Regularity

BY DOUGLAS N. HOOVER

Carnap's idea of comparing sizes of sets of real numbers in a way satisfying the axioms in Art. 6, §21 can be realized in large part by means of the construction of Parikh and Parnes in [1]. Briefly put, the Parikh–Parnes construction may be used (as outlined below) to define relations SEq and IS satisfying all of Carnap's axioms except 3(f), which is an axiom of countable additivity, and 7(p), which prescribes a harmony of the relations with the topology of the reals. These axioms are inconsistent with the others.

It should be noted that the proofs of inconsistency use only axioms that are above suspicion. And though we have discarded two axioms, we can add another which is conspicuously absent in Carnap: if A, B are Lebesgue measurable sets of positive, finite measure, then SEq (A, B) holds iff $\mu(A) \leq \mu(B)$. Further, inspection of the Parikh–Parnes construction shows that it yields a much finer gradation of sizes of sets of reals than that given by the two relations SEq and IS.

Proof of the Inconsistency of 3(f). Consider the usual example of a set that is not Lebesgue measurable: a set $S \subseteq [0, 1]$ such that for every $r \in \mathbf{R}$, S contains exactly one real number s such that $r - s$ is rational. By 7(h) and 3(a), (b) we have IS $(S, [0, 2])$. Hence, by 7(f), 3(c), and 7(c), IS (S, I) holds for any real interval I; *a fortiori* SEq (S, I) holds. By 3(a), (c), (f), SEq $(\mathbf{R}, J)$ holds where J is a finite interval (since $\bigcup_{q \in \mathbf{Q}} S + q = \mathbf{R}$ is a disjoint union. Write J as a union of countably many intervals.) But then $\mu(J) < \infty$ and $\mu(\mathbf{R}) = \infty$, so IS $(J, \mathbf{R})$ holds by 7(n). This with SEq $(\mathbf{R}, J)$ contradicts 7(b). ∎

Proof of the Inconsistency of 7(p).   Let $A = [0, 1]$, $B = A \cup \mathbf{Q}$. Then since $A \subseteq B$, SEq (A, B) holds. Now $A^{ac} = A$, but $B^{ac} = \mathbf{R}$ since $\mathbf{Q}$ is dense. Since $\mu(A) = 1$, $\mu(\mathbf{R} = \infty$. IS (A^{ac}, B^{ac}) holds by axiom 7(n). By 7(p), IS (A, B) holds. Since $B = A \cup \mathbf{Q}$, and IS (A, A) cannot hold, by 7(f) IS $(A, \mathbf{Q})$ follows. But A has positive Lebesgue measure, and $\mu(\mathbf{Q}) = 0$, so IS $(\mathbf{Q}, A)$ holds also. IS $(A, \mathbf{Q})$ and IS $(\mathbf{Q}, A)$ are inconsistent by 7(a), (b).   ■

It should be pointed out that as the Parikh–Parnes construction is not at all unique, the relations IS and SEq obtained will not be unique either. In fact there will be 2^c possible pairs of relations (c being the cardinality of the continuum).

The construction uses nonstandard measure theory. One may observe that Carnap's nonarchimedean number system Ω may be taken to be the nonnegative nonstandard reals used in the construction, modulo the equivalence relation

$$a \sim b \quad \text{iff} \quad \frac{a}{b} \text{ is noninfinitesmal and finite.}$$

IS and SEq are obtained as follows. Parikh and Parnes construct a nonstandard measure m (i.e. $m(\cdot, F)$ in the notation of their paper) on $*\mathscr{P}(\mathbf{R})$ having the following properties. (1) m is symmetric and invariant under translations by standard real numbers. (2) $m(*A) \neq 0$ for $A \subseteq \mathbf{R}$, $A \neq \emptyset$ (though of course one may have $m(*A) \approx 0$). (3) The measure $\bar{m}$ defined by

$$\bar{m}(A) = {}^\circ m(*A) = \text{the standard part of } m(*A), \qquad A \subseteq \mathbf{R}$$

is a finitely additive, translation invariant extension of Lebesgue measure. (4) The set function $p(\cdot, \cdot)$ defined by

$$p(A, B) = {}^\circ\!\left(\frac{m(AB)}{m(B)}\right), \qquad B \neq \emptyset$$

is a translation invariant extension of the conditional probability with respect to Lebesgue measure. If we define

$$\text{SEq } (A, B) \quad \text{iff} \quad A \neq \emptyset \quad \text{or} \quad B \neq \emptyset \quad \text{and} \quad {}^\circ\!\left(\frac{m(*A)}{m(*B)}\right) \leq 1$$

and

$$\text{IS } (A, B) \quad \text{iff} \quad {}^\circ\!\left(\frac{m(*A)}{m(*B)}\right) = 0,$$

then it is clear from (1)–(4) and the form of the definitions that the axioms for SEq (i.e. (3) and (9)) and all the axioms for IS not concerned with cardinalities of sets (7(a)–(i), (m), (n), the inconsistent 3(f) and 7(p) also being excepted) are satisfied. Satisfaction of 7(i), (k), (l) can be obtained by iterated use of the Parikh–Parnes lemma M in the construction of m.

REFERENCE

Parikh, Robert and Milton Parnes. "Conditional probabilities and uniform sets," in Albert Hurd and Peter Loeb eds. *Victoria Symposium on Nonstandard Analysis*. New York: Springer-Verlag, 1974.

INDEX
Volumes I and II

PREPARED BY ARON EDIDIN AND
PAUL BOGHOSSIAN